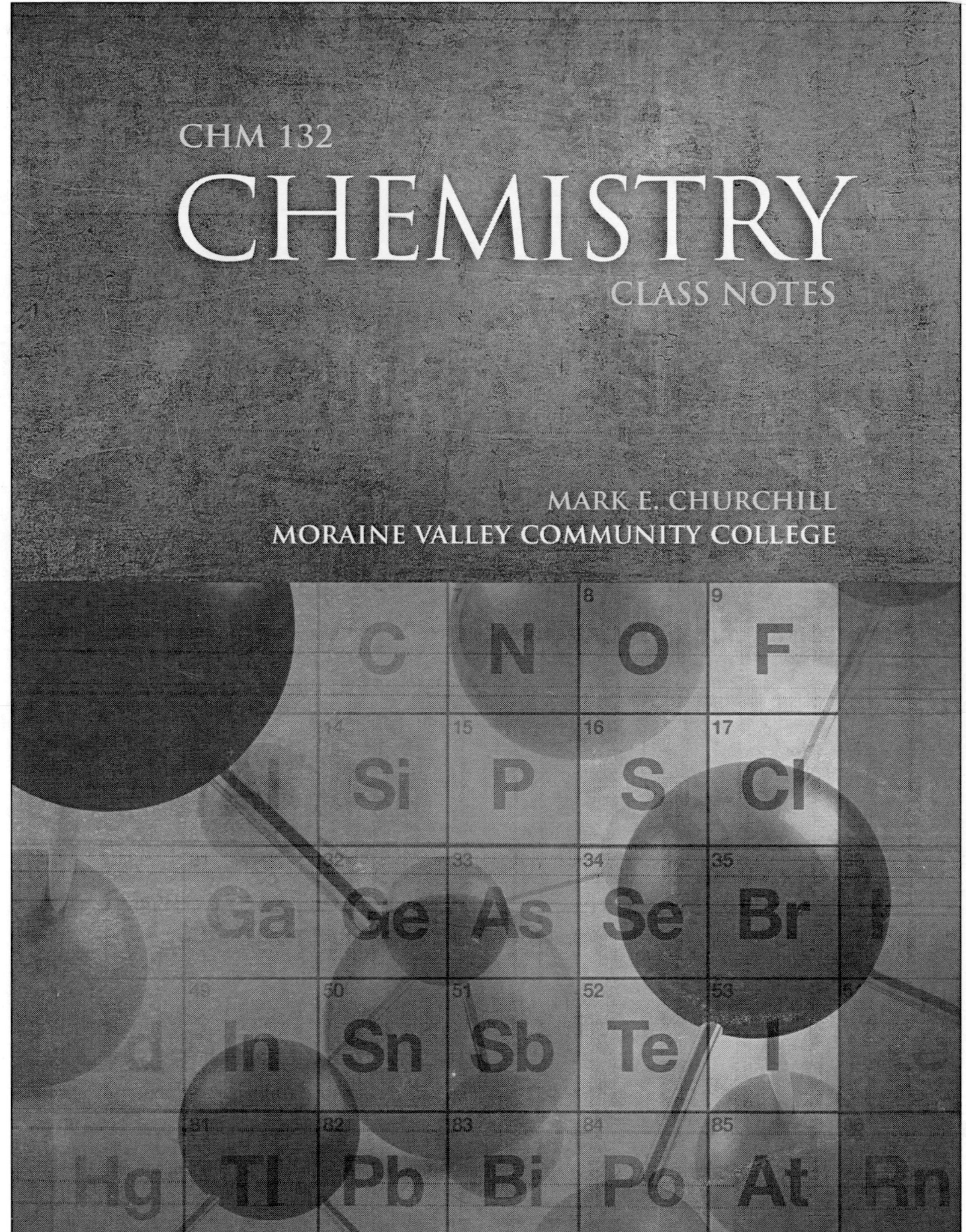

Mark E. Churchill
Moraine Valley Community College

President: Jon K. Earl

Senior Executive Publisher: Lucas Tomasso
Senior Executive Publisher: Al Grisanti
Senior Publisher: Dawn Earl

Senior Production Manager: Connie Dayton
Production Manager: Dan Woods
Production Manager: Amber Wahl
Production Manager: Julianne Prior
Assistant Production Manager: Ben Sweeney
Production Manager: Stephanie Larson
Project Manager: Peggy Li

Consulting Editors: Bruce D. Wingerd, M.S.
Suzanne S. Frucht, Ph.D.
Anna M. Kats, M.S., Florida Atlantic University
Michelle F. Cavallo, M.S., Florida Atlantic University
John F. Wiginton, Ph.D., University of Mississippi
Stephanie R. Dillon, Ph.D., Florida State University

Cover Design: Julianne Prior

ISBN-13: 978-1-59984-697-2

Published by bluedoor, LLC
10949 Bren Road East
Minneapolis, MN 55343-9613
800-979-1624
www.bluedoorpublishing.com

Printed in the United States of America.
14

Chemistry 132

Class Notes

Mark E. Churchill, Ph.D.

Moraine Valley Community College

Table of Contents

CHM-132 TABLES

Table 1

K_{sp} Values for Sparingly Soluble Salts

Name	Formula	K_{sp}
Bromides		
Copper(I) bromide	$CuBr$	6×10^{-19}
Lead bromide	$PbBr_2$	4.6×10^{-6}
Mercury(I) bromide	Hg_2Br_2	1.3×10^{-22}
Silver bromide	$AgBr$	5×10^{-13}
Carbonates		
Barium carbonate	$BaCO_3$	7×10^{-9}
Calcium carbonate	$CaCO_3$	1.7×10^{-8}
Cobalt(II) carbonate	$CoCO_3$	8×10^{-13}
Copper(II) carbonate	$CuCO_3$	2.5×10^{-10}
Iron(II) carbonate	$FeCO_3$	3.5×10^{-11}
Lead carbonate	$PbCO_3$	1.5×10^{-13}
Magnesium carbonate	$MgCO_3$	2.6×10^{-5}
Manganese(II) carbonate	$MnCO_3$	9×10^{-11}
Mercury(I) carbonate	Hg_2CO_3	9×10^{-17}
Nickel carbonate	$NiCO_3$	1.4×10^{-7}
Silver carbonate	Ag_2CO_3	8.2×10^{-12}
Strontium carbonate	$SrCO_3$	1.6×10^{-9}
Zinc carbonate	$ZnCO_3$	2×10^{-10}

Table 1 (Cont.) - K_{sp} Values

Name	Formula	K_{sp}
Chlorides		
Copper(I) chloride	$CuCl$	3.2×10^{-7}
Lead chloride	$PbCl_2$	1.6×10^{-5}
Mercury(I) chloride	Hg_2Cl_2	1.3×10^{-18}
Silver chloride	$AgCl$	1.8×10^{-10}
Chromates		
Barium chromate	$BaCrO_4$	8.5×10^{-11}
Lead chromate	$PbCrO_4$	2×10^{-16}
Mercury(I) chromate	Hg_2CrO_4	2.0×10^{-9}
Silver chromate	Ag_2CrO_4	1.9×10^{-12}
Strontium chromate	$SrCrO_4$	3.6×10^{-5}
Fluorides		
Barium fluoride	BaF_2	1.8×10^{-7}
Calcium fluoride	CaF_2	1.5×10^{-10}
Lead fluoride	PbF_2	7.1×10^{-7}
Magnesium fluoride	MgF_2	7×10^{-11}
Strontium fluoride	SrF_2	2.8×10^{-9}

Table 1 (Cont.) – K_{sp} Values

Name	Formula	K_{sp}
Hydroxides		
Aluminum hydroxide	$Al(OH)_3$	5×10^{-33}
Cadmium hydroxide	$Cd(OH)_2$	5.9×10^{-15}
Calcium hydroxide	$Ca(OH)_2$	1.3×10^{-6}
Chromium(II) hydroxide	$Cr(OH)_2$	1.0×10^{-17}
Chromium(III) hydroxide	$Cr(OH)_3$	6×10^{-31}
Cobalt(II) hydroxide	$Co(OH)_2$	1×10^{-15}
Cobalt(III) hydroxide	$Co(OH)_3$	1×10^{-43}
Copper(II) hydroxide	$Cu(OH)_2$	1.6×10^{-19}
Gold(III) hydroxide	$Au(OH)_3$	5.5×10^{-46}
Iron(II) hydroxide	$Fe(OH)_2$	2×10^{-15}
Iron(III) hydroxide	$Fe(OH)_3$	6×10^{-38}
Lead hydroxide	$Pb(OH)_2$	4×10^{-15}
Magnesium hydroxide	$Mg(OH)_2$	1×10^{-11}
Manganese(II) hydroxide	$Mn(OH)_2$	2×10^{-13}
Nickel hydroxide	$Ni(OH)_2$	1×10^{-15}
Palladium(II) hydroxide	$Pd(OH)_2$	1×10^{-31}
Platinum(II) hydroxide	$Pt(OH)_2$	1×10^{-35}
Zinc hydroxide	$Zn(OH)_2$	5×10^{-17}

Table 1 (Cont.) – K_{sp} Values

Name	Formula	K_{sp}
Iodides		
Bismuth iodide	BiI_3	8.1×10^{-19}
Copper(I) iodide	CuI	5.1×10^{-12}
Lead iodide	PbI_2	8.4×10^{-9}
Mercury(I) iodide	Hg_2I_2	5×10^{-29}
Silver iodide	AgI	1×10^{-16}
Oxalates		
Barium oxalate	BaC_2O_4	1.6×10^{-7}
Calcium oxalate	CaC_2O_4	2.3×10^{-9}
Copper(II) oxalate	CuC_2O_4	2.9×10^{-8}
Lead oxalate	PbC_2O_4	2.7×10^{-11}
Magnesium oxalate	MgC_2O_4	8.5×10^{-5}
Mercury(I) oxalate	$Hg_2C_2O_4$	1×10^{-13}
Silver oxalate	$Ag_2C_2O_4$	3.5×10^{-11}
Strontium oxalate	SrC_2O_4	5.6×10^{-8}
Zinc oxalate	ZnC_2O_4	1.4×10^{-9}
Phosphates		
Aluminum phosphate	$AlPO_4$	1×10^{-20}
Bismuth phosphate	$BiPO_4$	1.3×10^{-23}
Calcium phosphate	$Ca_3(PO_4)_2$	1×10^{-33}
Magnesium phosphate	$Mg_3(PO_4)_2$	1×10^{-24}
Silver phosphate	Ag_3PO_4	1×10^{-16}
Zinc phosphate	$Zn_3(PO_4)_2$	9.1×10^{-33}

Table 1 (Cont.) – K_{sp} Values

Name	Formula	K_{sp}
Sulfates		
Barium sulfate	$BaSO_4$	1.5×10^{-9}
Calcium sulfate	$CaSO_4$	2.4×10^{-5}
Lead sulfate	$PbSO_4$	1.3×10^{-8}
Mercury(I) sulfate	Hg_2SO_4	7.4×10^{-7}
Silver sulfate	Ag_2SO_4	1.6×10^{-5}
Strontium sulfate	$SrSO_4$	7.6×10^{-7}
Sulfides		
Bismuth sulfide	Bi_2S_3	1×10^{-99}
Cadmium sulfide	CdS	1×10^{-29}
Cobalt(II) sulfide	CoS	1×10^{-21}
Copper(I) sulfide	Cu_2S	1×10^{-48}
Copper(II) sulfide	CuS	6×10^{-36}
Iron(II) sulfide	FeS	6×10^{-18}
Lead sulfide	PbS	1×10^{-27}
Manganese(II) sulfide	MnS	7×10^{-16}
Mercury(I) sulfide	Hg_2S	1×10^{-45}
Mercury(II) sulfide	HgS	1×10^{-52}
Nickel sulfide	NiS	1×10^{-22}
Silver sulfide	Ag_2S	6×10^{-50}
Tin(II) sulfide	SnS	1×10^{-25}
Zinc sulfide	ZnS	2×10^{-20}

Table 2 – K_a Values of Weak Acids

Monoprotic Acids

Acid Name	Reaction	K_a	pK_a
Acetic	$HC_2H_3O_2 \rightleftharpoons H^+ + C_2H_3O_2^-$	1.8×10^{-5}	4.74
Ammonium ion	$NH_4^+ \rightleftharpoons H^+ + NH_3$	5.6×10^{-10}	9.25
Benzoic	$HC_7H_5O_2 \rightleftharpoons H^+ + C_7H_5O_2^-$	6.5×10^{-5}	4.19
Bisulfate ion	$HSO_4^- \rightleftharpoons H^+ + SO_4^{2-}$	1.3×10^{-2}	1.89
Chloroacetic	$HC_2H_2O_2Cl \rightleftharpoons H^+ + C_2H_2O_2Cl^-$	1.4×10^{-3}	2.85
Chlorous	$HClO_2 \rightleftharpoons H^+ + ClO_2^-$	1.1×10^{-2}	1.96
Formic	$HCHO_2 \rightleftharpoons H^+ + CHO_2^-$	1.7×10^{-4}	3.77
Hydrocyanic	$HCN \rightleftharpoons H^+ + CN^-$	4.9×10^{-10}	9.31
Hydrofluoric	$HF \rightleftharpoons H^+ + F^-$	7.1×10^{-4}	3.15
Hydrogen peroxide	$H_2O_2 \rightleftharpoons H^+ + HO_2^-$	2.4×10^{-12}	11.6
Hypobromous	$HBrO \rightleftharpoons H^+ + BrO^-$	2.1×10^{-9}	8.68
Hypochlorous	$HClO \rightleftharpoons H^+ + ClO^-$	3.0×10^{-8}	7.52
Hypoiodous	$HIO \rightleftharpoons H^+ + IO^-$	2.3×10^{-11}	10.6
Lactic	$HC_3H_5O_3 \rightleftharpoons H^+ + C_3H_5O_3^-$	8.4×10^{-4}	3.08
Nitrous	$HNO_2 \rightleftharpoons H^+ + NO_2^-$	4.5×10^{-4}	3.35

Polyprotic acids are on the back of this page.

Table 2 (Cont.) – K_a Values

Polyprotic Acids

Acid Name	Reaction	K_a	pK_a
Carbonic	$H_2CO_3 \rightleftharpoons H^+ + HCO_3^-$	4.2×10^{-7}	6.38
(Bicarbonate ion)	$HCO_3^- \rightleftharpoons H^+ + CO_3^{2-}$	4.8×10^{-11}	10.3
Hydrogen sulfide	$H_2S \rightleftharpoons H^+ + HS^-$	9.5×10^{-8}	7.02
	$HS^- \rightleftharpoons H^+ + S^{2-}$	Weaker than H_2O	----
Oxalic	$H_2C_2O_4 \rightleftharpoons H^+ + HC_2O_4^-$	6.5×10^{-2}	1.19
	$HC_2O_4^- \rightleftharpoons H^+ + C_2O_4^{2-}$	6.1×10^{-5}	4.21
Phosphoric	$H_3PO_4 \rightleftharpoons H^+ + H_2PO_4^-$	7.5×10^{-3}	2.12
	$H_2PO_4^- \rightleftharpoons H^+ + HPO_4^{2-}$	6.2×10^{-8}	7.21
	$HPO_4^{2-} \rightleftharpoons H^+ + PO_4^{3-}$	4.8×10^{-13}	12.3
Sulfuric	$H_2SO_4 \rightarrow H^+ + HSO_4^-$	**STRONG**	----
(Bisulfate ion)	$HSO_4^- \rightleftharpoons H^+ + SO_4^{2-}$	1.3×10^{-2}	1.89
Sulfurous	$H_2SO_3 \rightleftharpoons H^+ + HSO_3^-$	1.3×10^{-2}	1.89
(Bisulfite ion)	$HSO_3^- \rightleftharpoons H^+ + SO_3^{2-}$	6.3×10^{-8}	7.20

Table 3 – Reduction Potentials in Order of E^{o}_{red}

Acidic Solution

Reaction	E^{o}_{red}
$K^+ + e^- \longrightarrow K(s)$	−2.925
$Ba^{2+} + 2e^- \longrightarrow Ba(s)$	−2.90
$Sr^{2+} + 2e^- \longrightarrow Sr(s)$	−2.89
$Ca^{2+} + 2e^- \longrightarrow Ca(s)$	−2.87
$Na^+ + e^- \longrightarrow Na(s)$	−2.71
$Mg^{2+} + 2e^- \longrightarrow Mg(s)$	−2.37
$Al^{3+} + 3e^- \longrightarrow Al(s)$	−1.66
$Mn^{2+} + 2e^- \longrightarrow Mn(s)$	−1.18
$Cr^{2+} + 2e^- \longrightarrow Cr(s)$	−0.91
$Zn^{2+} + 2e^- \longrightarrow Zn(s)$	−0.763
$Cr^{3+} + 3e^- \longrightarrow Cr(s)$	−0.74
$Fe^{2+} + 2e^- \longrightarrow Fe(s)$	−0.440
$Cr^{3+} + e^- \longrightarrow Cr^{2+}$	−0.41
$Cd^{2+} + 2e^- \longrightarrow Cd(s)$	−0.403
$PbSO_4(s) + 2e^- \longrightarrow Pb(s) + SO_4^{2-}$	−0.356
$Co^{2+} + 2e^- \longrightarrow Co(s)$	−0.277
$Ni^{2+} + 2e^- \longrightarrow Ni(s)$	−0.250
$AgI(s) + e^- \longrightarrow Ag(s) + I^-$	−0.152
$Sn^{2+} + 2e^- \longrightarrow Sn(s)$	−0.136
$Pb^{2+} + 2e^- \longrightarrow Pb(s)$	−0.126
$2H^+ + 2e^- \longrightarrow H_2(g)$	0.000
$AgBr(s) + e^- \longrightarrow Ag(s) + Br^-$	+0.073
$SnCl_6^{2-} + 2e^- \longrightarrow SnCl_4^{2-} + 2Cl^-$	+0.10 (approximate)
$S(s) + 2H^+ + 2e^- \longrightarrow H_2S$	+0.141
$Sn^{4+} + 2e^- \longrightarrow Sn^{2+}$	+0.15
$Cu^{2+} + e^- \longrightarrow Cu^+$	+0.153
$SO_4^{2-} + 4H^+ + 2e^- \longrightarrow SO_2(g) + 2H_2O$	+0.155
$AgCl(s) + e^- \longrightarrow Ag(s) + Cl^-$	+0.222
$Cu^{2+} + 2e^- \longrightarrow Cu(s)$	+0.337
$Cu^+ + e^- \longrightarrow Cu(s)$	+0.521

Table 3 (Cont.) – E°_{red} Values

Acidic Solution

Reaction	E°_{red}
$O_2(g) + 2H^+ + 2e^- \longrightarrow H_2O_2$	+0.682
$Fe^{3+} + e^- \longrightarrow Fe^{2+}$	+0.771
$Ag^+ + e^- \longrightarrow Ag(s)$	+0.7991
$Hg^{2+} + 2e^- \longrightarrow Hg(\ell)$	+0.854
$NO_3^- + 3H^+ + 2e^- \longrightarrow HNO_2 + H_2O$	+0.94
$NO_3^- + 4H^+ + 3e^- \longrightarrow NO(g) + 2H_2O$	+0.96
$HNO_2 + H^+ + e^- \longrightarrow NO(g) + H_2O$	+0.99
$AuCl_4^- + 3e^- \longrightarrow Au(s) + 4Cl^-$	+1.001
$ClO_4^- + 2H^+ + 2e^- \longrightarrow ClO_3^- + H_2O$	+1.19
$2IO_3^- + 12H^+ + 10e^- \longrightarrow I_2 + 6H_2O$	+1.19
$O_2(g) + 4H^+ + 4e^- \longrightarrow 2H_2O$	+1.23
$MnO_2(s) + 4H^+ + 2e^- \longrightarrow Mn^{2+} + 2H_2O$	+1.23
$Cr_2O_7^{2-} + 14H^+ + 6e^- \longrightarrow 2Cr^{3+} + 7H_2O$	+1.33
$2ClO_3^- + 12H^+ + 10e^- \longrightarrow Cl_2 + 6H_2O$	+1.458
$Au^{3+} + 3e^- \longrightarrow Au(s)$	+1.50
$MnO_4^- + 8H^+ + 5e^- \longrightarrow Mn^{2+} + 4H_2O$	+1.51
$BiO_3^- + 6H^+ + 2e^- \longrightarrow Bi^{3+} + 3H_2O$	Greater than +1.51
$2BrO_3^- + 12H^+ + 10e^- \longrightarrow Br_2 + 6H_2O$	+1.52
$NiO_2(s) + 4H^+ + 2e^- \longrightarrow Ni^{2+} + 2H_2O$	+1.68
$H_2O_2 + 2H^+ + 2e^- \longrightarrow 2H_2O$	+1.77
$Co^{3+} + e^- \longrightarrow Co^{2+}$	+2.87

Table 3 (Cont.) – E°_{red} Values

Basic Solution

Reaction	E°_{red}
$Cr(OH)_3(s) + 3e^- \longrightarrow Cr(s) + 3OH^-$	-1.3
$Zn(OH)_2(s) + 2e^- \longrightarrow Zn(s) + 2OH^-$	-1.245
$Fe(OH)_2(s) + 2e^- \longrightarrow Fe(s) + 2OH^-$	-0.877
$2H_2O + 2e^- \longrightarrow H_2(g) + 2OH^-$	-0.828
$Co(OH)_2(s) + 2e^- \longrightarrow Co(s) + 2OH^-$	-0.73
$Ni(OH)_2(s) + 2e^- \longrightarrow Ni(s) + 2OH^-$	-0.66
$Fe(OH)_3(s) + e^- \longrightarrow Fe(OH)_2(s) + OH^-$	-0.56
$NO_2^- + H_2O + e^- \longrightarrow NO(g) + 2OH^-$	-0.46
$Cu(OH)_2(s) + 2e^- \longrightarrow Cu(s) + 2OH^-$	-0.224
$NO_3^- + 2H_2O + 3e^- \longrightarrow NO(g) + 4OH^-$	-0.140
$CrO_4^{2-} + 4H_2O + 3e \longrightarrow Cr(OH)_3(s) + 5OH^-$	-0.13
$MnO_2(s) + 2H_2O + 2e^- \longrightarrow Mn(OH)_2(s) + 2OH^-$	-0.05
$NO_3^- + H_2O + 2e^- \longrightarrow NO_2^- + 2OH^-$	+0.01
$ClO_4^- + H_2O + 2e^- \longrightarrow ClO_3^- + 2OH^-$	+0.17
$Co(OH)_3(s) + e^- \longrightarrow Co(OH)_2(s) + OH^-$	+0.17
$IO_3^- + 3H_2O + 6e^- \longrightarrow I^- + 6OH^-$	+0.26
$ClO_3^- + H_2O + 2e^- \longrightarrow ClO_2^- + 2OH^-$	+0.33
$O_2(g) + 2H_2O + 4e^- \longrightarrow 4OH^-$	+0.401
$NiO_2(s) + 2H_2O + 2e^- \longrightarrow Ni(OH)_2(s) + 2OH^-$	+0.49
$MnO_4^- + 2H_2O + 3e^- \longrightarrow MnO_2(s) + 4OH^-$	+0.588
$BrO_3^- + 3H_2O + 6e^- \longrightarrow Br^- + 6OH^-$	+0.61
$ClO_3^- + 3H_2O + 6e^- \longrightarrow Cl^- + 6OH^-$	+0.614
$ClO_2^- + H_2O + 2e^- \longrightarrow ClO^- + 2OH^-$	+0.66
$HO_2^- + H_2O + 2e^- \longrightarrow 3OH^-$	+0.88
$ClO^- + H_2O + 2e^- \longrightarrow Cl^- + 2OH^-$	+0.89

Either Acidic or Basic

Reaction	E°_{red}
$I_2 + 2e^- \longrightarrow 2I^-$	+0.5355
$Br_2 + 2e^- \longrightarrow 2Br^-$	+1.0652
$Cl_2 + 2e^- \longrightarrow 2Cl^-$	+1.3595
$F_2 + 2e^- \longrightarrow 2F^-$	+2.87

Table 4

Reduction Potentials by Element

*** = Basic Solution**
/ = Either Acidic or Basic Solution
No Symbol = Acidic Solution

	Reaction	E^o_{red}
	$Ag^+ + e^- \longrightarrow Ag(s)$	+0.7991
	$AgCl(s) + e^- \longrightarrow Ag(s) + Cl^-$	+0.222
	$AgBr(s) + e^- \longrightarrow Ag(s) + Br^-$	+0.073
	$AgI(s) + e^- \longrightarrow Ag(s) + I^-$	−0.152
	$Al^{3+} + 3e^- \longrightarrow Al(s)$	−1.66
	$Au^{3+} + 3e^- \longrightarrow Au(s)$	+1.50
	$AuCl_4^- + 3e^- \longrightarrow Au(s) + 4Cl^-$	+1.001
	$Ba^{2+} + 2e^- \longrightarrow Ba(s)$	−2.90
	$BiO_3^- + 6H^+ + 2e^- \longrightarrow Bi^{3+} + 3H_2O$	Greater than +1.51
/	$Br_2 + 2e^- \longrightarrow 2Br^-$	+1.0652
	$2BrO_3^- + 12H^+ + 10e^- \longrightarrow Br_2 + 6H_2O$	+1.52
*	$BrO_3^- + 3H_2O + 6e^- \longrightarrow Br^- + 6OH^-$	+0.61
	$Ca^{2+} + 2e^- \longrightarrow Ca(s)$	−2.87
	$Cd^{2+} + 2e^- \longrightarrow Cd(s)$	−0.403
/	$Cl_2 + 2e^- \longrightarrow 2Cl^-$	+1.3595
*	$ClO^- + H_2O + 2e^- \longrightarrow Cl^- + 2OH^-$	+0.89
*	$ClO_2^- + H_2O + 2e^- \longrightarrow ClO^- + 2OH^-$	+0.66
	$2ClO_3^- + 12H^+ + 10e^- \longrightarrow Cl_2 + 6H_2O$	+1.458
*	$ClO_3^- + H_2O + 2e^- \longrightarrow ClO_2^- + 2OH^-$	+0.33
*	$ClO_3^- + 3H_2O + 6e^- \longrightarrow Cl^- + 6OH^-$	+0.614
	$ClO_4^- + 2H^+ + 2e^- \longrightarrow ClO_3^- + H_2O$	+1.19
*	$ClO_4^- + H_2O + 2e^- \longrightarrow ClO_3^- + 2OH^-$	+0.17
	$Co^{2+} + 2e^- \longrightarrow Co(s)$	−0.277
	$Co^{3+} + e^- \longrightarrow Co^{2+}$	+2.87

Table 4 (Cont.) – Reduction Potentials by Element

*** = Basic Solution**

/ = Either Acidic or Basic Solution

No Symbol = Acidic Solution

	Reaction	E^o_{red}
*	$Co(OH)_2(s) + 2e^- \longrightarrow Co(s) + 2OH^-$	−0.73
*	$Co(OH)_3(s) + e^- \longrightarrow Co(OH)_2(s) + OH^-$	+0.17
	$Cr^{2+} + 2e^- \longrightarrow Cr(s)$	−0.91
	$Cr^{3+} + 3e^- \longrightarrow Cr(s)$	−0.74
	$Cr^{3+} + e^- \longrightarrow Cr^{2+}$	−0.41
	$Cr_2O_7^{2-} + 14H^+ + 6e^- \longrightarrow 2Cr^{3+} + 7H_2O$	+1.33
*	$Cr(OH)_3(s) + 3e^- \longrightarrow Cr(s) + 3OH^-$	−1.3
*	$CrO_4^{2-} + 4H_2O + 3e^- \longrightarrow Cr(OH)_3(s) + 5OH^-$	−0.13
	$Cu^+ + e^- \longrightarrow Cu(s)$	+0.521
	$Cu^{2+} + 2e^- \longrightarrow Cu(s)$	+0.337
	$Cu^{2+} + e^- \longrightarrow Cu^+$	+0.153
*	$Cu(OH)_2(s) + 2e^- \longrightarrow Cu(s) + 2OH^-$	−0.224
/	$F_2 + 2e^- \longrightarrow 2F^-$	+2.87
	$Fe^{2+} + 2e^- \longrightarrow Fe(s)$	−0.440
	$Fe^{3+} + e^- \longrightarrow Fe^{2+}$	+0.771
*	$Fe(OH)_2(s) + 2e^- \longrightarrow Fe(s) + 2OH^-$	−0.877
*	$Fe(OH)_3(s) + e^- \longrightarrow Fe(OH)_2(s) + OH^-$	−0.56

H_2, O_2, H_2O, HO_2^- and H_2O_2

	Reaction	E^o_{red}
	$2H^+ + 2e^- \longrightarrow H_2(g)$	0.000
	$O_2(g) + 4H^+ + 4e^- \longrightarrow 2H_2O$	+1.23
	$O_2(g) + 2H^+ + 2e^- \longrightarrow H_2O_2$	+0.682
*	$O_2(g) + 2H_2O + 4e^- \longrightarrow 4OH^-$	+0.401
*	$2H_2O + 2e^- \longrightarrow H_2(g) + 2OH^-$	−0.828
	$H_2O_2 + 2H^+ + 2e^- \longrightarrow 2H_2O$	+1.77
*	$HO_2^- + H_2O + 2e^- \longrightarrow 3OH^-$	+0.88

Table 4 (Cont.) – Reduction Potentials by Element

*** = Basic Solution**

/ = Either Acidic or Basic Solution

No Symbol = Acidic Solution

	Reaction	E°_{red}
	$Hg^{2+} + 2e^- \longrightarrow Hg(\ell)$	+0.854
/	$I_2 + 2e^- \longrightarrow 2I^-$	+0.5355
	$2IO_3^- + 12H^+ + 10e^- \longrightarrow I_2 + 6H_2O$	+1.19
*	$IO_3^- + 3H_2O + 6e^- \longrightarrow I^- + 6OH^-$	+0.26
	$K^+ + e \longrightarrow K(s)$	-2.925
	$Mg^{2+} + 2e^- \longrightarrow Mg(s)$	-2.37
	$Mn^{2+} + 2e^- \longrightarrow Mn(s)$	-1.18
	$MnO_2(s) + 4H^+ + 2e^- \longrightarrow Mn^{2+} + 2H_2O$	+1.23
	$MnO_4^- + 8H^+ + 5e^- \longrightarrow Mn^{2+} + 4H_2O$	+1.51
*	$MnO_2(s) + 2H_2O + 2e^- \longrightarrow Mn(OH)_2(s) + 2OH^-$	-0.05
*	$MnO_4^- + 2H_2O + 3e^- \longrightarrow MnO_2(s) + 4OH^-$	+0.588

HNO_2, NO_2^-, and NO_3^-

	Reaction	E°_{red}
	$HNO_2 + H^+ + e^- \longrightarrow NO(g) + H_2O$	+0.99
*	$NO_2^- + H_2O + e^- \longrightarrow NO(g) + 2OH^-$	-0.46
	$NO_3^- + 3H^+ + 2e^- \longrightarrow HNO_2 + H_2O$	+0.94
	$NO_3^- + 4H^+ + 3e^- \longrightarrow NO(g) + 2H_2O$	+0.96
*	$NO_3^- + H_2O + 2e^- \longrightarrow NO_2^- + 2OH^-$	+0.01
*	$NO_3^- + 2H_2O + 3e^- \longrightarrow NO(g) + 4OH^-$	-0.140

	Reaction	E°_{red}
	$Na^+ + e^- \longrightarrow Na(s)$	-2.71
	$Ni^{2+} + 2e^- \longrightarrow Ni(s)$	-0.250
*	$Ni(OH)_2(s) + 2e^- \longrightarrow Ni(s) + 2OH^-$	-0.66
	$NiO_2(s) + 4H^+ + 2e^- \longrightarrow Ni^{2+} + 2H_2O$	+1.68
*	$NiO_2(s) + 2H_2O + 2e^- \longrightarrow Ni(OH)_2(s) + 2OH^-$	+0.49

Table 4 (Cont.) – Reduction Potentials by Element

*** = Basic Solution**

/ = Either Acidic or Basic Solution

No Symbol = Acidic Solution

	Reaction	E^{o}_{red}
	$Pb^{2+} + 2e^{-} \longrightarrow Pb(s)$	−0.126
	$PbSO_4(s) + 2e^{-} \longrightarrow Pb(s) + SO_4^{2-}$	−0.356
	$S(s) + 2H^{+} + 2e^{-} \longrightarrow H_2S$	+0.141
	$SO_4^{2-} + 4H^{+} + 2e^{-} \longrightarrow SO_2(g) + 2H_2O$	+0.155
	$Sn^{2+} + 2e^{-} \longrightarrow Sn(s)$	−0.136
	$Sn^{4+} + 2e^{-} \longrightarrow Sn^{2+}$	+0.15
	$SnCl_6^{2-} + 2e^{-} \longrightarrow SnCl_4^{2-} + 2Cl^{-}$	+0.10 (approximate)
	$Sr^{2+} + 2e^{-} \longrightarrow Sr(s)$	−2.89
	$Zn^{2+} + 2e^{-} \longrightarrow Zn(s)$	−0.763
*	$Zn(OH)_2(s) + 2e^{-} \longrightarrow Zn(s) + 2OH^{-}$	−1.245

Table 5 - Common Ligands in Complexes

Monodentate Ligands

Neutral

NH_3	ammine
H_2O	aqua
CO	carbonyl

Anionic

Br^-	bromo
Cl^-	chloro
CO_3^{2-}	carbonato
CN^-	cyano
F^-	fluoro
OH^-	hydroxo
NO_2^-	nitro (when metal is bonded to **N** atom)
NO_2^-	nitrito (when metal is bonded to **O** atom)
SO_4^{2-}	sulfato
SCN^-	thiocyanato

Bidentate Ligands

Neutral

en	ethylenediamine, $H_2N(CH_2)_2NH_2$

Anionic

DMG^-	dimethylglyoxime, $C_4H_6N_2O_2H^-$
$C_2O_4^{2-}$	oxalato

Table 6 – Thermodynamic Data

	ΔH_f° (kJ/mol)	S° (kJ/K·mol)	ΔG_f° (kJ/mol) at 25°C
Ag(s)	0.0	+0.0426	0.0
AgBr(s)	-100.4	+0.1071	-96.9
AgCl(s)	-127.1	+0.0962	-109.8
AgI(s)	-61.8	+0.1155	-66.2
$AgNO_3$(s)	-124.4	+0.1409	-33.4
Ag_2O(s)	-31.0	+0.1213	-11.2
Al(s)	0.0	+0.0283	0.0
Al_2O_3(s)	-1675.7	+0.0509	-1582.3
Ba(s)	0.0	+0.0628	0.0
$BaCl_2$(s)	-858.6	+0.1237	-810.4
$BaCO_3$(s)	-1216.3	+0.1121	-1137.6
BaO(s)	-553.5	+0.0704	-525.1
$BaSO_4$(s)	-1473.2	+0.1322	-1362.3
Br_2(ℓ)	0.0	+0.1522	0.0
C(s)	0.0	+0.0057	0.0
CCl_4(ℓ)	-135.4	+0.2164	-65.3
$CHCl_3$(ℓ)	-134.5	+0.2017	-73.7
CH_4(g)	-74.8	+0.1862	-50.7
C_2H_2(g)	+226.7	+0.2008	+217.1
C_2H_4(g)	+52.3	+0.2195	+68.1
C_2H_6(g)	-84.7	+0.2295	-32.9
C_3H_8(g)	-103.8	+0.2699	-23.5
CH_3OH(ℓ)	-238.7	+0.1268	-166.3
C_2H_5OH(ℓ)	-277.7	+0.1607	-174.9
CO(g)	-110.5	+0.1976	-137.2
CO_2(g)	-393.5	+0.2136	-394.4
Ca(s)	0.0	+0.0414	0.0
$CaCl_2$(s)	-795.8	+0.1046	-748.1
$CaCO_3$(s)	-1206.9	+0.0929	-1128.8
CaO(s)	-635.1	+0.0398	-604.0
$Ca(OH)_2$(s)	-986.1	+0.0834	-898.5
$CaSO_4$(s)	-1434.1	+0.1067	-1321.8
Cd(s)	0.0	+0.0518	0.0
$CdCl_2$(s)	-391.5	+0.1153	-344.0
Cl_2(g)	0.0	+0.2230	0.0
Cr(s)	0.0	+0.0238	0.0
Cr_2O_3(s)	-1139.7	+0.0812	-1058.1
Cu(s)	0.0	+0.0332	0.0
CuO(s)	-157.3	+0.0426	-129.7
Cu_2O(s)	-168.6	+0.0931	-146.0
CuS(s)	-53.1	+0.0665	-53.6
Cu_2S(s)	-79.5	+0.1209	-86.2
$CuSO_4$(s)	-771.4	+0.1076	-661.9
F_2(g)	0.0	+0.2027	0.0
Fe(s)	0.0	+0.0273	0.0
$Fe(OH)_3$(s)	-823.0	+0.1067	-696.6
Fe_2O_3(s)	-824.2	+0.0874	-742.2
Fe_3O_4(s)	-1118.4	+0.1464	-1015.5
H_2(g)	0.0	+0.1306	0.0
HBr(g)	-36.4	+0.1986	-53.4
HCl(g)	-92.3	+0.1868	-95.3
HF(g)	-271.1	+0.1737	-273.2
HI(g)	+26.5	+0.2065	+1.7
HNO_3(ℓ)	-174.1	+0.1556	-80.8
H_2O(g)	-241.8	+0.1887	-228.6
H_2O(ℓ)	-285.8	+0.0699	-237.2

Table 6 (Cont.) -- Thermodynamic Data

	ΔH_f^o (kJ/mol)	S^o (kJ/K·mol)	ΔG_f^o (kJ/mol) at 25°C
$H_2S(g)$	-20.6	+0.2057	-33.6
$H_2SO_4(\ell)$	-814.0	+0.1569	-690.1
$Hg(\ell)$	0.0	+0.0760	0.0
$HgO(s)$	-90.8	+0.0703	-58.6
$I_2(s)$	0.0	+0.1161	0.0
$K(s)$	0.0	+0.0642	0.0
$KBr(s)$	-393.8	+0.0959	-380.7
$KCl(s)$	-436.7	+0.0826	-409.1
$KClO_3(s)$	-397.7	+0.1431	-296.3
$KClO_4(s)$	-432.8	+0.1510	-303.2
$KNO_3(s)$	-369.8	+0.1330	-394.9
$Mg(s)$	0.0	+0.0327	0.0
$MgCl_2(s)$	-641.3	+0.0896	-591.8
$MgCO_3(s)$	-1095.8	+0.0657	-1012.1
$MgO(s)$	-601.7	+0.0269	-569.4
$Mg(OH)_2(s)$	-924.5	+0.0632	-833.6
$MgSO_4(s)$	-1284.9	+0.0916	-1170.7
$Mn(s)$	0.0	+0.0320	0.0
$MnO(s)$	-385.2	+0.0597	-362.9
$MnO_2(s)$	-520.0	+0.0530	-465.2
$N_2(g)$	0.0	+0.1915	0.0
$NH_3(g)$	-46.1	+0.1923	-16.5
$NH_4Cl(s)$	-314.4	+0.0946	-203.0
$NH_4NO_3(s)$	-365.6	+0.1511	-184.0
$N_2H_4(\ell)$	+50.6	+0.1212	+149.2
$NO(g)$	+90.2	+0.2107	+86.6
$NO_2(g)$	+33.2	+0.2400	+51.3
$N_2O_4(g)$	+9.2	+0.3042	+97.9
$Na(s)$	0.0	+0.0512	0.0
$NaCl(s)$	-411.2	+0.0721	-384.2
$NaF(s)$	-573.6	+0.0515	-543.5
$NaOH(s)$	-425.6	+0.0645	-379.5
$Ni(s)$	0.0	+0.0299	0.0
$NiO(s)$	-239.7	+0.0380	-211.7
$O_2(g)$	0.0	+0.2050	0.0
$P_4(s)$	0.0	+0.1644	0.0
$PCl_3(g)$	-287.0	+0.3117	-267.8
$PCl_5(g)$	-374.9	+0.3645	-305.0
$Pb(s)$	0.0	+0.0648	0.0
$PbBr_2(s)$	-278.7	+0.1615	-261.9
$PbCl_2(s)$	-359.4	+0.1360	-314.1
$PbO(s)$	-219.0	+0.0665	-188.9
$PbO_2(s)$	-277.4	+0.0686	-217.4
$S(s)$	0.0	+0.0318	0.0
$SO_2(g)$	-296.8	+0.2481	-300.2
$SO_3(g)$	-395.7	+0.2567	-371.1
$Si(s)$	0.0	+0.0188	0.0
$SiO_2(s)$	-910.9	+0.0418	-856.7
$Sn(s)$	0.0	+0.0516	0.0
$SnO_2(s)$	-580.7	+0.0523	-519.6
$Zn(s)$	0.0	+0.0416	0.0
$ZnI_2(s)$	-208.0	+0.1611	-209.0
$ZnO(s)$	-348.3	+0.0436	-318.3
$ZnS(s)$	-206.0	+0.0577	-201.3

Objectives for Exams

OBJECTIVES FOR EXAM #1, CHM 132

After studying and doing problems from this section of the course, the student should be able to:

1. Do the following types of problems involving equilibrium:
   a. Write the K_{eq} expression for a reaction.
   b. Calculate the value of K_{eq} given equilibrium concentrations.
   c. Calculate the value of K_{eq} given initial concentrations and one equilibrium concentration.
   d. Calculate Q and use the value to determine the direction a reaction will shift to reach equilibrium.
   e. Use LeChatelier's Principle to predict the direction a reaction will shift to restore equilibrium.
2. Classify compounds as **ionic** or **covalent**.
3. Know **from memory** the names, charges and formulas of ions listed on pp. 49–51.
4. Write the formula of an ionic compound given the name (the cross method).
5. Classify a compound as an **acid, base,** or **salt.**
6. Classify an acid or base as **weak** or **strong.**
7. Write the dissolving equation for any given salt.
8. Know **from memory** the four solubility rules given in class and use them to determine whether a salt is soluble in water.
9. Write the K_{sp} expression for any insoluble salt.
10. Use K_{sp} values to determine which salt is most or least soluble.
11. Calculate Q and determine whether a precipitate will form, given the concentrations of two ions or two soluble compounds in solution.
12. Complete a double displacement (metathesis) precipitation reaction given the two reactants.
13. Write the net ionic equation for a metathesis precipitation reaction and identify the spectator ions.
14. Write the K_w expression for water and know that $K_w = 1.0 \times 10^{-14}$.
15. Interconvert $[H^+]$, $[OH^-]$, pH, and pOH. (Given one of them, calculate any of the others.)
16. Write the equation for ionization of a weak acid and the corresponding K_a expression.
17. Use K_a values to determine which acid is stronger or weaker.
18. Write the equation for each ionization step of a diprotic or triprotic acid.
19. Know that as polyprotic acids lose H^+ ions, the resulting acids become progressively weaker.

Objectives for Exam #1 continue on the back.

20. Know **from memory** the names, formulas, and charges of the following ions: HCO_3^-, HSO_4^-, HSO_3^-, $H_2PO_4^-$, and HPO_4^{2-}.
21. Write the equation for the reaction of a weak base with H_2O and the corresponding K_b expression.
22. Define and identify Bronsted acids and bases.
23. Calculate the K_b of a weak base given the K_a of the conjugate acid. (That is, use the equation $K_a \times K_b = 1 \times 10^{-14}$)
24. Use K_b values to determine which base is stronger or weaker.
25. Calculate the pH for a solution of a strong acid.
26. Calculate the pH and % ionization for a solution of a weak acid.
27. Calculate the pH and % ionization for a solution of a polyprotic acid (use only the first dissociation step)
28. Calculate the pH for a solution of a strong base.
29. Calculate the pH and % ionization for a solution of a weak base.

OBJECTIVES FOR EXAM #2, CHM 132

After studying and doing problems from this section of the course, the student should be able to:

1. Calculate the K_a of a weak acid given the molarity of the acid (or the # grams dissolved in a given volume of solution) and the pH of the solution.
2. Determine whether a salt will produce an acidic, basic, or neutral solution when dissolved in water (hydrolysis).
3. Calculate the pH of a salt solution given the molarity of the salt.
4. Know that, when a diprotic acid is dissolved in pure water, the concentration of the 2− ion equals the K_{a2} value ($[A^{2-}] = K_{a2}$).
5. Classify a given compound as a **strong, weak,** or **non-electrolyte**.
6. Calculate the oxidation number of any atom in a given compound or ion.
7. Explain the structure and operation of an electrochemical cell. For example, you should be able to determine:
   a. Which electrode is the anode and which is the cathode.
   b. Which way the electrons flow in the wire.
   c. Which way the cations and anions move in the solution.
   d. Which electrode dissolves and which one plates out.
8. Show on a table of reduction half-reactions which substances are good oxidizing agents and which are good reducing agents.
9. Balance a redox reaction in either acidic or basic solution, using a table of reduction half-reactions.
10. Write a balanced redox equation given the shorthand diagram of an electrochemical cell, such as:
    $Zn \mid Zn^{2+}(aq) \parallel Cu^{2+}(aq) \mid Cu$
11. Given a redox reaction, identify the oxidizing agent, reducing agent, substance oxidized, and substance reduced.
12. Write the net ionic equation for a neutralization reaction of any of the following types:
    a. Type 1, strong acid/strong base
    b. Type 2, weak acid/strong base
    c. Type 3a, strong acid/weak base (NH_3)
    d. Type 3b, strong acid/weak base (anion)

Objectives for Exam #2 continue on the back.

13. Explain how to prepare the following buffers: acetate buffer, ammonia buffer, sulfate buffer.
14. Write the net ionic equations showing how any given buffer neutralizes ("soaks up") added H^+ or OH^-.
15. Determine the pH of a given equimolar buffer.
16. Do problems involving the three forms of the molarity equation:

$$M = \frac{\#mol}{\#L} \qquad \#mol = M \times \#L \qquad \#L = \frac{\#mol}{M}$$

17. Determine whether a given pair of substances will form a buffer.
18. Determine what substance you would mix with another substance to form a buffer.
19. Choose an appropriate buffer for a given pH, and describe what substances you would mix to prepare the buffer.
20. Be able to determine answers to parts a, b, c, d, and e below, using the buffer equation (Henderson–Hasselbach equation):

$$pH = pK_a + \log\left(\frac{[base]}{[acid]}\right)$$

    a. Calculate the pH of a non–equimolar buffer, given [acid] (the concentrations of the weak acid in the buffer) and [base] (the concentration of the weak base in the buffer).
    b. Calculate the new pH of a buffer after addition of a known amount of H^+ or OH^- to the buffer.
    c. Determine the ratio [base]/[acid] needed to prepare a buffer of a given pH.
    d. Given [acid], determine [base] needed to give a buffer of a given pH.
    e. Given [base], determine [acid] needed to give a buffer of a given pH.
21. Explain the concept of buffer capacity.
22. Know that buffer capacity is greater:
    a. the greater the concentrations of weak acid and weak base used.
    b. the closer the concentrations of weak acid and weak base are to being equimolar.

OBJECTIVES FOR EXAM #3, CHM 132

After studying and doing problems from this section of the course, the student should be able to:

1. Calculate the K_{sp} of a slightly soluble salt given the solubility (in mol/L or g/L).
2. Calculate the solubility (in mol/L or g/L) of a slightly soluble salt given the K_{sp}.
3. Determine whether a precipitate will form given the concentrations of two aqueous ions or compounds. (These problems will not use the dilution equation.)
4. Determine whether a precipitate will form when known volumes of two aqueous solutions are mixed. (These problems will use the dilution equation $M_1V_1 = M_2V_2$.)
5. Given the concentration of one ion, determine the concentration of the other ion needed to start precipitation of a slightly soluble salt.
6. Determine the pH needed to start the precipitation of a hydroxide compound [like $Ca(OH)_2(s)$ or $Al(OH)_3(s)$].
7. Do problems involving fractional precipitation.
8. Calculate the solubility (in mol/L or g/L) of a slightly soluble salt in a solution that contains a common ion.
9. Determine which slightly soluble salts will be more soluble in an acid solution than in pure water.
10. Calculate the overall charge of a metal ion complex.
11. Calculate the charge of the metal ion in a metal ion complex.
12. Determine the coordination number of the central metal ion in a complex, given the formula of the complex.
13. Determine the molecular geometry of a metal ion complex if the coordination number is known.
14. Write the K_f expression, given the formula of a complex.
15. Know that colors of complexes are due to unpaired **d** electrons of the central metal ion.
16. Know that a slightly soluble salt is more soluble in a solution that contains a ligand with which the metal ion can form a complex.

Objectives for Exam #3 continue on the back.

17. This objective refers to chemical reactions that have **one** reactant. Be able to determine the answers to parts a, b, and c below, given data of the following type:

[A]	**Initial Rate**
.	.
.	.
.	.

   a. The order with respect to the reactant.
   b. The rate law.
   c. The value of the rate constant **k**.

18. This objective refers to chemical reactions that have **more than one** reactant. Be able to determine the answers to parts a, b, and c below, given data of the following type (a third reactant [C] could also be given):

[A]	**[B]**	**Initial Rate**
.	.	.
.	.	.
.	.	.

   a. The order with respect to each reactant.
   b. The rate law.
   c. The value of the rate constant **k**.

19. Know what happens to the rate of a **zero order**, **first order**, or **second order** reaction when the concentration of reactant is increased by a given number of times, for example, 2x, 5x, 10x, etc.

20. Be able to sketch the time (**x–axis**) vs. [A] (**y–axis**) graphs for **first order** and **second order** reactions. (See p. 296)

21. Be able to sketch the [A] (**x–axis**) vs. Initial Rate (**y–axis**) graphs for **zero order**, **first order**, and **second order** reactions. (See p. 296)

22. Be able to sketch the time (**x–axis**) vs. ln[A] (**y–axis**) graph for a **first order** reaction. (See p. 296)

23. Be able to determine the value of **k** for a first order reaction, given the following type of data:

time	**[A]**
.	.
.	.
.	.

(This problem involves making a third column (**ln[A]**) and calculating the slope.)

24. For a **first order** reaction, calculate the half-life ($t_{½}$) given **k**, or calculate **k** given $t_{½}$.

$$t_{½} = \frac{.693}{k} \quad \text{or} \quad k = \frac{.693}{t_{½}}$$

25. For a **first order** reaction, given the value of **k**, use the equation:

$$\ln\left(\frac{[A]_o}{[A]_t}\right) = kt$$

to calculate the concentration of reactant ($[A]_t$) left at time **t**, or the time **t** required for the concentration of reactant ($[A]_t$) to reach a given amount.

26. Be able to determine the value of **k** for a second order reaction, given the following type of data:

time	**[A]**
.	.
.	.
.	.

(This problem involves making a third column (**1/[A]**) and calculating the slope.)

27. For a **second order** reaction, calculate the half-life ($t_{½}$) given **k** and [A].

$$t_{½} = \frac{1}{k[A]}$$

Objectives for Exam #3 continue on the back.

28. Be able to sketch the time (**x–axis**) vs. 1/[A] (**y–axis**) graph for a **second order** reaction. (See p. 296)

29. For a **second order** reaction, given the value of **k**, use the equation:

$$\frac{1}{[A]_t} = kt + \frac{1}{[A]_o}$$

to calculate the concentration of reactant ($[A]_t$) left at time **t**, or the time **t** required for the concentration of reactant ($[A]_t$) to reach a given amount.

30. From the material given in class about the Collision Theory of Reaction Rates, be able to:
    a. state the basic assumption upon which the theory is based.
    b. define the term "diffusion-controlled" reaction.
    c. state the two requirements necessary for a collision to be successful.
    d. explain what is meant by the terms **transition state and activated complex.**
    e. sketch a graph of Potential Energy (y-axis) vs. Progress of Reaction (x-axis) for an exothermic or endothermic reaction.
    f. define the term activation energy (E_a).
    g. Describe the effect of an increase or decrease of E_a on reaction rate (Kinetics).
    h. Describe the effect of the relative potential energies of reactants and products on the position of equilibrium and the size of K_{eq} (Thermodynamics).

31. In regard to the material about **factors affecting reaction rate,** be able to:
    a. Describe the effect of subdivision of reactant particles on the rate of reaction.
    b. Describe the effect of increasing reactant concentrations on the rate of reaction.
    c. Know that the two variables affecting reaction rate the most are temperature and E_a.
    d. Describe the effect of increasing temperature on rate of reaction.
    e. Know that increasing the temperature of a reaction does not change E_a, but speeds up the reaction by increasing the number of reactant molecules that have enough energy to react
    f. Know that a catalyst speeds up a reaction by lowering E_a, but does not affect the position of equilibrium (that is, the relative potential energies of reactants and products).
    g. Know that the two variables that change reaction rate the most are temperature and E_a.

OBJECTIVES FOR EXAM #4, CHM 132

After studying and doing problems from this section of the course, the student should be able to:

1. Add the elementary steps in a reaction mechanism together to obtain the equation for the overall reaction.
2. Write the rate law for an elementary step in a reaction mechanism.
3. Write the rate law for an overall reaction given a reaction mechanism in which the first step is the slow step.
4. Determine for an overall reaction whether a given mechanism is consistent (might possibly be the right one) by comparing the experimentally determined rate law with the rate law predicted by the mechanism.
5. For a chemical reaction, know that if $\Delta G = 0$, the reaction is at equilibrium; if ΔG is negative, the reaction is spontaneous as written; if ΔG is positive, the reaction is nonspontaneous as written.
6. Explain the meaning of **enthalpy** and calculate ΔH°_{298} for a reaction from table values of ΔH°_f.
7. State the **Second Law of Thermodynamics**, explain the concept of **entropy**, and calculate ΔS° for a reaction from table values of S°.
8. Explain the concept of **free energy** and calculate ΔG°_{298} for a reaction from table values of ΔG°_f.
9. Know that a negative ΔH or a positive ΔS **tend** to make a reaction spontaneous, but whether the reaction is spontaneous or nonspontaneous can only be determined **for sure** by ΔG.
10. Given the signs of ΔH and ΔS, use the equation $\Delta G = \Delta H - T\Delta S$ to predict whether the reaction will be spontaneous or nonspontaneous at high or low temperatures.
11. Use the equation $\Delta G^\circ = \Delta H^\circ - T\Delta S^\circ$ to calculate ΔG° at any temperature.
12. Use the equation $\Delta G^\circ = \Delta H^\circ - T\Delta S^\circ$ to determine the temperature at which $\Delta G^\circ = 0$. (This temp is $T = \Delta H^\circ/\Delta S^\circ$)
13. Use the equation $\Delta G = \Delta G^\circ + RT(\ln Q)$ to calculate ΔG under nonstandard conditions.
14. Use the equation $\Delta G^\circ = -RT(\ln K_{eq})$ to calculate ΔG° or K_{eq}.
15. Know that the equation $\Delta G^\circ = -RT(\ln K_{eq})$ requires that a reaction with a negative ΔG° will have a large K_{eq} (greater than 1) and that a reaction with a positive ΔG° will have a small K_{eq} (less than 1).
16. Use a table of reduction potentials to calculate E°_{cell}, given a balanced redox reaction or a shorthand diagram of the cell, such as:

    $Zn \mid Zn^{2+}(aq) \parallel Cu^{2+}(aq) \mid Cu$

Objectives for Exam #4 continue on the back.

17. Know that a positive E°_{cell} means the reaction is spontaneous; a negative E°_{cell} means the reaction is nonspontaneous.

18. Write the oxidation and reduction half-reactions for the Standard Hydrogen Electrode and be able to draw a diagram of it.

19. Given two reduction half-reactions and their potentials, tell which species can spontaneously remove e^- from another species (the spontaneous direction of e^- flow is upper right to lower left when the reactions are listed with the most negative at the top.)

20. Use the equation $\Delta G^\circ = -nFE^\circ_{cell}$ to calculate ΔG° for a redox reaction; then use the equation $\Delta G^\circ = -RT\ln K_{eq}$ to calculate K_{eq} for the reaction.

21. Given a balanced redox reaction or a shorthand diagram of an electrochemical cell, use the Nernst Equation:

$$E_{cell} = E^\circ_{cell} - \frac{0.0591\ V}{n}\log Q$$

to calculate E_{cell} under nonstandard conditions.

22. Calculate how many grams of metal will plate out when a given number of moles of electrons pass through the circuit in an electrolytic cell (Faraday's Law of Electrolysis).

OBJECTIVES FOR FINAL EXAM, CHM 132

The final exam will have 7 questions on nuclear chemistry (material from the final lecture) and 26 comprehensive questions covering material from the entire semester. (Total of 33 questions.)

For the Nuclear Chemistry questions, students should be able to:

1. State the difference between stable and radioactive isotopes.
2. Describe the five basic types of radioactive decay: α-emission, β-emission, positron emission, electron capture, and γ-emission.
3. Describe the composition of α particles, β particles, positrons, and γ-rays and write the symbol for each.
4. Explain what happens in the nucleus when an isotope undergoes α-emission, β-emission, positron emission, electron capture, or γ-emission.
5. Write or complete nuclear reactions involving the five basic types of radioactive decay.
6. Define: **Curie (Ci), millicurie (mCi), and microcurie (μCi).**
7. Know that all radioactive decay processes are first order.
8. Calculate either the half-life (**$t_{1/2}$**) or the decay constant (**k**) of a radioactive isotope using the equations:

$$t_{1/2} = \frac{.693}{k} \quad \text{or} \quad k = \frac{.693}{t_{1/2}}$$

9. For a nuclear decay, given the initial amount of radioactive isotope (X_o) and its $t_{1/2}$ or **k** value, use the equation:

$$\ln\left(\frac{X_o}{X_t}\right) = kt$$

   to calculate the amount (X_t) or percentage of isotope left at time **t**, or to calculate the time **t** required for the isotope to decay to a given amount (X_t) or percentage.

10. Describe and distinguish between the following types of nuclear reactions: **nuclear fission, nuclear fusion, and nuclear bombardment.**
11. State that all elements larger than Uranium (element #92) are man-made by bombardment reactions.

Objectives for the Final Exam continue on the back

For the comprehensive questions, students should be able to:

1. Calculate the pH of a solution of a strong acid, a weak acid, a diprotic acid, a strong base, a weak base, or a salt.
2. Explain the structure and operation of an electrochemical cell.
3. Balance a redox equation in acidic or basic solution.
4. Write a balanced redox equation given the shorthand diagram of an electrochemical cell, such as:

   $Zn \mid Zn^{2+}(aq) \parallel Cu^{2+}(aq) \mid Cu$

5. Given a redox reaction, determine the oxidation number of any atom in the equation and identify the oxidizing agent, reducing agent, substance oxidized, and substance reduced.
6. Explain how a buffer is prepared and identify pairs of substances that will form a buffer.
7. Identify an appropriate buffer for a desired pH.
8. Write the net ionic equations describing how a buffer neutralizes ("soaks up") added acid or base.
9. Be able to determine answers to parts a, b, c and d below, using the buffer equation (Henderson–Hasselbach equation):

$$\mathbf{pH = pK_a + \log\left(\frac{[base]}{[acid]}\right)}$$

   a. Calculate the pH of a buffer given [acid] (the concentration of the weak acid in the buffer) and [base] (the concentration of the weak base in the buffer).
   b. Determine the ratio [base]/[acid] needed to prepare a buffer of a desired pH.
   c. Given [base], calculate [acid] needed to prepare a buffer of a desired pH.
   d. Given [acid], calculate [acid] needed to prepare a buffer of a desired pH.

10. Calculate the K_{sp} of a slightly soluble salt given the solubility (in mol/L or g/L).
11. Calculate the solubility (in mol/L or g/L) of a slightly soluble salt given the K_{sp}.
12. Determine whether a precipitate will form given the concentrations of two aqueous ions or compounds. (These problems will not use the dilution equation.)
13. Determine whether a precipitate will form when known volumes of two aqueous solutions are mixed. (These problems will use the dilution equation $M_1V_1 = M_2V_2$.)
14. Given the concentration of one ion, determine the concentration of the other ion needed to start precipitation of a slightly soluble salt.
15. Calculate the solubility (in mol/L or g/L) of a slightly soluble salt in a solution that contains a common ion.
16. Calculate the overall charge of a metal ion complex.
17. Calculate the charge of the metal ion in a metal ion complex.

18. Determine the coordination number of the central metal ion in a complex, given the formula of the complex.

19. Know what happens to the rate of a **zero order, first order,** or **second order** reaction when the concentration of reactant is increased by a given number of times, for example, 2x, 5x, 10x, etc.

20. This objective refers to chemical reactions that have **one** reactant. Be able to determine the rate law for a reaction, given data of the following type:

[A]	Initial Rate
.	.
.	.
.	.

21. This objective refers to chemical reactions that have **more than one** reactant. Be able to determine the rate law for a reaction, given data of the following type (a third reactant [C] could also be given):

[A]	[B]	Initial Rate
.	.	.
.	.	.
.	.	.

22. Be able to determine the value of **k** for a first order reaction, given the following type of data:

time	[A]
.	.
.	.
.	.

(This problem involves making a third column (**ln[A]**) and calculating the slope.)

23. For a **first order** reaction, calculate the half-life ($t_{1/2}$) given **k**, or calculate **k** given $t_{1/2}$.

$$t_{1/2} = \frac{.693}{k} \quad \text{or} \quad k = \frac{.693}{t_{1/2}}$$

Objectives for the Final Exam continue on the back.

24. For a **first order** reaction, given the value of **k**, use the equation:

$$\ln\left(\frac{[A]_o}{[A]_t}\right) = kt$$

to calculate the concentration of reactant ($[A]_t$) left at time **t**, or the time **t** required for the concentration of reactant ($[A]_t$) to reach a given amount.

25. Be able to determine the value of **k** for a second order reaction, given the following type of data:

time	[A]
.	.
.	.
.	.

(This problem involves making a third column (1/[A]) and calculating the slope.)

26. For a **second order** reaction, calculate the half-life ($t_{1/2}$) given **k** and [A].

$$t_{1/2} = \frac{1}{k[A]}$$

27. For a **second order** reaction, given the value of **k**, use the equation:

$$\frac{1}{[A]_t} = kt + \frac{1}{[A]_o}$$

to calculate the concentration of reactant ($[A]_t$) left at time **t**, or the time **t** required for the concentration of reactant ($[A]_t$) to reach a given amount.

28. Given the sign of ΔH and ΔS, use the equation $\Delta G = \Delta H - T\Delta S$ to predict whether the reaction will be spontaneous or nonspontaneous at high or low temperatures.
29. Use the equation $\Delta G^o = \Delta H^o - T\Delta S^o$ to calculate ΔG^o at any temperature.
30. Use the equation $\Delta G = \Delta G^o + RT(\ln Q)$ to calculate ΔG under nonstandard conditions.
31. Use the equation $\Delta G^o = -RT(\ln K_{eq})$ to calculate ΔG^o or K_{eq}.
32. Use a table of reduction potentials to calculate E^o_{cell} for a redox reaction.
33. Use the equation $\Delta G^o = -nFE^o_{cell}$ to calculate ΔG^o for a redox reaction.

Lecture Notes

Equilibrium, Ions and Formula Writing, and Dissolving

(Homework #1)

Chemical Equilibrium

Typical Reaction in CHM-131:

$$CO(g) + 3\,H_2(g) \longrightarrow CH_4(g) + H_2O(g)$$

Reactants **Products**

Many reactions are **reversible** = as soon as products start to form, they re-react to re-form reactants. These are written with a two-way or equilibrium arrow:

$$CO(g) + 3\,H_2(g) \rightleftharpoons CH_4(g) + H_2O(g)$$

Reactants **Products**

Because the reaction is reversible, which side is called Reactants and which side Products could be ambiguous. To avoid the problem, chemists define whatever is to the **left of the arrow as Reactants** and whatever is to the **right of the arrow as Products**, even for an equilibrium reaction.

If CO and H_2 are mixed, they begin to react to form CH_4 and H_2O. As CO and H_2 get used up, the forward reaction starts to slow down. As CH_4 and H_2O start to form, the reverse reaction gets faster. When the rate of the forward reaction equals the rate of the reverse reaction, it appears as though the amounts are not changing.

Dynamic Equilibrium = two opposing processes occurring at equal rates so that **no net change** is observed.

When the reaction above reaches equilibrium, there will be a mixture of all four substances. The amount of each substance at equilibrium depends on how fast the forward and reverse reactions are. Because chemists need a way to describe "where the reaction stops" and how much of each substance is present at equilibrium, they use a number called the **Equilibrium Constant, abbreviated K_{eq}**. This constant is defined as follows:

$$K_{eq} = \frac{\text{amount of PRODUCTS at} \rightleftharpoons}{\text{amount of REACTANTS at} \rightleftharpoons}$$

Amounts are expressed as **pressure in atm for gases** and as **Molarity (M or mol/L) for solutions**. For the reaction above:

$$K_{eq} = \frac{P(CH_4) \cdot P(H_2O)}{P(CO) \cdot P(H_2)^3}$$

Suppose ANY mixture of the four substances is placed in a flask and allowed to come to equilibrium. If the pressures at equilibrium are measured and plugged into the above expression, the same value of K_{eq} will be obtained no matter how much of each substance was in the starting mixture.

The following experiments demonstrate how the equilibrium constant works.

Review of Basic Equilibrium Chemistry – Chem. 132

What is the equilibrium constant?

$$CO(g) + 3H_2(g) \rightleftharpoons CH_4(g) + H_2O(g)$$

$$K_{eq} = \frac{P(CH_4) \cdot P(H_2O)}{P(CO) \cdot P(H_2)^3}$$

Experiment #1

	$CO(g)$	+	$3H_2(g)$	$\rightleftharpoons$	$CH_4(g)$	+	$H_2O(g)$
initial	10.0 atm		30.0 atm		0		0
at equilib.	6.1 atm		18.3 atm		3.9 atm		3.9 atm

$$K_{eq} = \frac{P(CH_4) \cdot P(H_2O)}{P(CO) \cdot P(H_2)^3} = \frac{(3.9) \cdot (3.9)}{(6.1) \cdot (18.3)^3} = \boxed{4.1 \times 10^{-4}}$$

Experiment #2

	$CO(g)$	+	$3H_2(g)$	$\rightleftharpoons$	$CH_4(g)$	+	$H_2O(g)$
initial	20.0 atm		50.0 atm		0		0
at equilib.	11.6 atm		24.8 atm		8.4 atm		8.4 atm

$$K_{eq} = \frac{P(CH_4) \cdot P(H_2O)}{P(CO) \cdot P(H_2)^3} = \frac{(8.4) \cdot (8.4)}{(11.6) \cdot (24.8)^3} = \boxed{4.0 \times 10^{-4}}$$

Experiment #3

	$CO(g)$	+	$3H_2(g)$	$\rightleftharpoons$	$CH_4(g)$	+	$H_2O(g)$
initial	0		0		10.0 atm		10.0 atm
at equilib.	6.1 atm		18.3 atm		3.9 atm		3.9 atm

$$K_{eq} = \frac{P(CH_4) \cdot P(H_2O)}{P(CO) \cdot P(H_2)^3} = \frac{(3.9) \cdot (3.9)}{(6.1) \cdot (18.3)^3} = \boxed{4.1 \times 10^{-4}}$$

Problem #1

For the following reaction (at 472°C): $2\,NH_3(g) \rightleftharpoons N_2(g) + 3\,H_2(g)$

Suppose the pressures **at equilibrium** were measured as:

$P(NH_3) = 0.122$ atm $\quad P(N_2) = 1.22$ atm $\quad P(H_2) = 7.59$ atm

What is the value of K_{eq}?

Solution:

$$K_{eq} = \frac{P(N_2) \cdot P(H_2)^3}{P(NH_3)^2} = \frac{(1.22) \cdot (7.59)^3}{(0.122)^2} = \boxed{\mathbf{3.58 \times 10^4}}$$

Problem #2

In the following reaction, suppose you start with 8.00 atm of HI(g) and no $H_2(g)$ or $I_2(g)$:

	$2\,HI(g)$	$\rightleftharpoons$ $H_2(g)$	+ $I_2(g)$
initial	8.00 atm	0	0

If the pressure of $H_2(g)$ is measured as 0.89 atm **at equilibrium**:

a. What are the pressures of all the substances at equilibrium?
b. What is the value of K_{eq}?

Solution:

a. First, suppose no equilibrium concentrations were given in the problem. Then, make a table in which you let x = the amount of $H_2(g)$ at equilibrium. This kind of table (which I refer to as an "ICE" table) can be used to solve many equilibrium problems.

	$2\,HI(g)$	$\rightleftharpoons$	$H_2(g)$	+ $I_2(g)$
***I**nitial*	8.00		0	0
***C**hange*	$-\,2x$		$+x$	$+x$
***E**quilibrium*	$8.00 - 2x$		x	x

The problem says that $P(H_2)$ at equilibrium, which is equal to x, is 0.89 atm. So, at equilibrium,

$$P(HI) = 8.00 - 2x = 8.00 - 2 \cdot (0.89) = \boxed{\mathbf{6.22\ atm}}$$

$$P(H_2) = x = \boxed{\mathbf{0.89\ atm}} \qquad P(I_2) = x = \boxed{\mathbf{0.89\ atm}}$$

b.

$$K_{eq} = \frac{P(H_2) \cdot P(I_2)}{P(HI)^2} = \frac{(0.89) \cdot (0.89)}{(6.22)^2} = \boxed{\mathbf{2.0 \times 10^{-2}} \text{ or } \mathbf{0.020}}$$

Problem #3

In the following reaction, suppose you start with 4.00 atm $Cl_2(g)$, 9.00 atm $H_2O(g)$ and no $HCl(g)$ or $O_2(g)$:

	$2\,Cl_2(g)$	+	$2\,H_2O(g)$	$\rightleftharpoons$	$4\,HCl(g)$	+	$O_2(g)$
initial	4.00 atm		9.00 atm		0		0

Suppose the pressure of $O_2(g)$ is measured as 0.659 atm **at equilibrium:**

a. What are the pressures of all the substances at equilibrium?
b. What is the value of K_{eq}?

Solution:

a. Let x = the amount of $O_2(g)$ at equilibrium:

	$2\,Cl_2(g)$	+	$2\,H_2O(g)$	$\rightleftharpoons$	$4\,HCl(g)$	+	$O_2(g)$
I	4.00		9.00		0		0
C	$-2x$		$-2x$		$+4x$		$+x$
E	$4.00-2x$		$9.00-2x$		$4x$		x

The problem says that $P(O_2)$ at equilibrium, which is equal to x, is 0.659 atm. So, at equilibrium,

$$P(Cl_2) = 4.00 - 2x = 4.00 - 2\cdot(0.659) = \boxed{2.68\text{ atm}}$$

$$P(H_2O) = 9.00 - 2x = 9.00 - 2\cdot(0.659) = \boxed{7.68\text{ atm}}$$

$$P(HCl) = 4x = 4\cdot(0.659)\text{ atm} = \boxed{2.64\text{ atm}} \qquad P(O_2) = x = \boxed{0.659\text{ atm}}$$

b.

$$K_{eq} = \frac{P(HCl)^4\cdot P(O_2)}{P(Cl_2)^2\cdot P(H_2O)^2} = \frac{(2.64)^4\cdot(0.659)}{(2.68)^2\cdot(7.68)^2} = \boxed{7.57\times 10^{-2}}$$

Problem #4

For the reaction: $2\,SO_3(g) \rightleftharpoons 2\,SO_2(g) + O_2(g)$

It is given that (at 700°C),

$$K_{eq} = \frac{P(SO_2)^2\cdot P(O_2)}{P(SO_3)^2} = 79.7$$

Suppose a chemist makes a reaction mixture that initially contains:

$P(SO_3) = 5$ atm $\qquad P(SO_2) = 100$ atm $\qquad P(O_2) = 30$ atm

Is the reaction at equilibrium? If not, which way does the reaction need to shift to reach equilibrium?

Solution:

First, use the same mathematical expression as given for K_{eq}, but plug in the ***initial*** pressures given in the problem. This value is referred to with the letter Q (for quotient). If $Q = K_{eq}$, the reaction is already at equilibrium, and no shift will occur. If $Q \neq K_{eq}$, the reaction will have to shift either to the right or to the left to reach equilibrium.

$$Q = \frac{P(SO_2)^2 \cdot P(O_2)}{P(SO_3)^2} = \frac{(100)^2 \cdot (30)}{(5)^2} = 1.2 \times 10^4 \text{ or } 12{,}000$$

$$\mathbf{Q > K_{eq}}$$

In order for Q to become equal to K_{eq}, the numerator must become smaller and/or the denominator larger. The way for this happen is for the reaction to **shift to the left, toward the reactants,** so that $P(SO_2)$ and $P(O_2)$ will decrease (↓), and $P(SO_3)$ will increase (↑).

Now suppose the chemist makes a new reaction mixture that contains:

$P(SO_3) = 75$ atm $\qquad P(SO_2) = 20$ atm $\qquad P(O_2) = 1$ atm

Q for this new reaction mixture will be:

$$Q = \frac{P(SO_2)^2 \cdot P(O_2)}{P(SO_3)^2} = \frac{(20)^2 \cdot (1)}{(75)^2} = 7.1 \times 10^{-2} \text{ or } 0.071$$

$$\mathbf{Q < K_{eq}}$$

In order for Q to become equal to K_{eq} this time, the numerator must become larger and/or the denominator smaller. The way for this to happen is for the reaction to **shift to the right, toward the products,** so that $P(SO_2)$ and $P(O_2)$ will increase (↑), and $P(SO_3)$ will decrease (↓).

In summary, the following table is true for reactions in general:

If $\mathbf{Q > K_{eq}}$	shifts to the **left** (toward reactants)
If $\mathbf{Q = K_{eq}}$	**at equilibrium**
If $\mathbf{Q < K_{eq}}$	shifts to the **right** (toward products)

← Q has a large #

← Q is a small number

Please note the following:

1. For any reaction, Q and K_{eq} have the same mathematical expression, but they are **very different** in meaning. **Q** is the number obtained when ***initial*** values from a problem are plugged in, but the number obtained is $\mathbf{K_{eq}}$ **only** when values measured ***at equilibrium*** are plugged in.

2. **Q** can have **many different values** for the same equation; it depends on what the chemist chooses to place in the initial reaction mixture.

3. $\mathbf{K_{eq}}$ has **one and only one value** for the same reaction at the same temperature, because any reaction mixture that is allowed to come to equilibrium will give the same value of K_{eq} ; that is the reason K_{eq} is referred to as the equilibrium **constant.**

4. When comparing the values of Q and K_{eq}, you are really comparing ***initial conditions*** with ***known equilibrium conditions*** to determine whether the reaction mixture given in the problem is at equilibrium or whether it must shift in order to get there.

5. If the initial values contain a zero (in other words, there is none of that substance present initially), no calculation of Q is needed because it is already clear that **the reaction must shift toward the side with the zero** in order to reach equilibrium.

States of Matter of Substances in Equilibrium Expressions

1. Solids (s) and liquids (ℓ) are not included in $\rightleftharpoons$ expressions because their concentrations do not vary much with conditions. **Solids and liquids DO NOT appear in $\rightleftharpoons$ expressions.**

2. Gases (g) and aqueous substances (aq) are included in equilibrium expressions because their concentrations can change relatively easily. **Gases and aqueous substances DO appear in $\rightleftharpoons$ expressions.**

3. The concentrations of a **gases in an $\rightleftharpoons$ expression are given as pressure (atm).**

4. When an aqueous substance is included in an $\rightleftharpoons$ expression, it is enclosed in square brackets to indicate that its concentration is in given as molarity (M). **Square brackets in $\rightleftharpoons$ expressions mean molarity (M) of aqueous substances.**

Examples:

Write the equilibrium expressions for the following reactions:

a. $3\,Fe(s) + 4\,H_2O(g) \rightleftharpoons Fe_3O_4(s) + 4\,H_2(g)$

$$K_{eq} = \frac{P(H_2)^4}{P(H_2O)^4}$$

b. $NH_3(aq) + H_2O(\ell) \rightleftharpoons NH_4^+(aq) + OH^-(aq)$

$$K_{eq} = \frac{[NH_4^+][OH^-]}{[NH_3]}$$

c. $CaO(s) + SO_3(g) \rightleftharpoons CaSO_4(s)$

$$K_{eq} = \frac{1}{P(SO_3)}$$

LeChatelier's Principle

When a stress is applied to a system at $\rightleftharpoons$, the $\rightleftharpoons$ shifts so as to relieve the stress.

Although a system can be stressed in several ways, including changing pressure, temperature and/or concentrations, CHM-132 is mostly concerned with changes in concentration.

Suppose a reaction is at $\rightleftharpoons$, and the concentration of one of the substances is suddenly changed.

1. If you **remove** some of a substance from one side of an $\rightleftharpoons$, the reaction will shift **toward that side** until $\rightleftharpoons$ is reached again.

2. If you **add** more of a substance to one side of the $\rightleftharpoons$, the reaction will shift **away from** that side until $\rightleftharpoons$ is reached again.

Example:

Suppose the reaction:

$$CO(g) + 3H_2(g) \rightleftharpoons CH_4(g) + H_2O(g)$$

is at equilibrium. The following are **all true**:

1. If some **$CO(g)$ is removed** from the mixture, the reaction will **shift to the left**. (Think of the reaction trying to "replace" the $CO(g)$ that was removed.) As the reaction shifts, $P(CO)$ and $P(H_2)$ will $\uparrow$, while the $P(CH_4)$ and $P(H_2O)$ will $\downarrow$.

2. If some **$CH_4(g)$ is removed** from the mixture, the reaction will shift to the **right**. As the reaction shifts, $P(CO)$ and $P(H_2)$ will $\downarrow$, and $P(H_2O)$ and $P(CH_4)$ will $\uparrow$.

3. If some **$H_2(g)$ is added** to the mixture, the reaction will **shift to the right**. (Think of the reaction trying to "use up" the "extra" $H_2(g)$ that was added.) As the reaction shifts, $P(CO)$ and $P(H_2)$ will $\downarrow$, and $P(H_2O)$ and $P(CH_4)$ will $\uparrow$. (Same as in #2 above.)

4. If some **$H_2O(g)$ is added** to the mixture, the reaction will **shift to the left**. As the reaction shifts, $P(CO)$ and $P(H_2)$ will $\uparrow$, while the $P(CH_4)$ and $P(H_2O)$ will $\downarrow$. (Same as in #1 above.)

Classification of Chemical Compounds and Dissolving

Classification I – Covalent/Ionic

Covalent = compounds that do not contain a metal (only nonmetals and metalloids).

1. Consist of **molecules.**
2. Molecules held together by **covalent bonds.**
3. No electrical charge.

Examples: H_2O NH_3 CO_2 $AsCl_3$ $C_6H_{12}O_6$

Ionic = consist of + **ions** or **cations** (metals or NH_4^+) bound to – **ions** or **anions** (nonmetals or polyatomic ions).

1. **No molecules** – smallest unit is **ions.**
2. Ions held together by **electrostatic attractions** (+ to –).
3. The **ions** are electrically charged. The **overall compound** is neutral (charges of ions add up to zero).

General Form

Metal		Nonmetal
or	**combined with**	or
NH_4^+		Polyatomic ion

Examples of each type:

NaCl	Sodium chloride
$Ba(NO_3)_2$	Barium nitrate
$(NH_4)_2S$	Ammonium sulfide
$(NH_4)_3PO_4$	Ammonium phosphate

5. **Types of ions**

Monatomic ion = charged **individual** atoms, ide ending when –

Polyatomic ion = charged **group** of atoms

+1 ions

Monatomic

Cs^+	Cesium
Cu^+	Copper(I) or Cuprous
H^+	Hydrogen
Li^+	Lithium
K^+	Potassium
Rb^+	Rubidium
Ag^+	Silver

Polyatomic

NH_4^+	Ammonium

+2 ions

Monatomic

Ba^{2+}	Barium
Cd^{2+}	Cadmium
Ca^{2+}	Calcium
Cr^{2+}	Chromium(II)
Co^{2+}	Cobalt(II)
Cu^{2+}	Copper(II) or Cupric
Fe^{2+}	Iron(II) or Ferrous
Pb^{2+}	Lead(II)
Mg^{2+}	Magnesium
Mn^{2+}	Manganese(II)
Hg^{2+}	Mercury(II) or Mercuric
Ni^{2+}	Nickel
Sr^{2+}	Strontium
Sn^{2+}	Tin(II)
Zn^{2+}	Zinc

Polyatomic

Hg_2^{2+}	Mercury(I) or Mercurous

+3 ions

Monatomic

Al^{3+}	Aluminum
Bi^{3+}	Bismuth
Cr^{3+}	Chromium(III)
Co^{3+}	Cobalt(III)
Fe^{3+}	Iron(III) or Ferric
Ga^{3+}	Gallium
Mn^{3+}	Manganese(III)

+4 ions

Monatomic

Pb^{4+}	Lead(IV)
Sn^{4+}	Tin(IV)

−1 ions

Monatomic

Br^-	Bromide
Cl^-	Chloride
F^-	Fluoride
I^-	Iodide

Polyatomic

$C_2H_3O_2^-$ or CH_3COO^-	Acetate
HCO_3^-	Bicarbonate
ClO_3^-	Chlorate
ClO_2^-	Chlorite
CN^-	Cyanide
OH^-	Hydroxide
ClO^-	Hypochlorite
NO_3^-	Nitrate
NO_2^-	Nitrite
ClO_4^-	Perchlorate
MnO_4^-	Permanganate

−2 ions

Monatomic

O^{2-}	Oxide
S^{2-}	Sulfide

Polyatomic

CO_3^{2-}	Carbonate
CrO_4^{2-}	Chromate
$Cr_2O_7^{2-}$	Dichromate
$C_2O_4^{2-}$	Oxalate
O_2^{2-}	Peroxide
SO_4^{2-}	Sulfate
SO_3^{2-}	Sulfite

−3 ions

Monatomic

N^{3-}	Nitride
P^{3-}	Phosphide

Polyatomic

BO_3^{3-}	Borate
PO_4^{3-}	Phosphate

	IA	IIA											IIIA	IVA	VA	VIA	VIIA	VIIIA
1	1 **H**																	
2	3 **Li** +1	4 **Be** +2													7 **N** -3	8 **O** -1 -2	9 **F** -1	
3	11 **Na** +1	12 **Mg** +2											13 **Al** +3		15 **P** -3	16 **S** -2	17 **Cl** -1	
4	19 **K** +1	20 **Ca** +2				24 **Cr** +2 +3	25 **Mn** +2 +3	26 **Fe** +2 +3	27 **Co** +2 +3	28 **Ni** +2	29 **Cu** +1 +2	30 **Zn** +2	31 **Ga** +3				35 **Br** -1	
5	37 **Rb** +1	38 **Sr** +2									47 **Ag** +1	48 **Cd** +2		50 **Sn** +2 +4			53 **I** -1	
6	55 **Cs** +1	56 **Ba** +2										80 **Hg** +1 +2		82 **Pb** +2 +4	83 **Bi** +3			
7																		

Naming Ions

You are responsible for knowing the names, formulas, and charges of the ions listed in the Blue Book, pp. 49-51. The monatomic ions are also shown in the Periodic Table on p. 52.

Cations

1. If the metal ion can have only one charge, the name of the ion is the same as the name of the metal:

Examples:

K^+ Potassium ion Ca^{2+} Calcium ion Zn^{2+} Zinc ion

2. If the metal can have more than one charge, there are two systems, both of which are still in use.
   A. Put the charge in Roman numerals in parentheses after the name.
   B. Add the suffix **ic** to the name (often the Latin name) of the ion with the higher charge and **ous** to the name of the ion with the smaller charge.

Examples:

Fe^{2+} Iron(II) ion or Ferrous ion

Fe^{3+} Iron(III) ion or Ferric ion

Cu^{+} Copper(I) ion or Cuprous ion

Cu^{2+} Copper(II) ion or Cupric ion

3. The ion Mercury(I) or Mercurous has been found to have a unique property that is reflected in how the formula is written. Mercury(I) ions do not exist singly, but are always found in pairs connected by a covalent bond. **The formula of Mercury(I) must, therefore, be written as Hg_2^{2+}.** Mercury(II) ions exist singly as expected.

Mercury(I) or Mercurous $Hg^+ - Hg^+$ **Formula MUST be written as Hg_2^{2+}**

Mercury(II) or Mercuric Hg^{2+}

4. The other positive ion for which you are responsible is NH_4^+ = **ammonium** ion. It is a polyatomic ion and acts "like a metal ion" in chemical formulas because it has a + charge. Therefore, compounds containing NH_4^+ are **IONIC.**

NH_3	**ammonia**	a neutral compound
NH_4^+	**ammonium ion**	a positive ion

Anions

1. **Monatomic anions** are named by removing the end of the element name and adding the suffix **ide**.

   Examples:

   Cl^- Chloride I^- Iodide O^{2-} Oxide N^{3-} Nitride

2. **Polyatomic anions** are named as shown on p. 51.

   A. Most of the polyatomic anions listed contain oxygen combined with another element. The names of these ions include the name of the element that is combined with oxygen.

   Examples:

   PO_4^{3-} Phosphate SO_3^{2-} Sulfite CO_3^{2-} Carbonate

   B. The names of the oxygen-containing polyatomic anions end in **ite** or **ate**. The ion with the name ending in **ite** always has **one less oxygen** than the one ending in **ate**.

   Examples:

   NO_3^- Nitrate SO_4^{2-} Sulfate

   NO_2^- Nitrite SO_3^{2-} Sulfite

   Note that the suffix **ate** DOES NOT refer to any particular number of oxygen atoms: you must learn how many oxygen atoms the **ate** ion has for each element.

   C. Some elements form FOUR different ions with oxygen, so more names are needed than just **ate** and **ite**. For these ions, the one with more oxygen atoms than **ate** also includes the prefix **per**. The one with less oxygen atoms than **ite** includes the prefix **hypo**.

   ClO^- Hypochlorite ClO_3^- Chlorate

   ClO_2^- Chlorite ClO_4^- Perchlorate

   The elements bromine (Br) and iodine (I) also have four ions each named the same way.

   D. Please note the following two oxygen-containing ions that do not follow the rules above. Because of their importance in chemistry, these names must be memorized separately.

   OH^- hydroxide O_2^{2-} Peroxide

   E. The ion CN^-, which does not contain oxygen, is called **cyanide**.

Writing Formulas of Ionic Compounds

Ionic Compounds

Cation	combined with	Anion
(Metal or NH_4^+)		(Nonmetal ion or Polyatomic ion)

Since ionic compounds are electrically neutral, the total number of positive charges must equal the total number of negative charges in the formula. The following method always gives the correct formula if a few additional rules are followed.

Cross Method

1. Write formulas (including the charges) of ions side by side with the + ion first. Place polyatomic ions in parentheses.
2. Cross the numbers (place the charge of the first ion as the subscript of the second and the charge of the second as the subscript of the first).
3. **Erase the charges.**
4. Reduce the formula if necessary.
5. Remove parentheses from polyatomic ions if the subscript is 1.
6. Write the final formula neatly.

Examples:

Aluminum Chromate

$$Al^{3+}(CrO_4)^{2-}$$

$$Al_2^{+}(CrO_4)_3^{-}$$

$$Al_2(CrO_4)_3$$

Iron(II) Sulfate

or

Ferrous Sulfate

$Fe^{2+}(SO_4)^{2-}$

$Fe_2^{+}(SO_4)_2^{-}$

$Fe_2(SO_4)_2$

$FeSO_4$

Iron(III) Sulfate

or

Ferric Sulfate

$Fe^{3+}(SO_4)_3^{2-}$

$Fe_2^{+}(SO_4)_3^{-}$

$Fe_2(SO_4)_3$

Aluminum Sulfide

$Al_2^{3+}S_3^{2-}$

Al_2S_3

Mercury(I) Phosphate

or

Mercurous Phosphate

$(Hg_2)^{2+}(PO_4)^{3-}$

$(Hg_2)_3^{+}(PO_4)_2^{-}$

$(Hg_2)_3(PO_4)_2$

Determining the Charge of the Metal Ion in a Compound

Since the charges in an ionic compound must add up to zero, the charge of a metal ion can be determined if the formula of the compound is known.

Example:

Determine the charge of **Cr** in $Cr_2(CO_3)_3$

Method 1 – Algebraic

Let x = the charge of Cr

$2x + 3 \cdot (-2) = 0$

$2x - 6 = 0$

$2x = 6, \quad x = 3$

Answer: +3

Method 2 – Uncrossing

$Cr_2(CO_3)_3$

Answer: +3

Uncrossing works any time the subscripts are different numbers. If the subscripts are both 1, however, it will not always work.

Example:

Determine the charge of **Mn** in $MnPO_4$

This formula is equivalent to $Mn_1(PO_4)_1$. Uncrossing the 1 would give Mn a +1 charge, which is not a possibility for Mn (it has charges of +2 and +3). The reason is that the formula with the 1 on each was reduced.

If both subscripts are 1, the metal ion has the same charge as the negative ion, except positive.

Since PO_4 is a −3 ion, the Mn in $MnPO_4$ must be +3 in order to make the compound neutral.

Answer: +3

Formula Writing Practice

Directions: Write formulas for the following ionic compounds.

Potassium nitrate	KNO_3	Cuprous bicarbonate	$CuHCO_3$
Sodium sulfate	Na_2SO_4	Cadmium chromate	$CdCrO_4$
Lithium phosphate	Li_3PO_4	Lead(II) fluoride	PbF_2
Magnesium chloride	$MgCl_2$	Strontium carbonate	$SrCO_3$
Nickel chromate	$NiCrO_4$	Sodium peroxide	Na_2O_2
Zinc phosphate	$Zn_3(PO_4)_2$	Tin(IV) oxide	SnO_2
Manganese(II) sulfite	$MnSO_3$	Cobalt(II) nitrite	$Co(NO_2)_2$
Tin(II) sulfide	SnS	Cesium permanganate	$CsMnO_4$
Chromium(III) hydroxide	$Cr(OH)_3$	Iron(II) acetate	$Fe(C_2H_3O_2)_2$
Cobalt(III) dichromate	$Co_2(Cr_2O_7)_3$	Sodium hypochlorite	$NaClO$
Ferric carbonate	$Fe_2(CO_3)_3$	Cobalt(III) chlorate	$Co(ClO_3)_3$
Bismuth phosphate	$BiPO_4$	Gallium chlorite	$Ga(ClO_2)_3$
Silver oxalate	$Ag_2C_2O_4$	Calcium permanganate	$Ca(MnO_4)_2$
Aluminum cyanide	$Al(CN)_3$	Magnesium chromate	$MgCrO_4$
Mercury(I) bromide	Hg_2Br_2	Barium dichromate	$BaCr_2O_7$
Mercuric phosphate	$Hg_3(PO_4)_2$	Silver nitride	Ag_3N
Mercuric sulfate	$HgSO_4$	Manganese(II) phosphide	Mn_3P_2
Copper(II) sulfide	CuS	Mercury(I) oxalate	$Hg_2C_2O_4$
Ammonium perchlorate	NH_4ClO_4	Ammonium acetate	$NH_4C_2H_3O_2$

Directions: Determine the charge of the metal ion in the compounds below.

$Fe_3(PO_4)_2$	Fe^{2+}	Cu_3N	Cu^+	$Cr(CN)_2$	Cr^{2+}
Cu_2SO_4	Cu^+	$Fe_2(CrO_4)_3$	Fe^{3+}	$CoCr_2O_7$	Co^{2+}
$MnCO_3$	Mn^{2+}	Hg_2Cl_2	Hg_2^{2+}	$Co_2(SO_3)_3$	Co^{3+}
$CuNO_3$	Cu^+	Mn_2S_3	Mn^{3+}	Hg_2SO_4	Hg_2^{2+}
$CrPO_4$	Cr^{3+}	$HgCl_2$	Hg^{2+}	Cu_2S	Cu^+
$Cu_3(PO_4)_2$	Cu^{2+}	$Hg_3(PO_4)_2$	Hg^{2+}	SnO	Sn^{2+}
$Co(C_2H_3O_2)_3$	Co^{3+}	CuC_2O_4	Cu^{2+}	Mn_3P_2	Mn^{2+}

Classification II – Acid/Base/Salt

Acids = form H^+ ions in water

Bases = form OH^- ions in water

Acid

		Nonmetal
H	**combined with**	or
		Polyatomic ion

Examples: HCl HBr H_2SO_4 HNO_3

Base

Metal **combined with** OH^-

Examples: $NaOH$ KOH $Ba(OH)_2$

Salt

Metal		Nonmetal
or	**combined with**	or
NH_4^+		Polyatomic ion (**not** OH^-)

When an **acid** reacts with a **base (neutralization reaction)**: $H^+ + OH^- \longrightarrow H_2O$

Also, H^+ partner combines with OH^- partner to form a **salt**.

$$HCl(aq) + NaOH(aq) \longrightarrow NaCl(aq) + H_2O(\ell)$$

$$H_2SO_4(aq) + 2\,KOH(aq) \longrightarrow K_2SO_4(aq) + 2\,H_2O(\ell)$$

acid **base** **salt** **water**

Classification III – Electrolytes/Nonelectrolytes

Electrolytes = form ions when they dissolve in water, so the solution conducts electricity.

Compounds that are electrolytes:

1. acids
2. bases
3. soluble salts

Nonelectrolytes = do not form ions in water, so solution does not conduct electricity.

Most covalent compounds other than acids are nonelectrolytes.

1. Pure, distilled water
2. Sugars ($C_6H_{12}O_6$, $C_{12}H_{22}O_{11}$)
3. Alcohols (CH_3OH, C_2H_5OH)
4. Covalent compounds other than acids.

Electrolytes

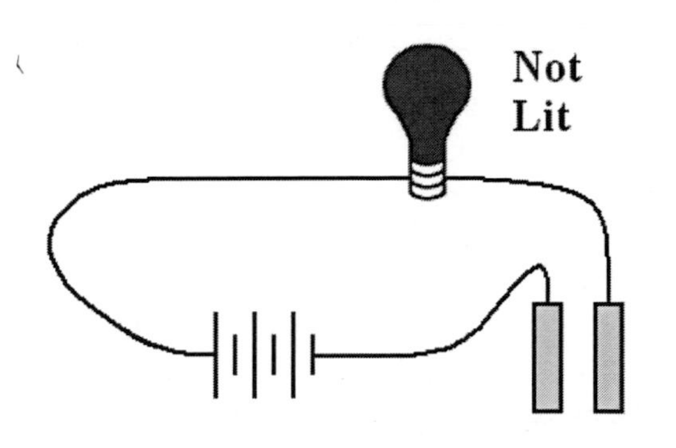

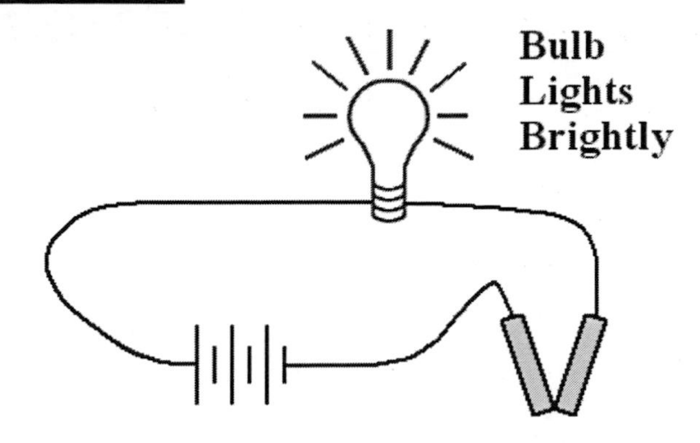

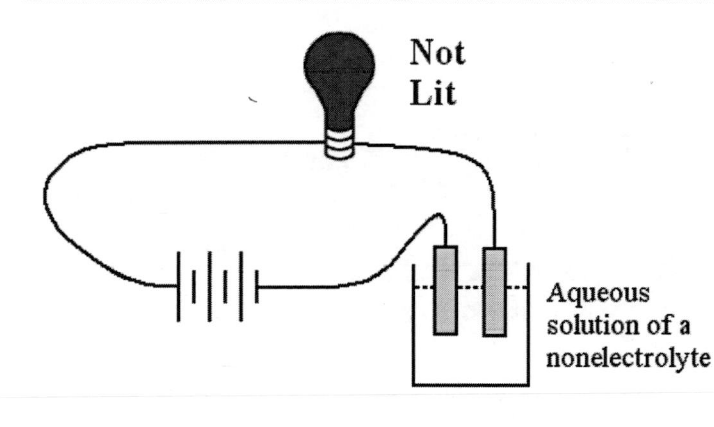

Nonelectrolyte = produces no ions when dissolved in water.

1. Pure H_2O
2. sugars
3. alcohols
4. most covalent substances

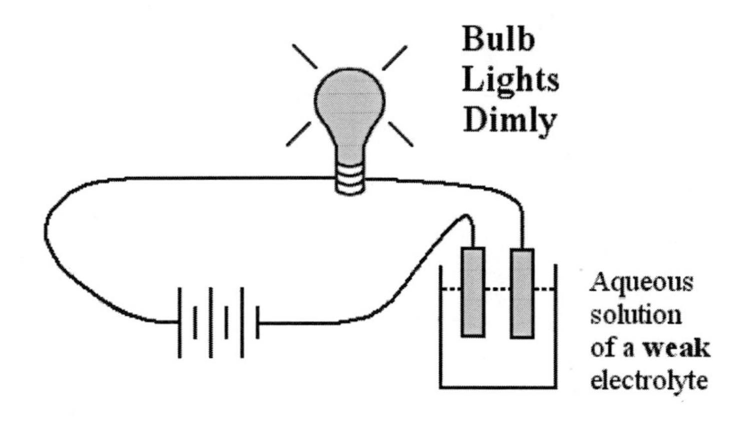

Weak electrolyte = only a few ions when dissolved in water.

1. weak acids
2. weak base (NH_3)

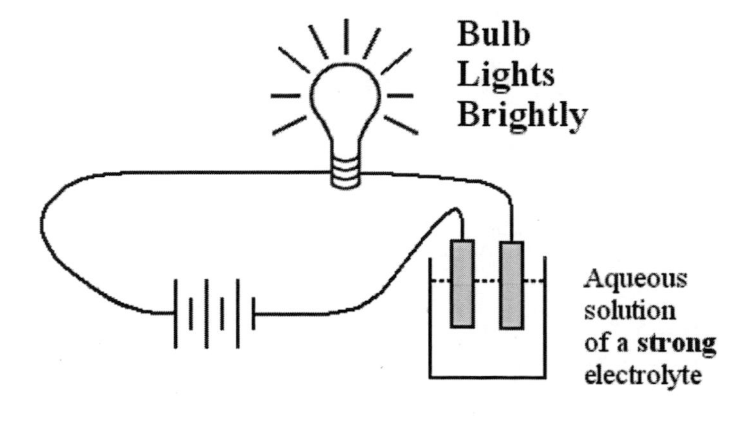

Strong electrolyte = produces 100% ions when dissolved in water.

1. soluble ionic substances
2. strong acids
3. strong bases

Precipitation Reactions

Example:

$$2\,KI(aq) + Pb(NO_3)_2(aq) \longrightarrow 2\,KNO_3(aq) + PbI_2(s)$$

Covalent Substances

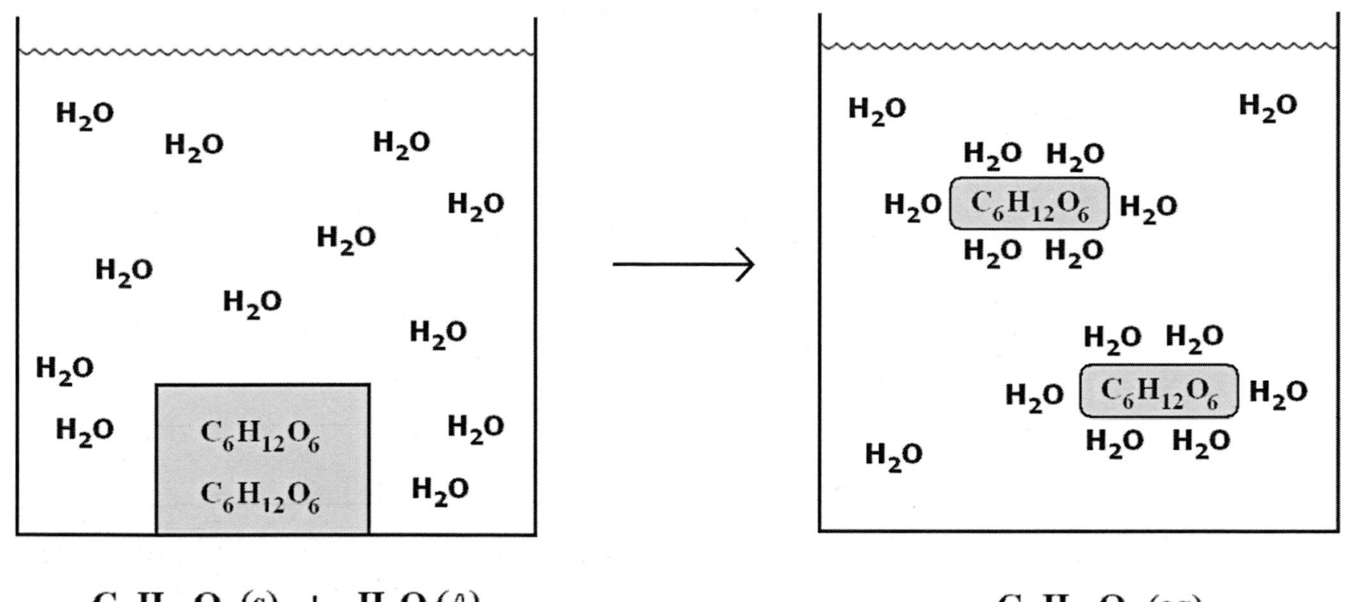

Equation: $C_6H_{12}O_6(s) \xrightarrow{H_2O} C_6H_{12}O_6(aq)$

Ionic Substances

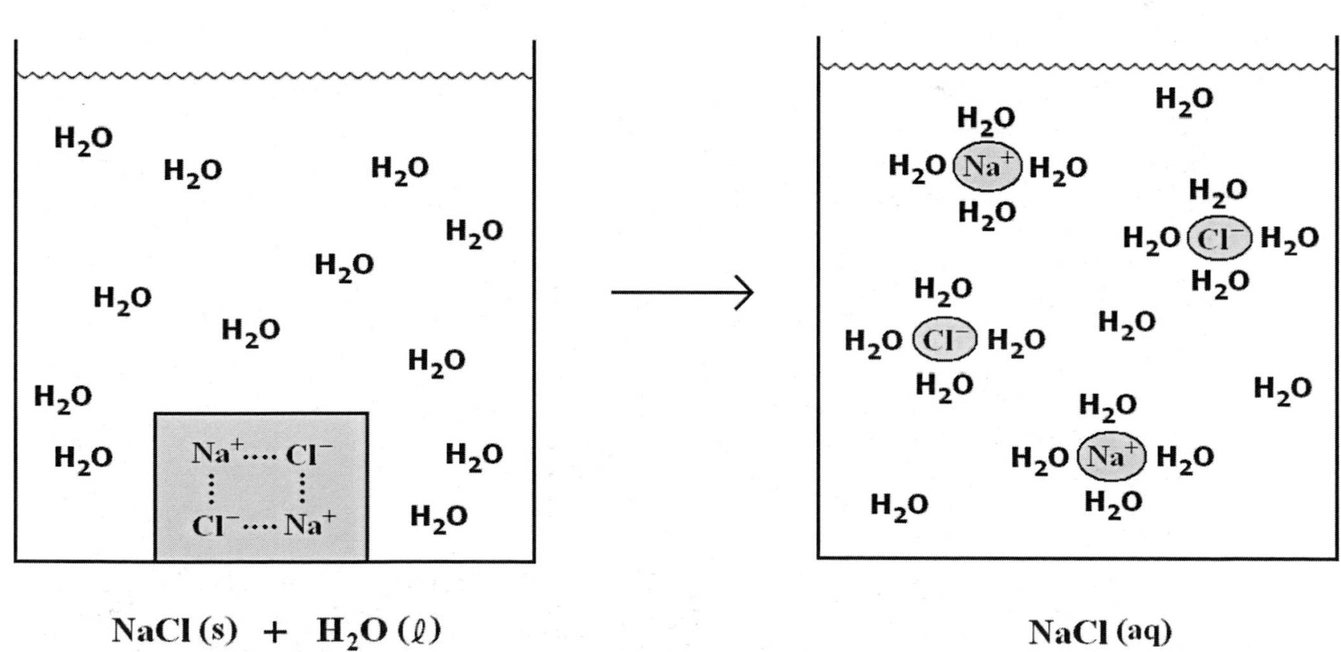

Equation: $NaCl(s) \xrightarrow{H_2O} Na^+(aq) + Cl^-(aq)$

Dissolving Equations

$$CaCl_2\,(s) \longrightarrow Ca^{2+}\,(aq) + 2\,Cl^-\,(aq)$$

Ca^{2+} Cl^-

Cl^-

$$K_2SO_4 \longrightarrow 2\,K^+ + SO_4^{2-}$$

K^+ SO_4^{2-}

K^+

Further Examples:

$$Al(NO_3)_3 \longrightarrow Al^{3+} + 3\,NO_3^-$$

$$Fe_2(SO_4)_3 \longrightarrow 2\,Fe^{3+} + 3\,SO_4^{2-}$$

$$(NH_4)_2CO_3 \longrightarrow 2\,NH_4^+ + CO_3^{2-}$$

Solubility is
357 g per L

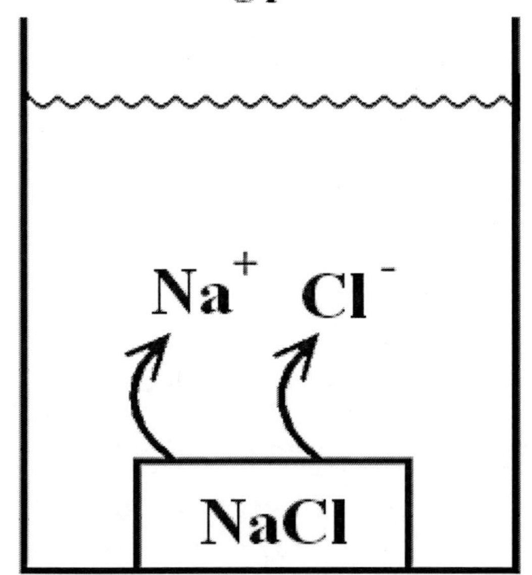

$NaCl\,(s) \longrightarrow Na^{+}(aq) + Cl^{-}(aq)$

One-way Arrow

"Soluble"
Salt

Solubility is
.002 g per L

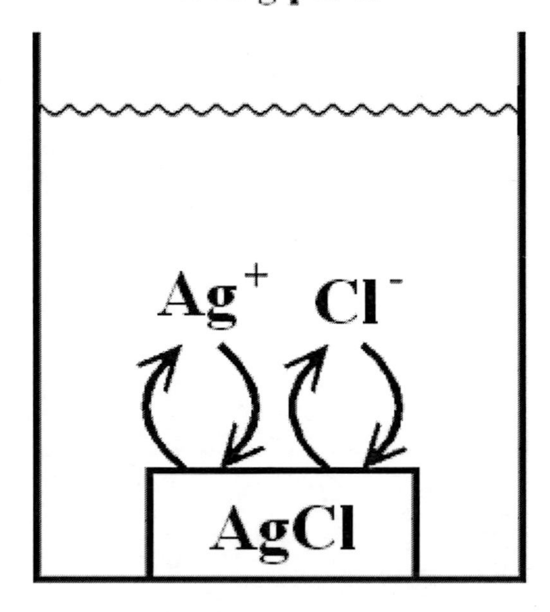

$AgCl\,(s) \rightleftharpoons Ag^{+}(aq) + Cl^{-}(aq)$

Equilibrium Arrow

"Insoluble"
or
"Sparingly soluble"
Salt

Solubility of Ionic Compounds in Water (at Room Temperature)

S = soluble SS = slightly soluble I = insoluble

	Al^{3+}	NH_4^+	Ba^{2+}	Ca^{2+}	Co^{2+}	Cr^{3+}	Cu^{2+}	Fe^{2+}	Fe^{3+}	Pb^{2+}	Mg^{2+}	Mn^{2+}	Hg_2^{2+}	Hg^{2+}	Ni^{2+}	K^+	Ag^+	Na^+	Sr^{2+}	Sn^{2+}	Zn^{2+}
Acetate ($C_2H_3O_2^-$)	S	S	S	S	S	S	S	S	S	S	S	S	S	S	S	S	SS	S	S	S	S
Bromide (Br^-)	S	S	S	S	S	S	S	S	S	I	S	S	I	S	S	S	I	S	S	S	S
Carbonate (CO_3^{2-})	I	S	I	I	I	I	I	I	I	I	SS	I	I	I	I	S	I	S	I	I	I
Chloride (Cl^-)	S	S	S	S	S	S	S	S	S	I	S	S	I	S	S	S	I	S	S	S	S
Chromate (CrO_4^{2-})	I	S	I	I	I	I	I	I	I	I	S	I	I	I	I	S	I	S	I	I	I
Hydroxide (OH^-)	I	-----	S	I	I	I	I	I	I	I	I	I	I	I	I	S	I	S	S	I	I
Iodide (I^-)	S	S	S	S	S	S	-----	S	S	I	S	S	I	S	S	S	I	S	S	SS	S
Nitrate (NO_3^-)	S	S	S	S	S	S	S	S	S	S	S	S	S	S	S	S	S	S	S	S	S
Phosphate (PO_4^{3-})	I	S	I	I	I	I	I	I	I	I	I	I	I	I	I	S	I	S	I	I	I
Sulfate (SO_4^{2-})	S	S	I	SS	S	S	S	S	S	I	S	S	I	SS	S	S	SS	S	SS	S	S
Sulfite (SO_3^{2-})	I	S	I	I	I	I	I	I	I	I	I	I	I	I	I	S	I	S	I	I	I
Sulfide (S^{2-})	I	S	-----	I	I	I	I	I	I	I	-----	I	I	I	I	S	I	S	I	I	I

Basic Solubility Rules

1. Salts of alkali metals (Group IA) and NH_4^+ are **soluble**.

   soluble: $NaCl$ KBr $(NH_4)_2C_2O_4$ Li_2SO_4 Cs_2CrO_4 NH_4NO_2

2. Salts of Cl^-, NO_3^-, and $C_2H_3O_2^-$ are **soluble**.

   Exceptions: $AgCl$, $PbCl_2$, and Hg_2Cl_2 are **insoluble**.

   soluble: $AgNO_3$ $Fe(NO_3)_2$ $Ba(C_2H_3O_2)_2$ $Al(C_2H_3O_2)_3$ $SrCl_2$ $FeCl_3$

   insoluble: $AgCl$ $PbCl_2$ Hg_2Cl_2

3. Metal hydroxides (bases) are **insoluble.**

   Exceptions: a. those from Rule 1 above [where the metal ion is an alkali metal (Group IA)] are **soluble**.

   b. $Sr(OH)_2$ and $Ba(OH)_2$ are **soluble**.

   insoluble: $Pb(OH)_2$ $Al(OH)_3$ $Fe(OH)_2$

   soluble: $NaOH$ KOH $Sr(OH)_2$ $Ba(OH)_2$

4. Salts of CO_3^{2-} and PO_4^{3-} are **insoluble.**

   Exceptions: those from Rule 1 above [where the positive ion is an alkali metal (Group IA) or NH_4^+] are **soluble**.

   insoluble: $PbCO_3$ $Ca_3(PO_4)_2$ $Fe_2(CO_3)_3$ $CrPO_4$

   soluble: Na_2CO_3 K_3PO_4 $(NH_4)_2CO_3$ Li_3PO_4

$$2\,KI(aq) + Pb(NO_3)_2(aq) \longrightarrow 2\,KNO_3(aq) + PbI_2(s)$$

$$\cancel{2K^+} + 2\,I^- + Pb^{2+} + \cancel{2NO_3^-} \longrightarrow \cancel{2K^+} + \cancel{2NO_3^-} + PbI_2(s)$$

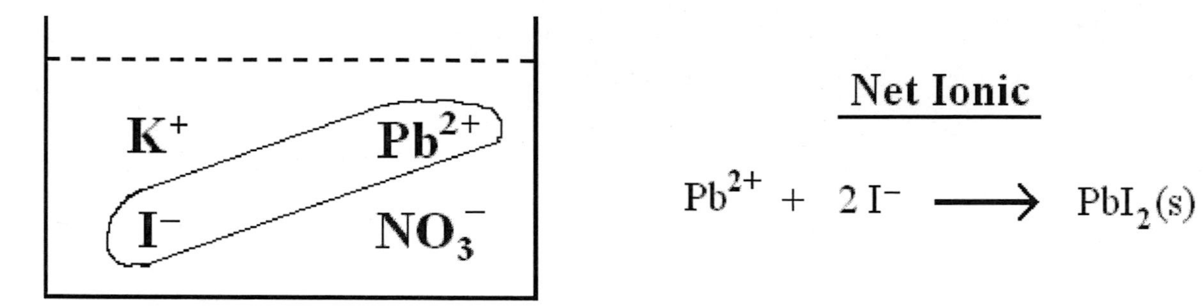

K$^+$ and NO$_3^-$ are "Spectator Ions"

$$NaI(aq) + 2\,Pb(NO_3)_2(aq) \longrightarrow 2\,NaNO_3(aq) + PbI_2(s)$$

$$\cancel{2Na^+} + 2\,I^- + Pb^{2+} + \cancel{2NO_3^-} \longrightarrow \cancel{2Na^+} + \cancel{2NO_3^-} + PbI_2(s)$$

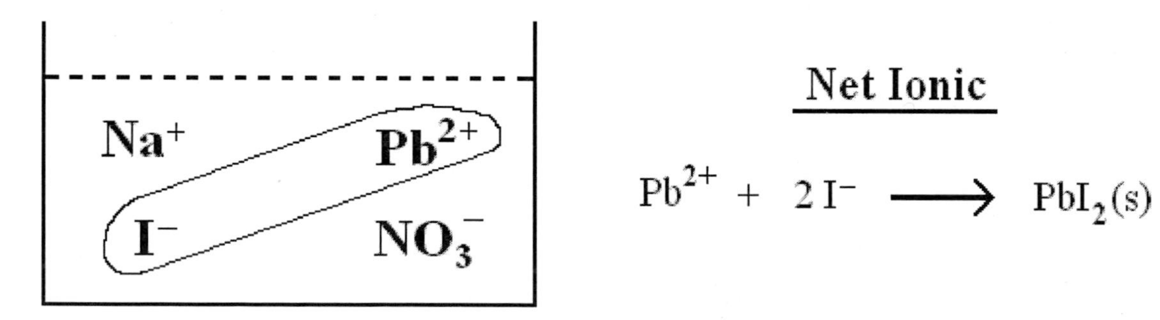

Na$^+$ and NO$_3^-$ are "Spectator Ions"

Write the net ionic equations for precipitation and dissolving of $BaCO_3$

Precipitation Reaction

$$Ba^{2+} + CO_3^{2-} \longrightarrow BaCO_3$$

Dissolving Equation

$$BaCO_3 \rightleftharpoons Ba^{2+} + CO_3^{2-}$$

Precipitation

Ba^{2+} CO_3^{2-}

Ba^{2+} CO_3^{2-}

$BaCO_3$

Dissolving

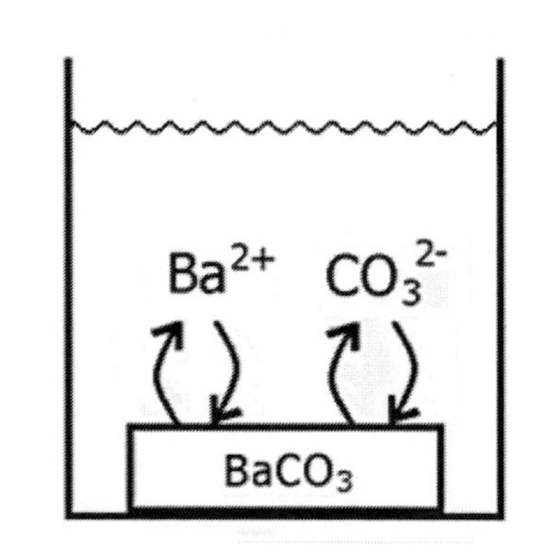

K_{sp} and pH

(Homework #2)

Equilibrium Constant For Precipitates

Soluble salts = solubility can be visually observed

$$NaCl(s) \longrightarrow Na^+(aq) + Cl^-(aq)$$

One-way arrow

Insoluble salts = no apparent solubility by eye

$$AgCl(s) \rightleftharpoons Ag^+(aq) + Cl^-(aq)$$

Equilibrium arrow

The equilibrium expression for AgCl(s) dissolving is:

$$K_{eq} = [Ag^+][Cl^-]$$

← it only has the product cause the reactant is a solid

[AgCl] would be the denominator, but **solids are not included in K_{eq} expressions.**

When the K_{eq} is for dissolving of an insoluble salt, use K_{sp}.

* the higher the # the more soluble

$$K_{sp} = [Ag^+][Cl^-]$$

Another example: $PbCl_2(s) \rightleftharpoons Pb^{2+}(aq) + 2\ Cl^-(aq)$

$$K_{sp} = [Pb^{2+}][Cl^-]^2$$

Problem:

Write the dissolving equation and K_{sp} expression for the insoluble salt $Ca_3(PO_4)_2$.

$$Ca_3(PO_4)_2 \rightleftharpoons 3\ Ca^{2+} + 2\ PO_4^{3-}$$

$$K_{sp} = [Ca^{2+}]^3[PO_4^{3-}]^2$$

K_{sp} values are obtained in the lab by an experiment. A chemist weighs out a known amount of the pure solid, stirs until maximum dissolving occurs, and determines how much dissolved.

Problem:

Suppose that, when a chemist dissolves $Ag_2CrO_4(s)$ in water, the following concentrations of ions are measured:

$[Ag^+] = 1.56 \times 10^{-4}$ M

$[CrO_4^{2-}] = 7.80 \times 10^{-5}$ M

What is the value of K_{sp}?

Solution:

$$Ag_2CrO_4(s) \rightleftharpoons 2\,Ag^+ + CrO_4^{2-}$$

↙ you have to balance the charges first

$$K_{sp} = [Ag^+]^2[CrO_4^{2-}] = (1.56 \times 10^{-4})^2(7.80 \times 10^{-5}) = \mathbf{1.9 \times 10^{-12}}$$

On a graphing calculator:

1.56 [EE] (−)4 ^ 2 * 7.80 [EE] (−)5 [Enter] (No Parentheses Needed)

On the display: 1.56E−4^2*7.80E−5

Alternate way:

(1.56 * 10^(−)4) ^ 2 * (7.80 * 10^(−)5) [Enter] **(MUST USE PARENTHESES!!)**

On display: (1.56 * 10^−4)^2 * (7.80 * 10^−5)

On a "regular" calculator:

1.56 [EE] [+/−] 4 [y^x] 2 * 7.80 [EE] [+/−] 5 =
or [EXP] (for [EE]); or [x^2] (for [y^x])

Table of K_{sp} values – **Table 1**, pp. 3 - 7

Arranged in alphabetical order by negative ion name.

Relative Solubilities of Salts

Problem: Which salt is more soluble, $BaCrO_4$ or $SrCrO_4$?

$BaCrO_4(s) \rightleftharpoons Ba^{2+} + CrO_4^{2-}$

$K_{sp} = [Ba^{2+}][CrO_4^{2-}] = 8.5 \times 10^{-11}$

$SrCrO_4(s) \rightleftharpoons Sr^{2+} + CrO_4^{2-}$

$K_{sp} = [Sr^{2+}][CrO_4^{2-}] = 3.6 \times 10^{-5}$

Larger number ➜ more ions ➜ **more soluble**

Smaller number ➜ fewer ions ➜ **less soluble**

8.5×10^{-11} is .000000000085

3.6×10^{-5} is .000036 ➜ Larger number

$3.6 \times 10^{-5} > 8.5 \times 10^{-11}$

$SrCrO_4$ is more soluble than $BaCrO_4$. Now include AgCl.

$AgCl(s) \rightleftharpoons Ag^+(aq) + Cl^-(aq)$

$K_{sp} = [Ag^+][Cl^-] = 1.8 \times 10^{-10}$

Problem: Rank the compounds AgCl, $SrCrO_4$ and $BaCrO_4$ in order from most soluble to least soluble.

Solution:

Most soluble

↓

$SrCrO_4$ 3.6×10^{-5}

AgCl 1.8×10^{-10}

$BaCrO_4$ 8.5×10^{-11}

↓

Least soluble

If the salt Ag_2CrO_4 is included in the comparison:

$$Ag_2CrO_4(s) \rightleftharpoons 2\ Ag^+ + CrO_4^{2-}$$

$$K_{sp} = [Ag^+]^2[CrO_4^{2-}] = \mathbf{1.9 \times 10^{-12}}$$

It appears to be the least soluble of all four (smallest K_{sp} value).

This conclusion is **not valid** because the exponents the K_{sp} expressions of $SrCrO_4$, AgCl and $BaCrO_4$ are the same (all 1's), but $[Ag^+]$ in the K_{sp} of Ag_2CrO_4 is **squared**. It requires a math problem to be done in a future class (HW 8) in order to determine where Ag_2CrO_4 fits into the group.

Problem: What is the value of K_{sp} for a soluble salt like NaCl?

$$NaCl \longrightarrow Na^+ + Cl^-$$

$$\text{"}K_{sp}\text{"} = \frac{[Na^+][Cl^-]}{[NaCl]}$$

Under the conditions of our experiments, [NaCl] = 0. That is, since NaCl is completely soluble, **no solid** is left after dissolving, only aqueous ions. Using the value 1 for the denominator for insoluble salts assumes that there will be some solid left after maximum dissolving.

Since dividing by 0 is not allowed, **K_{sp} values for soluble salts are considered to be undefined.**

Summary Rules:

- The larger the K_{sp} value, the more soluble the salt (if the exponents in the K_{sp} expressions are all the same.)

- The K_{sp} values of soluble salts are undefined.

"Will a ppt form?" Problems

Will a ppt form if you mix 7.1×10^{-3} M Ag^+ (aq) with 4.2×10^{-4} M CrO_4^{2-} (aq)?

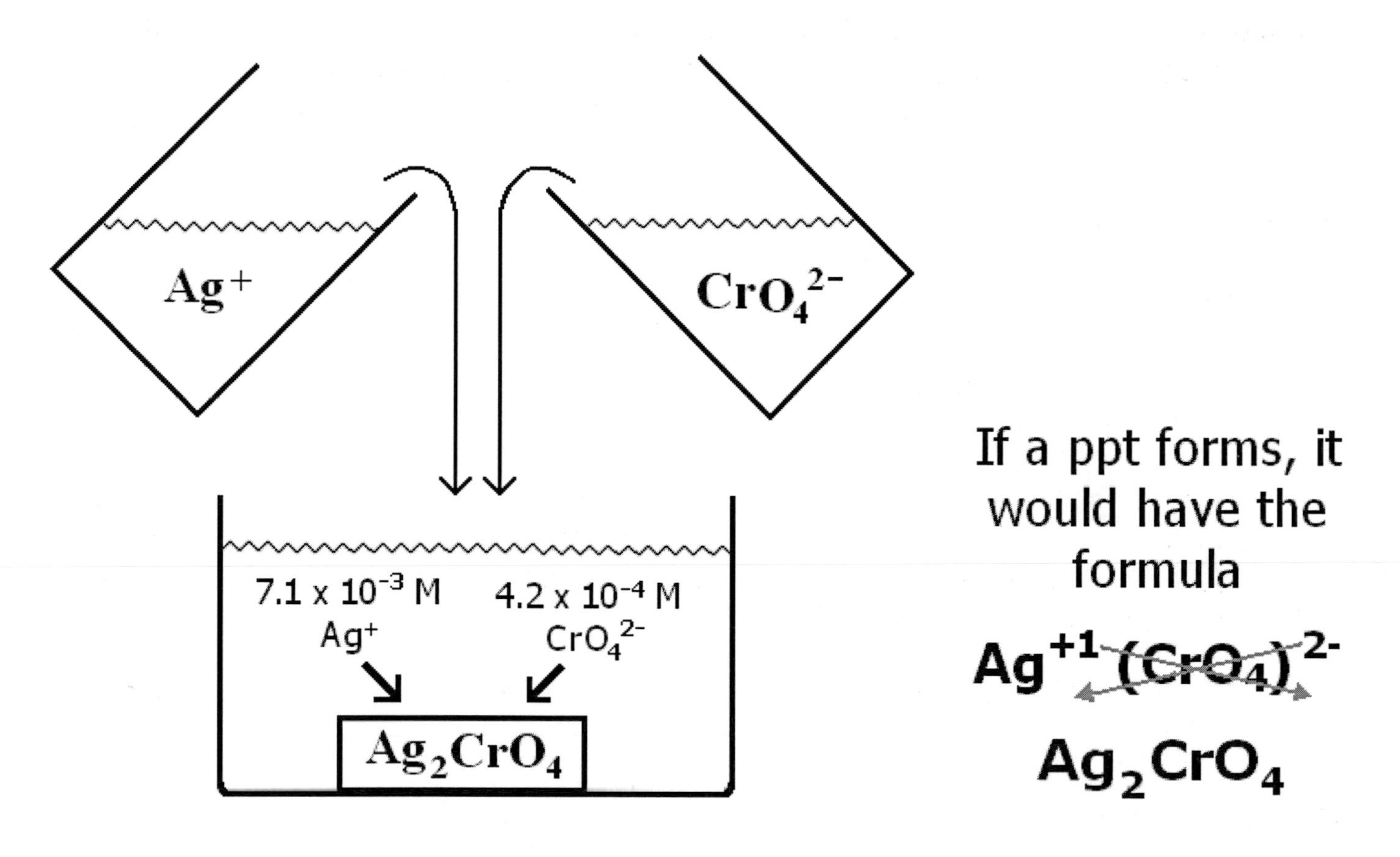

Even though Ag_2CrO_4 is "insoluble," it still dissolves a little. The concentration of ions must be **large enough** to exceed the solubility limit, or no ppt forms.

Even though it is not necessary, sometimes the ppt that would form is specified in the problem.

Problem: Will a ppt (of Ag_2CrO_4) form if you mix 7.1×10^{-3} M Ag^+ (aq) with 4.2×10^{-4} M CrO_4^{2-} (aq)?

Procedure for Solving "Will a ppt form?" Problems

$Ag_2CrO_4 \rightleftharpoons 2Ag^+ + CrO_4^{2-}$ $K_{sp} = 1.9 \times 10^{-12}$

← Value from TABLE 1

$Q = [Ag^+]^2[CrO_4^{2-}]$

$= (7.1 \times 10^{-3})^2(4.2 \times 10^{-4}) = 2.1 \times 10^{-8}$

$Q > K_{sp}$ ppt forms

Reaction shifts LEFT (Toward the Solid)

New Problem: Will a ppt of $Ag_2CrO_4(s)$ form if you mix 1.3×10^{-6} M Ag^+ (aq) with 4.7×10^{-3} M CrO_4^{2-} (aq)?

$Q = [Ag^+]^2[CrO_4^{2-}] = (1.3 \times 10^{-6})^2(4.7 \times 10^{-3}) = 7.9 \times 10^{-15}$

$Q < K_{sp}$ no ppt

Reaction shifts RIGHT (Toward the Ions)

Mixing Ions In the Lab

- Ag^+(aq) cannot exist in solution alone.
- There must be a – ion with it.
- Similarly, there must be a + ion with CrO_4^{2-} (aq).
- The additional ions will be spectators, but must be present.

"Real" Problem

Will a ppt (of Ag_2CrO_4) form if you mix 4.9×10^{-4} M $AgNO_3$ (aq) with 8.3×10^{-5} M K_2CrO_4 (aq)?

1) write the dissolving eq for Ag_2CrO_4

2) Calculate the concentr of each needed ion

3) Find the Q

4) compare it to the ksp from the table

Ag^+ NO_3^-	+	K^+ CrO_4^{2-}
100 % IONS		100% IONS

- If a ppt forms, it will be Ag_2CrO_4 (s).
- K^+ and NO_3^- are ions that "make everything soluble," so they are spectators.

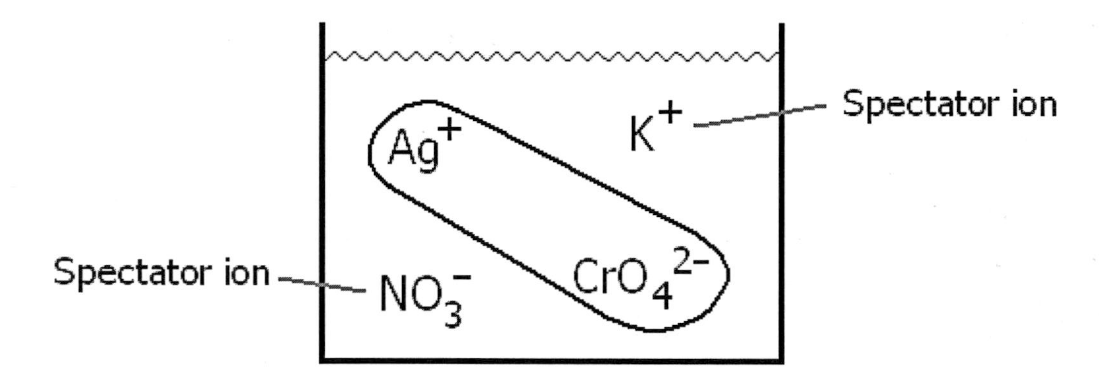

To solve the problem, we need a value for Q.

$Ag_2CrO_4 (s) \rightleftharpoons 2Ag^+ (aq) + CrO_4^{2-} (aq)$ $K_{sp} = 1.9 \times 10^{-12}$

$Q = [Ag^+]^2[CrO_4^{2-}]$

- However, the problem does not give values for $[Ag^+]$ and $[CrO_4^{2-}]$ directly.
- They can be determined for the data given in the problem.

$AgNO_3$ and K_2CrO_4 both produce 100% ions in water.

	$AgNO_3 (aq)$	$\rightarrow$	$Ag^+ (aq)$	+	~~$NO_3^- (aq)$~~
Initial	4.9×10^{-4} M		0		~~0~~
After	0		4.9×10^{-4} M		~~4.9×10^{-4} M~~ spectator

	$K_2CrO_4 (aq)$	$\rightarrow$	~~$2K^+ (aq)$~~	+	$CrO_4^{2-} (aq)$
Initial	8.3×10^{-5} M		~~0~~		0
After	0		~~$2 \times 8.3 \times 10^{-5} = 1.56 \times 10^{-4}$ M~~ spectator		8.3×10^{-5} M

It is allowable to "cross out" the spectators because they do not end up in the ppt.

"Real" Problem (from p. 78)

Will a ppt (of Ag_2CrO_4) form if you mix 4.9×10^{-4} M $AgNO_3$ (aq) with 8.3×10^{-5} M K_2CrO_4 (aq)?

$Ag_2CrO_4 \rightleftharpoons 2Ag^+ + CrO_4^{2-}$ $\qquad K_{sp} = 1.9 \times 10^{-12}$

$Q = [Ag^+]^2[CrO_4^{2-}]$

$= (4.9 \times 10^{-4})^2(8.3 \times 10^{-5}) = 2.0 \times 10^{-11}$

$Q > K_{sp}$ ppt forms

Problem:

Complete and balance the following metathesis (double displacement) reaction and write the net ionic equation for the precipitation.

$AgNO_3$ (aq) + K_2CrO_4 (aq) →

STEP 1

"Switch" the metal ions:

$AgNO_3 + K_2CrO_4 \rightarrow K^+(NO_3)^- + Ag^+(CrO_4)^{2-}$

STEP 2

"Cross" the charges to get the correct formula:

$AgNO_3 + K_2CrO_4 \rightarrow KNO_3 + Ag_2CrO_4$

STEP 3

Balance:

$2AgNO_3 + K_2CrO_4 \rightarrow 2KNO_3 + Ag_2CrO_4$

STEP 4

Determine which product is the ppt.

- KNO_3 cannot be a ppt because K^+ and NO_3^- both "make everything soluble".
- Ag_2CrO_4 is found in TABLE 1, which contains only insoluble compounds.

$$2\,AgNO_3\,(aq) + K_2CrO_4\,(aq) \longrightarrow 2\,KNO_3\,(aq) + Ag_2CrO_4\,(s)$$

STEP 5 (Optional)

Split soluble compounds up into ions and cancel spectators.

$$2\,Ag^+ + \cancel{2\,NO_3^-} + \cancel{2\,K^+} + CrO_4^{2-} \longrightarrow \cancel{2\,K^+} + \cancel{2\,NO_3^-} + Ag_2CrO_4\,(s)$$

STEP 6

Write the final net ionic equation.

$$2\,Ag^+ + CrO_4^{2-} \longrightarrow Ag_2CrO_4\,(s)$$

Why do we use the dissolving equation, rather than the precipitation equation, to do the "Will a ppt form?" problems?

- Tradition = Chemists have chosen to record the dissolving constant, K_{sp}, rather than the precipitation constant, in tables.
- The problem can be done either way. All that is required is to determine which way the equilibrium shifts by comparing Q to K (either K_{sp} or a "precipitation constant.").
- If the reaction shifts toward the solid, a ppt forms.
- If the reaction shifts toward the ions, no ppt forms.

Problem:

Will a ppt of $Al(OH)_3$ (s) form if you mix 4.3×10^{-8} M $Al(C_2H_3O_2)_3$ (aq) with 7.2×10^{-5} M NaOH (aq)?

Solution:

$Al(OH)_3\,(s) \rightleftharpoons Al^{3+} + 3\,OH^-$ $\quad K_{sp} = 5 \times 10^{-33}$

$Q = [Al^{3+}][OH^-]^3$

How do we get values for $[Al^{3+}]$ and $[OH^-]$?

Answer: Just "cross out" the spectators.

Will a ppt of $Al(OH)_3$ (s) form if you mix 4.3×10^{-8} M $Al(C_2H_3O_2)_3$ (aq) with 7.2×10^{-5} M NaOH (aq)?

$Al(OH)_3\,(s) \rightleftharpoons Al^{3+} + 3\,OH^-$ $\quad K_{sp} = 5 \times 10^{-33}$

$Q = [Al^{3+}][OH^-]^3$

$= (4.3 \times 10^{-8})(7.2 \times 10^{-5})^3 = 1.6 \times 10^{-20}$

$Q > K_{sp}$ ppt forms

Suppose you were not given the formula of the ppt in the previous problem but were asked to determine it yourself.

Problem:

Complete and balance the following metathesis (double displacement) reaction and write the net ionic equation for the precipitation.

$Al(C_2H_3O_2)_3\ (aq) + NaOH\ (aq) \longrightarrow$

STEP 1

"Switch" the metal ions:

$Al(C_2H_3O_2)_3 + NaOH \longrightarrow Na^+(C_2H_3O_2)^- + Al^{3+}(OH)^-$

STEP 2

"Cross" the charges to get the correct formula:

$Al(C_2H_3O_2)_3 + NaOH \longrightarrow NaC_2H_3O_2 + Al(OH)_3$

STEP 3

Balance:

$Al(C_2H_3O_2)_3 + 3\ NaOH \longrightarrow 3\ NaC_2H_3O_2 + Al(OH)_3$

STEP 4

Determine which product is the ppt.

- $NaC_2H_3O_2$ cannot be a ppt because Na^+ and $C_2H_3O_2^-$ both "make everything soluble".
- $Al(OH)_3$ is found in TABLE 1, which contains only insoluble compounds.
- $Al(OH)_3$ is insoluble according to solubility rule 3 (p. 67).

$$Al(C_2H_3O_2)_3\ (aq) + 3\ NaOH\ (aq) \longrightarrow 3\ NaC_2H_3O_2\ (aq) + Al(OH)_3\ (s)$$

STEP 5 (Optional)

Split soluble compounds up into ions and cancel spectators.

$$Al^{3+} + \cancel{3\,C_2H_3O_2^-} + \cancel{3\,Na^+} + 3\,OH^- \rightarrow \cancel{3\,Na^+} + \cancel{3\,C_2H_3O_2^-} + Al(OH)_3\,(s)$$

STEP 6

Write the final net ionic equation.

$$Al^{3+} + 3\,OH^- \rightarrow Al(OH)_3\,(s)$$

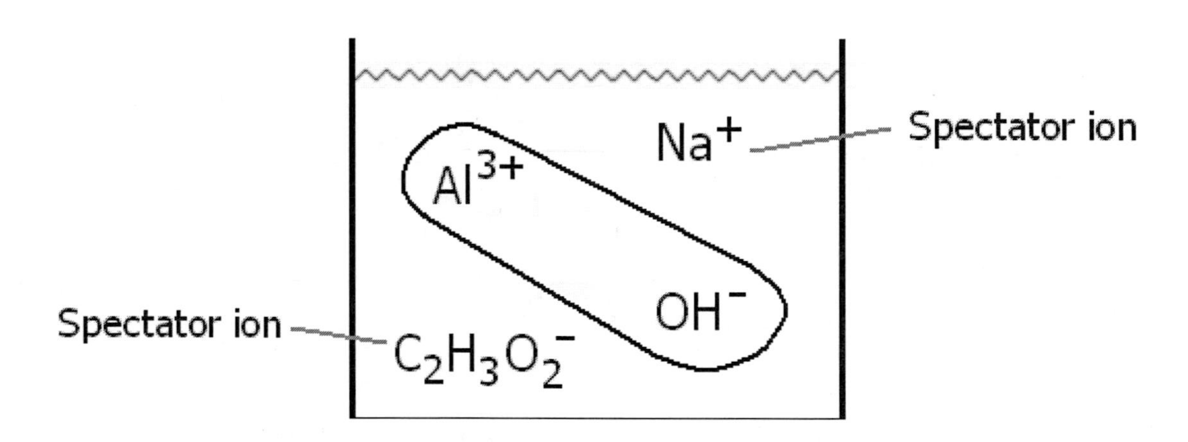

Measurement of Acidity – pH

Acids ionize in water to give $H^+(aq)$.

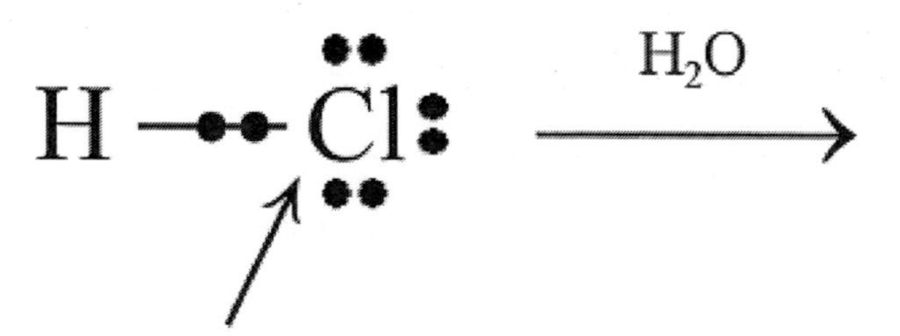

$$\xrightarrow{H_2O} \quad H^+ + :Cl:^-$$

- Higher Electronegativity, so e^- already "closer" to Cl.
- H_2O "completes" the process of splitting the bond.

Called a "**hydrogen ion**" or a "**proton**."

- Actually, H^+ does not exist as a "free" ion in water.
- It connects to H_2O molecules by a type of bond called a "**coordinate covalent**" or "**dative**" bond in which **both e^-** in the bond come from the **same atom**:

$$H^+ \quad :\ddot{O}(H)-H \quad \longrightarrow \quad \left[H \leftarrow \ddot{O}(H)-H \right]^+$$

H_3O^+ is called "hydronium ion" and is actually what is meant by $H^+(aq)$.

Although we balance equations using H^+, it is sometimes important to realize that H^+ is actually being carried by a water molecule rather than being a "free" ion.

Bases produce OH^- when they dissolve in water (soluble ionic compounds split up into ions in solution).

$$NaOH(s) \xrightarrow{H_2O} Na^+(aq) + OH^-(aq)$$

Pure water has a very small, but significant, number of $H^+(aq)$ and $OH^-(aq)$ ions.

These ions come from the **autoionization of water:**

$$H_2O(\ell) \rightleftharpoons H^+(aq) + OH^-(aq)$$

$$\mathbf{K_w} = [H^+] \cdot [OH^-] = 1.0 \times 10^{-14}$$

$H_2O(\ell)$, just like any liquid, does not appear in the $\mathbf{K_{eq}}$ expression (called "$\mathbf{K_w}$" for water). The value of K_w has been determined to two significant figures (1.0×10^{-14}) at room temperature.

In pure water, the concentrations of H^+ and OH^- are equal (one of each ion forms when water splits apart):

$$[H^+] = [OH^-]$$

Because the value of K_w is a constant, the expression

$$[H^+] \cdot [OH^-] = 1.0 \times 10^{-14}$$

shows that, in any aqueous solution, if you increase the $[H^+]$, the $[OH^-]$ decreases. Likewise, if you decrease the $[H^+]$, the $[OH^-]$ increases.

The **pH** measures tells **how acidic a solution is (how much H^+ is present)** according to the following mathematical definition:

$$\mathbf{pH = -\log_{10} [H^+]}$$

A lowercase **p** in front of a variable is often used to indicate "**$-\log_{10}$**" in math and science.

Description of logarithms

number = 10^y

"antilog" (arrow to number)
2nd log
INV log

logarithm (arrow to y)

The **logarithm** of a number is the **exponent to which 10 must be raised** to give the number.

In pure water, $[H^+]$ and $[OH^-]$ can be calculated as follows:

Let $x = [H^+] = [OH^-]$

Since $K_w = [H^+] \cdot [OH^-] = 1.0 \times 10^{-14}$

$$(x) \cdot (x) = 1.0 \times 10^{-14}$$

$$\sqrt{x^2} = \sqrt{1.0 \times 10^{-14}}$$

$$x = 1.0 \times 10^{-7}\text{ M} = [H^+] = [OH^-]$$

$$\mathbf{pH} = \mathbf{-log_{10}[H^+]} = -\log_{10}(1 \times 10^{-7}) = -(-7) = \textcircled{7}$$

A similar definition exists for pOH

$$\mathbf{pOH} = \mathbf{-log_{10}[OH^-]} = -\log_{10}(1 \times 10^{-7}) = -(-7) = \textcircled{7}$$

pH 7 is referred to as "neutral" = the solution does not act either acidic or basic. Because of the way pH and pOH are defined, in any aqueous solution:

$$\mathbf{pH + pOH = 14}$$

A useful formula for interconverting $[H^+]$ and $[OH^-]$ can be obtained from

$$\mathbf{[H^+] \cdot [OH^-] = 1 \times 10^{-14}}$$

Dividing both sides by $[H^+]$ gives:

$$\frac{\cancel{[H^+]} \cdot [OH^-]}{\cancel{[H^+]}} = \frac{1 \times 10^{-14}}{[H^+]}$$

$$\mathbf{[OH^-]} = \frac{\mathbf{1 \times 10^{-14}}}{\mathbf{[H^+]}}$$

Switching $[H^+]$ and $[OH^-]$ gives a similar formula for calculating $[H^+]$:

$$\mathbf{[H^+]} = \frac{\mathbf{1 \times 10^{-14}}}{\mathbf{[OH^-]}}$$

How pH changes with changes in $[H^+]$

We showed above that a **neutral** solution has $[H^+]$ **= 1.0 x 10^{-7} M** and **pH** = 7.

Problem: What is the pH of a solution for which $[H^+] = 3.7 \times 10^{-3}$ M?

$$pH = -\log(3.7 \times 10^{-3}) = -(-2.43) = \boxed{2.43}$$

calculator: (−) log 3.7 EE (−) 3 Enter OR

(−) log (3.7 * 10^(−)3) Enter

Since 3.7×10^{-3} M > 1.0×10^{-7} M, this problem shows that ↑$[H^+]$ causes ↓pH.

Because of the definition of pH, **the higher the $[H^+]$, the lower the pH**. Therefore, **acidic** solutions have **low pH values.**

$$[H^+] \cdot [OH^-] = 1 \times 10^{-14}$$

Dissolve an **acid** in water	:	↑$[H^+]$	↓$[OH^-]$	↓pH
Dissolve a **base** in water	:	↓$[H^+]$	↑$[OH^-]$	↑pH

Acidic solutions have a pH Below 7

Basic (Alkaline) solutions have a pH Above 7

The pH Scale

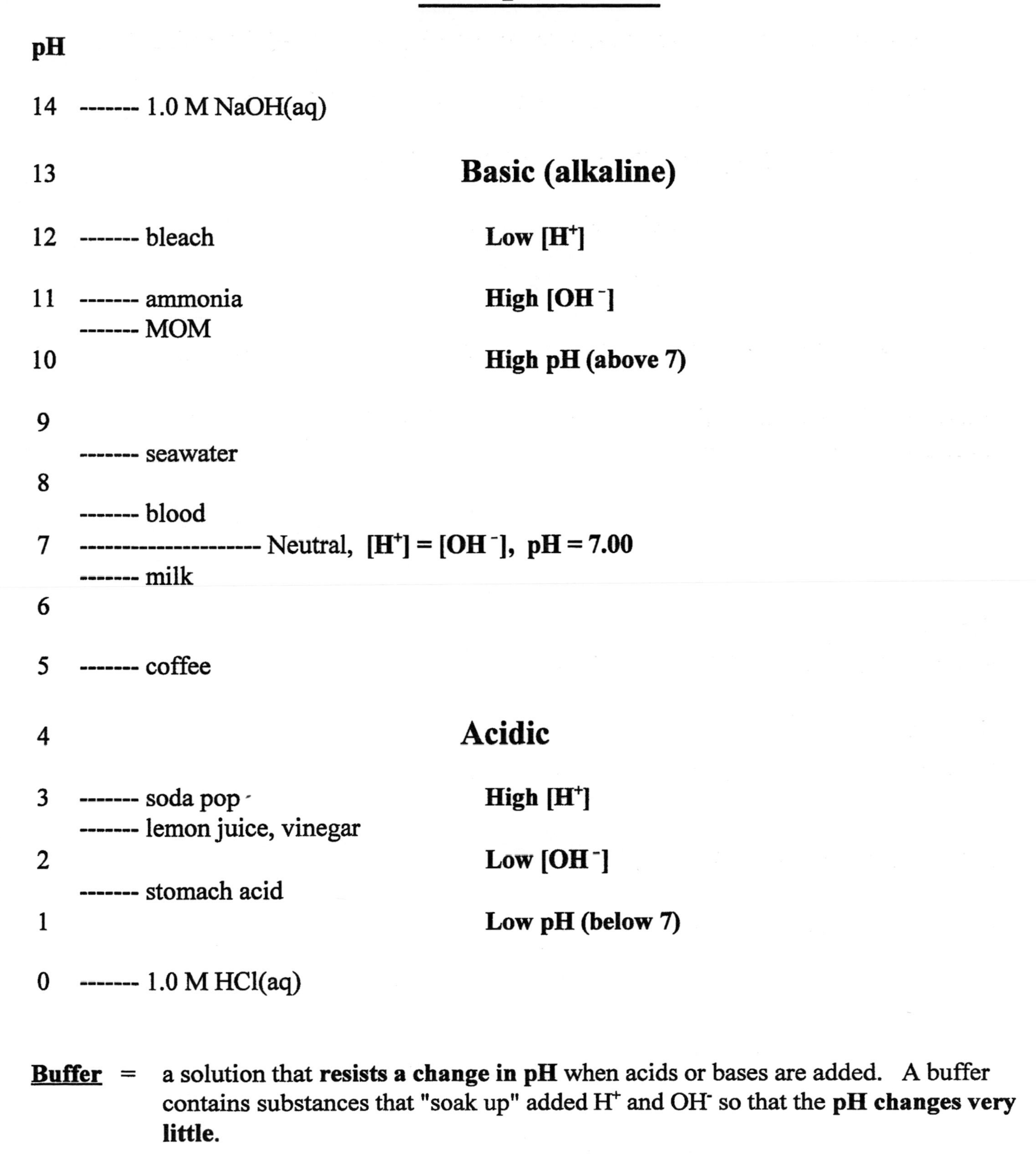

Buffer = a solution that **resists a change in pH** when acids or bases are added. A buffer contains substances that "soak up" added H^+ and OH^- so that the **pH changes very little.**

	$[H^+]$	$[OH^-]$	pH	pOH
	1.0×10^{-14} M	1.0 M	14	0
	2.3×10^{-11} M	4.3×10^{-4} M	10.63	3.37
neutral	1.0×10^{-7} M	1.0×10^{-7} M	7	7
	7.8×10^{-7} M	1.3×10^{-8} M	6.11	7.89
	1.7×10^{-3} M	5.9×10^{-12} M	2.77	11.23
	1.0 M	1.0×10^{-14} M	0	14

If $[H^+] = 2.3 \times 10^{-11}$ M, what is the pH?

$$pH = -\log(2.3 \times 10^{-11}) = \boxed{10.63}$$

What is the pOH?

$$pOH = 14 - pH = 14 - 10.63 = \boxed{3.37}$$

What is $[OH^-]$?

$$[OH^-] = \frac{1 \times 10^{-14}}{[H^+]} = \frac{1 \times 10^{-14}}{2.3 \times 10^{-11}} = \boxed{4.3 \times 10^{-4}\ M}$$

How to convert from pH to $[H^+]$

$$pH = -\log [H^+]$$

(multiply both sides by −1)

$$-pH = \log [H^+]$$

(turn equation around)

$$\log [H^+] = -pH$$

(take INV log of both sides)

$$\textbf{INV log} \ (\log [H^+]) = \textbf{INV log} \ (-pH)$$

(INV log removes log)

$$\mathbf{[H^+] = INV\ log\ (-pH)}$$ ← ***Final conversion equation***

Problem:

If pH = 6.11, what is $[H^+]$?

$$[H^+] = \text{INV log} (-6.11) = 7.8 \times 10^{-7} \text{ M}$$

What is pOH?

$$pOH = 14 - pH = 7.89$$

What is $[OH^-]$?

2 alternatives:

$$[OH^-] = \frac{1 \times 10^{-14}}{[H^+]} = \frac{1 \times 10^{-14}}{7.8 \times 10^{-7}} = \boxed{\mathbf{1.3 \times 10^{-8}\ M}}$$

$$[OH^-] = \text{INV log} (-pOH) = \text{INV log} (-7.89) = \boxed{\mathbf{1.3 \times 10^{-8}\ M}}$$

Summary of pH Conversion Formulas

$pH = -\log [H^+]$

$pOH = -\log [OH^-]$

$[H^+] = \text{INV} \log (-pH)$

$[OH^-] = \text{INV} \log (-pOH)$

$$[H^+] = \frac{1 \times 10^{-14}}{[OH^-]}$$

$$[OH^-] = \frac{1 \times 10^{-14}}{[H^+]}$$

$pH + pOH = 14$

In Words

Convert $[H^+] \rightarrow pH$ or $[OH^-] \rightarrow pOH$: $-\log$

Convert $pH \rightarrow [H^+]$ or $pOH \rightarrow [OH^-]$: Inv log(-)

For $[H^+]$ and $[OH^-]$: $\dfrac{1 \times 10^{-14}}{\text{one of them}} = \text{the other}$

For pH and pOH: 14 − one of them = the other

pH of Solutions of Acids and Bases

(Homework #3)

pH of Solutions of Acids and Bases

Acids

		nonmetal
H	***combined with***	**or**
		polyatomic

Strong Acids = ionize (dissociate) 100 % into ions.

Hydrochloric	$HCl(aq) \longrightarrow H^+(aq) + Cl^-(aq)$	(100 % ions)
Nitric	$HNO_3(aq) \longrightarrow H^+(aq) + NO_3^-(aq)$	(100 % ions)

There are **six strong acids** commonly used in lab. The other four are:

HBr	Hydrobromic
HI	Hydroiodic
$HClO_4$	Perchloric
H_2SO_4	Sulfuric

You need to be able to **recognize these 6 strong acids**, because you can assume that any others are weak.

Weak acids = ionize (dissociate) less than 100 %, often less than 5 %.

Hydrofluoric	$HF(aq) \rightleftharpoons H^+(aq) + F^-(aq)$	($\cong$ 1 % ions)
Nitrous	$HNO_2(aq) \rightleftharpoons H^+(aq) + NO_2^-(aq)$	($\cong$ 1 % ions)
Acetic	$HC_2H_3O_2(aq) \rightleftharpoons H^+(aq) + C_2H_3O_2^-(aq)$	($\cong$ 1 % ions)

For weak acids, **almost all** the acid remains as **molecules** with the H still attached, and **only a few molecules** split up into **ions** (1 % ionization means 1 molecule out of 100 forms ions. The other 99 remain as molecules.)

How do chemists determine whether an acid is weak or strong?

pH values can be measured in the lab with a device called a **pH meter.**

Example:

If you make the following solutions, the pH values measured will be approximately:

Solution	pH
0.1 M HCl(aq)	1
0.1 M HF(aq)	3

- As stated above, the **lower the pH**, the **more H^+(aq)** ions are present.
- HCl, a strong acid, produces **more H^+(aq) ions** than the weak acid HF, even though both acids have the same concentration.
- Another way to say it is that HCl **splits up into ions more extensively** than HF.

The amount that an acid dissociates in water can be measured by the appropriate equilibrium constant.

Equilibrium Constant (K_{eq}) for Acids:

The Acid Dissociation Constant, K_a

$$HNO_2(aq) \rightleftharpoons H^+(aq) + NO_2^-(aq)$$

$$K_a = \frac{[H^+]\,[NO_2^-]}{[HNO_2]}$$

- Note that $[HNO_2]$ does appear in the denominator.
  HNO_2 dissolves, but only a small number of HNO_2 molecules **ionize.**
- In K_{sp}, on the other hand, the solid does not appear in the denominator because it remains **undissolved unless it splits up into ions.**
- By contrast, **acids dissolve whether they split up into ions or not.**

Values of K_a

- K_a values are recorded in **Table 2** (pp. 9 and 10).
- They are **small numbers** (– power of 10) because only a few ions form.
- The **larger the K_a**, the more ions, and the **stronger the acid.**

Stronger

↓	HNO_2	$K_a = 4.5 \times 10^{-4}$
↓	$HC_2H_3O_2$	$K_a = 1.8 \times 10^{-5}$
↓	HCN	$K_a = 4.9 \times 10^{-10}$

Weaker

Terminology used for acids:

★ All strong acids ionize 100 %.

★ All weak acids ionize less than 100 %, usually less than 5 %.

★ Some weak acids are stronger (ionize more) than others.

Strong acids have a K_a that is **undefined.**

$$HCl(aq) \longrightarrow H^+(aq) + Cl^-(aq)$$

$$K_a = \frac{[H^+]\,[Cl^-]}{[HCl]}$$

Since HCl dissociates 100 %, [HCl] = 0 and division by zero is not allowed.

Diprotic and Triprotic Acids

- Some acids have two or three H's that can be lost.
- These acids lose the H's one at a time in separate steps.
- Some examples are shown on the second page of **Table 2** (p. 10).

Example:

$$H_2CO_3 \rightleftharpoons H^+ + HCO_3^- \qquad K_{a1} = 4.2 \times 10^{-7}$$

$$HCO_3^- \rightleftharpoons H^+ + CO_3^{2-} \qquad K_{a2} = 4.8 \times 10^{-11}$$

✖ H_2CO_3 is a stronger acid than HCO_3^-, as the K_a values show.

✖ In the K_{a1} step, where H_2CO_3 ionizes, H^+ separates from the −1 ion HCO_3^-.

✖ In the K_{a2} step, where HCO_3^- ionizes, H^+ must separate from the −2 ion CO_3^{2-}.

✖ It makes sense that it would be easier for a +1 H to separate from a −1 ion than from a −2 ion.

✖ This general principle is true for all polyprotic acids; **the first acid** in the series is the **strongest**, and the acids always **get progressively weaker** as you go down.

H_2SO_4 has a first ionization step that occurs 100 %, but the second step is weak and has a defined K_{a2} value.

$$H_2SO_4 \rightarrow H^+ + HSO_4^- \qquad K_{a1} = \text{undefined} \quad \textbf{(STRONG)}$$

$$HSO_4^- \rightleftharpoons H^+ + SO_4^{2-} \qquad K_{a2} = 1.3 \times 10^{-2} \quad \textbf{(weak)}$$

H_3PO_4 can lose all 3 H's.

$$H_3PO_4 \rightleftharpoons H^+ + H_2PO_4^- \qquad K_{a1} = 7.5 \times 10^{-3}$$

$$H_2PO_4^- \rightleftharpoons H^+ + HPO_4^{2-} \qquad K_{a2} = 6.2 \times 10^{-8}$$

$$HPO_4^{2-} \rightleftharpoons H^+ + PO_4^{3-} \qquad K_{a3} = 4.8 \times 10^{-13}$$

Naming of Ions from Polyprotic Acids

- The ions from these acids that **still contain some H's** have a naming system of their own.
- The prefix **bi**– is used for the ion from a diprotic acid that still has an H attached. An alternate system uses "Hydrogen" in the name:

$\mathbf{HCO_3^-}$	Bicarbonate or Hydrogen Carbonate
$\mathbf{HSO_4^-}$	Bisulfate or Hydrogen Sulfate
$\mathbf{HSO_3^-}$	Bisulfite or Hydrogen Sulfite

The ions from triprotic acids **are not** given the prefix **bi**– :

$\mathbf{H_2PO_4^-}$	Dihydrogen Phosphate
$\mathbf{HPO_4^{2-}}$	Monohydrogen Phosphate (**NOT** Biphosphate!)

Write the formula of Barium Dihydrogen Phosphate

Ba^{2+} $(H_2PO_4)^{1-}$ cross the charges $\longrightarrow$ $\mathbf{Ba(H_2PO_4)_2}$

Write the formula of Ammonium Monohydrogen Phosphate

NH_4^{1+} $(HPO_4)^{2-}$ cross the charges $\longrightarrow$ $(NH_4)_2HPO_4$

Calculating the pH of Strong Acid solutions

Problem: What is the pH of .0079 M $HClO_4(aq)$?

Solution: $HClO_4$ is a strong acid (one of the six listed earlier). So, it ionizes 100%.

	$HClO_4(aq)$	$\longrightarrow$	$H^+(aq)$	+	$ClO_4^-(aq)$
before ionizing	.0079 M		0		0
after ionizing	0		.0079 M		.0079 M

$$pH = -\log [H^+] = -\log(.0079) = \boxed{2.1}$$

➻ **General Rule: To calculate the pH of a strong acid solution, pH = −log [acid]**

pH of Weak Acid Solutions

Problem: Calculate the pH and % ionization of .0079 M $HC_2H_3O_2(aq)$.

Solution: Since $HC_2H_3O_2$ is a weak acid, ionization is not 100%, so an **ICE** table must be used to determine how much of the acid splits into ions.

	$HC_2H_3O_2$	$\rightleftharpoons$	H^+	+	$C_2H_3O_2^-$
I	.0079		0		0
C	$-x$		$+x$		$+x$
E	$.0079 - x$		x		x

$$K_a = \frac{[H^+][C_2H_3O_2^-]}{[HC_2H_3O_2]} = \frac{x \cdot x}{.0079 - x} = \frac{x^2}{.0079 - x} = 1.8 \times 10^{-5}$$

Value from **Table 2, p. 9**

* This quadratic equation would have to be solved by the quadratic formula.

* Since $HC_2H_3O_2$ is a weak acid which splits into ions about 5 % or less, x is small compared to the original .0079 M concentration.

* The answer will not change very much if x is ignored relative to .0079

* The equation will then be solvable without the quadratic formula.

$$\frac{x^2}{.0079 \cancel{-x}} = 1.8 \times 10^{-5}$$

$$\frac{x^2}{.0079} = 1.8 \times 10^{-5}$$

$$\cancel{.0079} \cdot \frac{x^2}{\cancel{.0079}} = 1.8 \times 10^{-5} \cdot .0079$$

$$\sqrt{x^2} = \sqrt{1.42 \times 10^{-7}}$$

$$x = 3.77 \times 10^{-4} \text{M} = [H^+]$$

$$\text{pH} = -\log(3.77 \times 10^{-4}) = \boxed{\mathbf{3.42}}$$

(If x is not ignored and the equation is solved using the quadratic formula:

$x = 3.68 \times 10^{-4}$M $= [H^+]$, pH $=$ **3.43**

This difference is negligible.)

% ionization refers to the percentage of the original acid that forms ions.

$$\% \text{ ionization} = \frac{x \text{ or } [H^+]}{\text{original conc. acid}} \times 100\%$$

$$= \frac{3.77 \times 10^{-4}}{.0079} \times 100\% = \boxed{4.8\%}$$

➽ **The 5 % Rule:**

If the % ionization of an acid is 5 % or less, **it is acceptable to ignore *x*** relative to the original acid concentration.

pH of Solutions of Diprotic Acids

Problem:

Calculate the pH and % ionization of 0.1 M H_2CO_3 (aq).

$H_2CO_3 \rightleftharpoons H^+ + HCO_3^-$ $K_{a1} = 4.2 \times 10^{-7}$

$HCO_3^- \rightleftharpoons H^+ + CO_3^{2-}$ $K_{a2} = 4.8 \times 10^{-11}$

* H_2CO_3 is 10^4 or 10,000 times stronger an acid than HCO_3^-.
* It is expected that the K_{a1} step produces about 10,000 times more H^+ than step 2.
* So, for calculating the pH of a diprotic acid solution, use only the K_{a1} step and ignore step 2.

	H_2CO_3	$\rightleftharpoons$	H^+	+	HCO_3^-
I	0.1		0		0
C	$-x$		$+x$		$+x$
E	$0.1 - x$		x		x

$$K_{a1} = \frac{[H^+][HCO_3^-]}{[H_2CO_3]} = \frac{x \cdot x}{0.1 - x} = \frac{x^2}{0.1 - x} = 4.2 \times 10^{-7}$$

Value from Table 2, p. 10

$$\frac{x^2}{0.1 \not{-} \not{x}} = 4.2 \times 10^{-7}$$

$$\frac{x^2}{0.1} = 4.2 \times 10^{-7}$$

$$\not{0.1} \cdot \frac{x^2}{\not{0.1}} = 4.2 \times 10^{-7} \cdot 0.1$$

$$\sqrt{x^2} = \sqrt{4.2 \times 10^{-8}}$$

$$x = 2.05 \times 10^{-4} M = [H^+]$$

$$pH = -\log(2.05 \times 10^{-4}) = \boxed{3.69}$$

$$\% \text{ ionization} = \frac{x \text{ or } [H^+]}{\text{original conc. acid}} \times 100\%$$

$$= \frac{2.05 \times 10^{-4}}{0.1} \times 100\% = \boxed{.205\%}$$

➻ **Rule:** **When calculating the pH of a diprotic acid, ignore the 2nd step (K_{a2} step).**

Calculating the pH of Strong Base solutions

Strong Bases

Metal Ion ***combined with*** **OH^-**

The base is soluble in water when the metal ion is:

- ✓ from Group I of the Periodic Table
- ✓ Ba^{2+} or Sr^{2+}

Examples: LiOH NaOH KOH CsOH $Ba(OH)_2$ $Sr(OH)_2$

Problem: What is the pH of .0079 M NaOH(aq)?
(Sometimes you must calculate the molarity. For example, the solution could have been given as 1.17 g of NaOH(s) dissolved in 3700 mL of solution.)

Solution: NaOH is a strong base, so it ionizes 100 %.

	NaOH (aq)	$\longrightarrow$	$Na^+(aq)$	+	$OH^-(aq)$
before ionizing	.0079 M		0		0
after ionizing	0		.0079 M		.0079 M

This time, −log of the concentration is **pOH**.

$$pOH = -\log [OH^-] = -\log(.0079) = 2.1$$

$$pH = 14 - 2.1 = \boxed{\mathbf{11.9}}$$

Problem: What is the pH of .0079 M $Ba(OH)_2$ (aq)?

Solution: $Ba(OH)_2$ is a strong base, so it ionizes 100%.

	$Ba(OH)_2$ (aq)	$\longrightarrow$	Ba^{2+}(aq)	+	2 OH^-(aq)
before ionizing	.0079 M		0		0
after ionizing	0		.0079 M		2 x .0079 M = .0158 M

The .0079 is multiplied by 2 because $Ba(OH)_2$ has 2 OH^- in the formula, so every time 1 $Ba(OH)_2$ unit dissolves, 2 OH^- are produced.

pOH = $-\log [OH^-]$ = $-\log (.0158)$ = **1.8**

pH = 14 − 1.8 = 12.2

If the $[OH^-]$ is 2 times greater for $Ba(OH)_2$ than for NaOH, why did the pH not become twice as large (23.8)?

Answer: Because pH is a logarithm, it does not change as much as $[H^+]$ and $[OH^-]$.

number = 10^x

or

$[H^+]$ = INV log (−pH) = 10^{-pH}

- Suppose $[H^+]$ in a problem starts at 1.0×10^{-6} M so that pH = $-\log(1.0 \times 10^{-6})$ = 6
- Now suppose that enough acid is added so that $[H^+] = 1.0 \times 10^{-4}$. What is the new pH?
- **Answer:** pH = $-\log(1.0 \times 10^{-4}) = 4$
- When the $[H^+]$ changed 100 or 10^2 times, the pH changed 2 units.

➻ **General Rule:** When the pH changes x units, $[H^+]$ and $[OH^-]$ change 10^x times.

In the NaOH/$Ba(OH)_2$ problem, **$[OH^-]$ changed 2 times**, but the **pH changed only 0.3 units**. The reason is that $10^{0.3}$ = 2.

Problem: Suppose enough acid is added to a pH 5 solution that $[H^+]$ becomes 1000 times greater. What is the new pH?

Solution: Since 1000 is 10^3, the pH changes (goes down) by 3 units to **pH = 2**

Weak Bases

Definition: Substances that cause an ↑$[OH^-]$ when they dissolve in water, but do not contain OH^- in their formula. They **react with water** to produce OH^-.

There are two kinds of weak bases: Neutral molecules and Anions (−ions). We will discuss neutral molecules first.

Neutral Molecules That Are Weak Bases

The **only one** of these that we will consider is $\mathbf{NH_3}$ (although there are many others, both inorganic and especially organic). Ammonia is by far the most significant one we deal with in inorganic chemistry.

NH_3 reacts with water to remove H^+, which produces OH^-. NH_3 is referred to as a weak base because the following reaction occurs only about 2 % in water:

$$NH_3(aq) + H_2O(\ell) \rightleftharpoons NH_4^+(aq) + OH^-(aq) \qquad \text{(occurs about 2 \%)}$$

$$\begin{matrix} & H & \\ & | & \\ H- & \ddot{N}: & \\ & | & \\ & H & \end{matrix} \; + \; \begin{matrix} H- & \ddot{O}: \\ & | \\ & H \end{matrix} \; \rightleftharpoons \; \left[\begin{matrix} & H & \\ & | & \\ H- & N & -H \\ & | & \\ & H & \end{matrix}\right]^+ \; + \; \begin{matrix} :\ddot{O}:^- \\ | \\ H \end{matrix}$$

NH_3 dissolved in water has several names used by chemists:

"ammonia water"
"ammonium hydroxide"
$\mathbf{NH_3(aq)}$ **or "aqueous ammonia"**

Equilibrium Constant (K_{eq}) for Bases:

The Base Dissociation Constant, K_b

$$NH_3(aq) + H_2O(\ell) \rightleftharpoons NH_4^+(aq) + OH^-(aq)$$

$$K_b = \frac{[NH_4^+][OH^-]}{[NH_3]}$$

Like any liquid, $H_2O(\ell)$ does not appear in the K_b expression.

Values for the K_b of neutral weak bases can be found in tables, but values for weak bases that are anions are not usually included. **We will obtain K_b values by calculating them,** as discussed below.

In order to discuss weak base anions and how to calculate K_b values, we will first review the **Bronsted Theory of Acids and Bases.**

Bronsted Theory of Acids and Bases

- H^+ ions do not exist in the free state in water.
- They are attached either to water in the form of H_3O^+ or to some other molecule or ion.
- Bronsted Theory takes into account that H^+ is always attached to something else.

Bronsted acid: substance that donates H^+ (a proton) to another substance

Bronsted base: substance that accepts H^+ (a proton) from another substance

Because we write H^+ (aq) rather than H_3O^+ (aq), we write the dissociation of HF as follows:

$$HF(aq) \rightleftharpoons H^+(aq) + F^-(aq)$$

But a more complete equation would show that the H^+ is attached to water:

$$HF(aq) + H_2O(\ell) \rightleftharpoons H_3O^+(aq) + F^-(aq)$$

HF donates an H^+ to H_2O, and so is acting as an **acid.** **H_2O** accepts an H^+, and so is acting as a **base.**

Since the reaction is reversible, it could be viewed as occurring in the other direction: in that case **H_3O^+** donates an H^+ to F^-, and so acts as an **acid,** while **F^-** accepts an H^+, and so acts as a **base.** In the reaction above:

<u>**Acids**</u>: HF and H_3O^+
<u>**Bases**</u>: H_2O and F^-

The word **conjugate** is used in Bronsted Theory to refer to a substance that differs from another substance by 1 H^+: the substance with the **H^+ attached** is the **acid,** and the substance **without the H^+** is the **base.**

Substances that differ by 1 H^+ are referred to as a **"conjugate acid/base pair"**.

HF / F^- is a conjugate acid/base pair.

H_3O^+ / H_2O is a conjugate acid/base pair.

✚ Any time you **remove an H^+** from an acid, you **produce the "conjugate base"** of that acid.

✚ Any time you **add an H^+** to a base, you **produce the "conjugate acid"** of that base.

✚ Conjugate acid base pairs **differ by only 1 H^+**. In diprotic and triprotic acids, there are ions that differ by more than one H^+, but these are **not** considered to be conjugate acid/base pairs.

Problem: What is the conjugate base of HCN? **Ans:** CN^-

Problem: What is the conjugate acid of ClO^-? **Ans:** HClO

Problem: What is the conjugate acid of CO_3^{2-}? **Ans:** HCO_3^-

Problem: What is the conjugate base of $H_2PO_4^-$? **Ans:** HPO_4^{2-}

Using the K_a Table (Table 2) to Locate Acids and Bases

Everything to the LEFT of the arrow is an ACID

Everything to the RIGHT of the arrow is a BASE

Reaction	K_a
$HC_2H_3O_2 \rightleftharpoons H^+ + C_2H_3O_2^-$	1.8×10^{-5}
$NH_4^+ \rightleftharpoons H^+ + NH_3$	5.6×10^{-10}
$HC_7H_5O_2 \rightleftharpoons H^+ + C_7H_5O_2^-$	6.5×10^{-5}
$HSO_4^- \rightleftharpoons H^+ + SO_4^{2-}$	1.3×10^{-2}
$HC_2H_2O_2Cl \rightleftharpoons H^+ + C_2H_2O_2Cl^-$	1.4×10^{-3}
$HClO_2 \rightleftharpoons H^+ + ClO_2^-$	1.1×10^{-2}
$HCHO_2 \rightleftharpoons H^+ + CHO_2^-$	1.7×10^{-4}
$HCN \rightleftharpoons H^+ + CN^-$	4.9×10^{-10}
$HF \rightleftharpoons H^+ + F^-$	7.1×10^{-4}
$H_2O_2 \rightleftharpoons H^+ + HO_2^-$	2.4×10^{-12}
$HBrO \rightleftharpoons H^+ + BrO^-$	2.1×10^{-9}
$HClO \rightleftharpoons H^+ + ClO^-$	3.0×10^{-8}
$HIO \rightleftharpoons H^+ + IO^-$	2.3×10^{-11}
$HC_3H_5O_3 \rightleftharpoons H^+ + C_3H_5O_3^-$	8.4×10^{-4}
$HNO_2 \rightleftharpoons H^+ + NO_2^-$	4.5×10^{-4}

Relationship between K_a and K_b

If HF is dissolved in pure water, an acidic solution results:

$$HF(aq) \rightleftharpoons H^+(aq) + F^-(aq)$$

Makes the pH of the solution **acidic**

$$K_a = \frac{[H^+][F^-]}{[HF]} = 7.1 \times 10^{-4}$$

Value in **Table 2**

If F^- is dissolved in water (for example, in the form of the salt NaF, with Na^+ as the spectator), a basic solution results.

$$F^-(aq) + H_2O(\ell) \rightleftharpoons HF(aq) + OH^-(aq)$$

Makes the pH of the solution **basic**

$$K_b = \frac{[HF][OH^-]}{[F^-]} = ?$$

Value to be calculated

A formula for calculating K_b can be derived as follows:

$$K_a \cdot K_b = \frac{[H^+]\cancel{[F^-]}}{\cancel{[HF]}} \cdot \frac{\cancel{[HF]}[OH^-]}{\cancel{[F^-]}} = [H^+] \cdot [OH^-] = 1 \times 10^{-14} \ (K_w)$$

The final formula is:

$$K_a \cdot K_b = 1 \times 10^{-14}$$ **(where the acid and base are conjugates)**

This equation can be used in either of the following forms:

$$K_a = \frac{1 \times 10^{-14}}{K_b} \qquad K_b = \frac{1 \times 10^{-14}}{K_a}$$

Problem: Calculate the K_b of F^-.

Solution: The equation for F^- acting as a base is:

$$F^-(aq) + H_2O(\ell) \rightleftharpoons HF(aq) + OH^-(aq)$$

The K_a of HF is listed in **Table 2** as 7.1×10^{-4}.
Since F^- is the conjugate base, K_b can be calculated as:

$$K_b = \frac{[HF][OH^-]}{[F^-]} = \frac{1 \times 10^{-14}}{K_a} = \frac{1 \times 10^{-14}}{7.1 \times 10^{-4}} = \boxed{\mathbf{1.4 \times 10^{-11}}}$$

Problem: Calculate the K_b of NH_3.

Solution: The equation for NH_3 acting as a base is:

$$NH_3(aq) + H_2O(\ell) \rightleftharpoons NH_4^+(aq) + OH^-(aq)$$

The K_a of NH_4^+ (Ammonium ion) is listed in **Table 2** as 5.6×10^{-10}
Since NH_3 is the conjugate base, K_b can be calculated as:

$$K_b = \frac{[NH_4^+][OH^-]}{[NH_3]} = \frac{1 \times 10^{-14}}{K_a} = \frac{1 \times 10^{-14}}{5.6 \times 10^{-10}} = \boxed{\mathbf{1.8 \times 10^{-5}}}$$

Problem: Calculate the K_b of CO_3^{2-}.

Solution: The equation for CO_3^{2-} acting as a base is:

$$CO_3^{2-}(aq) + H_2O(\ell) \rightleftharpoons HCO_3^-(aq) + OH^-(aq)$$

The K_a of HCO_3^- (aq) (Bicarbonate ion) is listed in **Table 2** as 4.8×10^{-11}
(We **do not** use the K_a of H_2CO_3 because it is not the conjugate base of CO_3^{2-})
Since CO_3^{2-} is the conjugate base of HCO_3^-, K_b can be calculated as:

$$K_b = \frac{[HCO_3^-][OH^-]}{[CO_3^{2-}]} = \frac{1 \times 10^{-14}}{K_a} = \frac{1 \times 10^{-14}}{4.8 \times 10^{-11}} = \boxed{2.1 \times 10^{-4}}$$

K_b values can be used for comparing strengths of weak bases.
The **larger the K_b**, the **stronger the base.**

Stronger

CO_3^{2-}	$K_b = 2.1 \times 10^{-4}$
NH_3	$K_b = 1.8 \times 10^{-5}$
F^-	$K_b = 1.4 \times 10^{-11}$

Weaker

Using the K_a Table (Table 2) to Locate Acids and Bases

Everything to the **LEFT** of the arrow is an **ACID**

The K_a value is for the **ACID** on the **LEFT**

Reaction	K_a
$HC_2H_3O_2 \rightleftharpoons H^+ + C_2H_3O_2^-$	1.8×10^{-5}
$NH_4^+ \rightleftharpoons H^+ + NH_3$	5.6×10^{-10}
$HC_7H_5O_2 \rightleftharpoons H^+ + C_7H_5O_2^-$	6.5×10^{-5}
$HSO_4^- \rightleftharpoons H^+ + SO_4^{2-}$	1.3×10^{-2}
$HC_2H_2O_2Cl \rightleftharpoons H^+ + C_2H_2O_2Cl^-$	1.4×10^{-3}
$HClO_2 \rightleftharpoons H^+ + ClO_2^-$	1.1×10^{-2}
$HCHO_2 \rightleftharpoons H^+ + CHO_2^-$	1.7×10^{-4}
$HCN \rightleftharpoons H^+ + CN^-$	4.9×10^{-10}
$HF \rightleftharpoons H^+ + F^-$	7.1×10^{-4}
$H_2O_2 \rightleftharpoons H^+ + HO_2^-$	2.4×10^{-12}
$HBrO \rightleftharpoons H^+ + BrO^-$	2.1×10^{-9}
$HClO \rightleftharpoons H^+ + ClO^-$	3.0×10^{-8}
$HIO \rightleftharpoons H^+ + IO^-$	2.3×10^{-11}
$HC_3H_5O_3 \rightleftharpoons H^+ + C_3H_5O_3^-$	8.4×10^{-4}
$HNO_2 \rightleftharpoons H^+ + NO_2^-$	4.5×10^{-4}

Everything to the **RIGHT** of the arrow is a **BASE**

The K_b value ($= 1 \times 10^{-14}/K_a$) is for the **BASE** on the **RIGHT**

!!! **THE MOST CRITICAL SKILL REQUIRED TO MASTER ANY MATERIAL IN THIS CLASS RELATED TO ACIDS, BASES, AND BUFFERS IS THE ABILITY TO CLASSIFY A MOLECULE OR ION AS A STRONG ACID, WEAK ACID, STRONG BASE, OR WEAK BASE.**

!!! **THE PROCEDURE FOR DOING THIS MUST BE COMMITTED TO MEMORY SO THAT IT BECOMES AUTOMATIC.**

Strong acids: **One of the 6** listed earlier in this class (HCl, HBr, HI, $HClO_4$, HNO_3, H_2SO_4)

Weak acids: The formula has an H that can be lost, but is **not one of the 6** strong acids listed above. **All acids in Table 2** (except H_2SO_4) **are weak.**

Strong base: An **ionic compound** consisting of a **metal ion combined with OH^-**. (If the metal ion Ba^{2+}, Sr^{2+}, or an ion from Group I of the Periodic Table, the base is soluble in water.)

Weak base: Substance formed when a weak acid loses an H^+. All substances on the **right side of the $\rightleftharpoons$ arrows in Table 2** are weak bases. (All except NH_3 are anions.)

Note: There is only **one strong base ion, OH^-**, in water. If a base stronger than OH^- is dissolved in water, the substance will immediately remove H^+ from H_2O to form OH^-.

Problem: Classify the following as a **strong acid, strong base, weak acid** or **weak base.**

HBr **Strong Acid** (One of the six.)

$HBrO$ **Weak Acid** (Not one of the six strong ones. Also, it is found in **Table 2**.)

NH_3 **Weak Base** (**Please memorize!** NH_3 is on the **right side of the $\rightleftharpoons$ arrow** in **Table 2**.)

NH_4^+ **Weak Acid** (**Please memorize!** It has an H that can be lost, but is not one of the six strong acids. Also, it is found in **Table 2**.)

CN^- **Weak Base** (It is on the **right side of the $\rightleftharpoons$ arrow** in **Table 2**.)

CO_3^{2-} **Weak Base** (It is on the right side of the $\rightleftharpoons$ arrow in **Table 2**. It comes from a diprotic acid and is on p. 10, and these are weak bases also.)

$NaOH$ **Strong Base** (It contains a metal ion combined with OH^-.)

HNO_2 **Weak Acid** (Not one of the six strong ones.)

HF **Weak Acid** (Not one of the six strong ones.)

$H_2C_2O_4$ **Weak Acid** (Not one of the six strong ones. It is found in **Table 2** on p. 10; Diprotic acids are weak, except for H_2SO_4)

Problems involving NH_3 and NH_4^+

- The conjugate acid/base pair NH_4^+/NH_3 is sometimes confusing because the formulas look similar.
- Students must make a **mental note** that NH_4^+ is a **weak acid** and NH_3 is a **weak base.**

Problem: Calculate the pH and % ionization of 0.1 M NH_4^+(aq).

Solution: Because NH_4^+ is a weak acid, this problem is done like any other weak acid problem:

	NH_4^+	$\rightleftharpoons$	H^+	+	NH_3
I	0.1		0		0
C	$-x$		$+x$		$+x$
E	$0.1 - x$		x		x

$$K_a = \frac{[H^+][NH_3]}{[NH_4^+]} = \frac{x \cdot x}{0.1 - x} = \frac{x^2}{0.1 - x} = 5.6 \times 10^{-10}$$

↑ **Value from Table 2, p. 9**

$$\frac{x^2}{0.1 \not{-x}} = 5.6 \times 10^{-10}$$

$$\frac{x^2}{0.1} = 5.6 \times 10^{-10}$$

$$\not{0.1} \cdot \frac{x^2}{\not{0.1}} = 5.6 \times 10^{-10} \cdot 0.1$$

$$\sqrt{x^2} = \sqrt{5.6 \times 10^{-11}}$$

$$x = 7.5 \times 10^{-6}\text{M} = [H^+]$$

$$\text{pH} = -\log(7.5 \times 10^{-6}) = \boxed{5.12}$$

$$\%\text{ ionization} = \frac{x \text{ or } [H^+]}{\text{original conc. acid}} \times 100\%$$

$$= \frac{7.5 \times 10^{-6}}{0.1} \times 100\% = \boxed{.0075\%}$$

Calculating the pH of Weak Base Solutions

This problem involves **two additional steps** compared with the weak acid problem.

Problem: Calculate the pH and % ionization of .05 M NH_3 (aq).

Before beginning, it is **essential** to classify NH_3 as a **weak base** (found on the right side of the $\rightleftharpoons$ arrow in **Table 2**). Therefore, the pH **must** come out to be **above** 7.

The equation for a weak base reacting with water always looks like the following:

	NH_3 (aq)	+ $H_2O(\ell)$ $\rightleftharpoons$	NH_4^+(aq)	+ OH^- (aq)
I	0.05	X	0	0
C	$-x$		$+x$	$+x$
E	$0.05 - x$		x	x

Additional Step 1: You must write a K_b because NH_3 is a base, but that means you must **calculate K_b from the K_a value for NH_4^+.**

$$K_b = \frac{[NH_4^+][OH^-]}{[NH_3]} = \frac{x \cdot x}{.05 - x} = \frac{x^2}{.05} = 1.8 \times 10^{-5}$$

Use the K_b value

$$K_b = \frac{1 \times 10^{-14}}{K_a} = \frac{1 \times 10^{-14}}{5.6 \times 10^{-10}} = 1.8 \times 10^{-5}$$

$$\frac{x^2}{.05} = 1.8 \times 10^{-5}$$

$$\cancel{0.05} \cdot \frac{x^2}{\cancel{0.05}} = 1.8 \times 10^{-5} \cdot 0.05$$

$$\sqrt{x^2} = \sqrt{9.0 \times 10^{-7}}$$

$$x = 9.5 \times 10^{-4}\text{M} = [OH^-]$$

Additional Step 2: Since NH_3 is a base, pOH must be converted back to pH at the end.

$$pOH = -\log(9.5 \times 10^{-4}) = 3.0$$

$$pH = 14 - 3.0 = \boxed{11.0}$$

$$\% \text{ ionization} = \frac{x \text{ or } [OH^-]}{\text{original conc. base}} \times 100\%$$

$$= \frac{9.5 \times 10^{-4}}{0.05} \times 100\% = \boxed{1.9\%}$$

Problem: Calculate the pH and % ionization of 0.25 M IO^- (aq).

Before beginning, it is **essential** to classify IO^- as a **weak base** (found on the right side of the $\rightleftharpoons$ arrow in **Table 2**). Therefore, the pH **must** come out to be **above 7**.

The equation for a weak base reacting with water always looks like the following:

$$IO^-(aq) + H_2O(\ell) \rightleftharpoons HIO(aq) + OH^-(aq)$$

	IO^- (aq)	$H_2O(\ell)$	$HIO(aq)$	OH^- (aq)
I	0.25	X	0	0
C	$-x$	X	$+x$	$+x$
E	$0.25 - x$	X	x	x

Additional Step 1: You must write a K_b because IO^- is a base, but that means you must calculate K_b from the K_a value for HIO.

$$K_b = \frac{[HIO]\,[OH^-]}{[IO^-]} = \frac{x \cdot x}{.25\ HH} = \frac{x^2}{.25} = 4.3 \times 10^{-4}$$

Use the K_b value

$$K_b = \frac{1 \times 10^{-14}}{K_a} = \frac{1 \times 10^{-14}}{2.3 \times 10^{-11}} = 4.3 \times 10^{-4}$$

$$\frac{x^2}{.25} = 4.3 \times 10^{-4}$$

$$0.25 \cdot \frac{x^2}{0.25} = 4.3 \times 10^{-4} \cdot 0.25$$

$$x^2 = 1.1 \times 10^{-4}$$

$$\sqrt{x^2} = \sqrt{1.1 \times 10^{-4}}$$

$$x = 1.05 \times 10^{-2}\,M = [OH^-]$$

Additional Step 2: Since IO^- is a base, pOH must be converted back to pH at the end.

$$pOH = -\log(1.05 \times 10^{-2}) = 1.98$$

$$pH = 14 - 1.98 = \boxed{12.02}$$

$$\%\text{ ionization} = \frac{x \text{ or } [OH^-]}{\text{original conc. base}} \times 100\%$$

$$= \frac{1.05 \times 10^{-2}}{0.25} \times 100\% = \boxed{4.2\%}$$

Relative Strengths of Acids and Bases

The K_a of a weak acid and the K_b of its conjugate base are related by the formula:

$$\mathbf{K_a \cdot K_b = 1 \times 10^{-14}}$$

This formula predicts that:

★ **The stronger the acid (↑K_a), the weaker the conjugate base (↓K_b).**

★ **The reverse is also true: the weaker the acid (↓K_a), the stronger the conjugate base (↑K_b).**

Suppose we consider first a strong acid like HCl:

$$HCl(aq) \longrightarrow H^+(aq) + Cl^-(aq) \qquad \textbf{(100 \% ionization)}$$

The Cl^- formed shows no tendency to act as a base in water, that is, it does not accept any of the H^+. The HCl is such a strong acid in water that it has a conjugate base, Cl^-, that does not even act as a base in water.

If a weak acid like HF is analyzed the same way:

$$HF(aq) \rightleftharpoons H^+(aq) + F^-(aq) \qquad \textbf{(less than 5 \% ionization)}$$

The F^- not only shows a "tendency" to accept H^+, it is so good at accepting H^+ that over 95 % of the H^+ remains attached to F^- at equilibrium.

For weak acids in general, the better the – ion is at accepting H^+, the weaker the acid will be.

Relative Strengths of Conjugate Acids and Bases

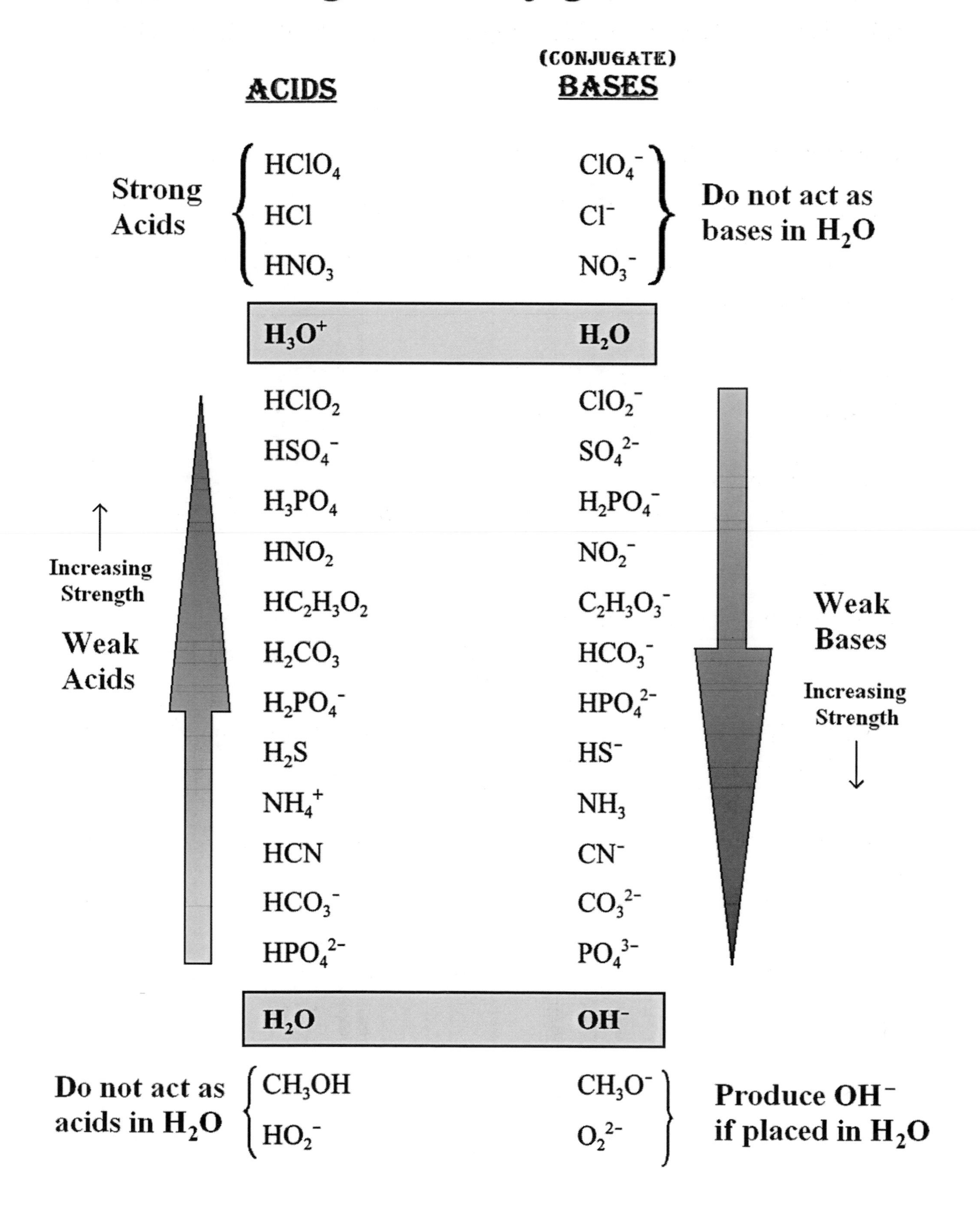

pH of Salts, Diprotic Acids, and Introduction to Redox

(Homework #4)

Determining K_a Values Experimentally

Problem: When 3.85 g of the weak acid Phenol (HC_6H_5O, MM = 94.12) is dissolved in 500 mL of water, a pH of 5.49 is measured for the solution. What is the value of K_a for Phenol?

Solution: Because HC_6H_5O is a weak acid, this problem begins with an ICE table.

First, we need to calculate the molarity of the solution:

$$\#mol = 3.85 \text{ g} \times \frac{1 \text{ mol}}{94.12 \text{ g}} = .0409 \text{ mol}$$

$$M = \frac{\#mol}{\#L} = \frac{.0409 \text{ mol}}{.5 \text{ L}} = .0818 \text{ M}$$

	HC_6H_5O	$\rightleftharpoons$	H^+	+	$C_6H_5O^-$
I	.0818		0		0
C	$-x$		$+x$		$+x$
E	$.0818 - x$		x		x

$$K_a = \frac{[H^+][C_6H_5O^-]}{[HC_6H_5O]} = \frac{x \cdot x}{.0818 \cancel{-x}} = \frac{x^2}{.0818} = ?$$

In the problem from last class, the K_a value could be obtained from **Table 2**.

In the present problem, we can determine x from the given pH, plug it in, and then **calculate K_a**.

$$x = [H^+] = \text{INV log}(-5.49) = 3.24 \times 10^{-6} \text{ M}$$

$$\frac{(3.24 \times 10^{-6})^2}{.0818} = \boxed{\mathbf{1.3 \times 10^{-10}}}$$

Another Example:

Problem: When 2.07 g of **cacodylic acid** ($HAsC_2H_6O_2$, MM = 138.00), which is a weak acid, is dissolved in 250 mL of water, a pH of 3.71 is measured for the solution. What is the value of K_a for cacodylic acid?

Solution: First, we need to calculate the molarity of the solution:

$$\#mol = 2.07\,\cancel{g} \times \frac{1\text{ mol}}{138.00\,\cancel{g}} = .015\text{ mol}$$

$$M = \frac{\#mol}{\#L} = \frac{.015\text{ mol}}{.25\text{ L}} = .06\text{ M}$$

	$HAsC_2H_6O_2$	$\rightleftharpoons$	H^+	+	$AsC_2H_6O_2^-$
I	.06		0		0
C	$-x$		$+x$		$+x$
E	$.06 - x$		x		x

$$K_a = \frac{[H^+][AsC_2H_6O_2^-]}{[HAsC_2H_6O_2]} = \frac{x \cdot x}{.06 \cancel{-x}} = \frac{x^2}{.06} = ?$$

$$x = [H^+] = \text{INV log}(-3.71) = 1.95 \times 10^{-4}\text{ M}$$

$$\frac{(1.95 \times 10^{-4})^2}{.06} = \boxed{6.4 \times 10^{-7}}$$

Diprotic Acids: Concentration of the −2 ion

When calculating the pH of a diprotic acid solution in water, ignore the K_{a2} step. (See pp. 102-103.)

When determining the pH of the −2 ion, however, the K_{a2} step cannot be ignored because that step contains the ion of interest. (Can lose another H^+)

$$H_2A \rightleftharpoons H^+ + HA^- \quad (K_{a1} \text{ step})$$

$H_2CO_3 \rightleftharpoons H^+ + HCO_3^-$ k_{a1}

$$HA^- \rightleftharpoons H^+ + A^{2-} \quad (K_{a2} \text{ step})$$

$HCO_3^- \rightleftharpoons H^+ + CO_3^{-2}$ k_{a2}

From the first step, it can be seen that $[H^+] = [HA^-]$. The amount that HA^- splits apart in step 2 is very small. Therefore, when the K_{a2} expression is written, $[H^+]$ and $[HA^-]$ cancel:

$$K_{a2} = \frac{[H^+][A^{2-}]}{[HA^-]} = [A^{2-}]$$

$k_{a2} = \frac{[H^+][CO_3^{-2}]}{[HCO_3^-]} = [CO_3^{-2}]$

It does not matter what the $[H_2A]$ is because $[H^+]$ always equals $[HA^-]$, so the following is true at any $[H_2A]$.

> **General Rule**: For **any** diprotic acid H_2A at **any** $[H_2A]$,
>
> $$[A^{2-}] = K_{a2}$$
>
> when the acid is dissolved in pure water.

* Rule #1: for diprotic acids, concentration of the conjugate base in step 2 = k_{a2}

$k_{a2} = [A^{-2}]$

* Rule #2: for diprotic acids, pH depends only on the concentration of H^+ in step 1. (* use k_{a1} to setup the ICE Table)

Problem:

What is $[SO_3^{2-}]$ in a 0.558 M $H_2SO_3(aq)$ solution?

Answer: The K_{a2} value for H_2SO_3 is 6.3×10^{-8} (see p. 10). Therefore,

$$[SO_3^{2-}] = 6.3 \times 10^{-8} \text{ M}$$

Rules for diprotic acids:

1. **When calculating the pH, ignore the 2nd step (K_{a2}) step.**
2. **When asked for $[A^{2-}]$, it equals K_{a2}.**

pH of Salt Solutions ("Hydrolysis" of salts)

Salts are another kind of substance that can potentially change the pH of a solution.

Salt

Metal ion ***combined with*** **– ion** (except OH^-)

Examples of how salts change pH

When the following salts are dissolved, the pH can become **more acidic, more basic, or remain unchanged**, depending on the salt, as shown below:

NaCl **No pH change**

KCN Solution becomes more **Basic**

NH_4NO_3 Solution becomes more **Acidic**

* any Ion that comes from group A is neutral
2A
3A

* neutral means no reaction to water

In order to predict how a salt will change pH, the **effect of the individual ions** (the cation and the anion) must first be determined **separately.**

Ions can affect the pH of solutions in the following known ways:

1. **Neutral Cations (+ ions)** = **Metal Ions from Groups I and II** in the Periodic Table do not react with H_2O and do not change the pH:

$Na^+ + H_2O \not\rightarrow$ No Reaction

$Ca^{2+} + H_2O \not\rightarrow$ No Reaction

Other examples: Li^+ K^+ Rb^+ Cs^+ Mg^{2+} Sr^{2+} Ba^{2+}

2. **Acidic Cation** = We discuss **one + ion** that makes **acidic** solutions: $\mathbf{NH_4^+}$.
Ammonium ion is a weak acid.

$$NH_4^+(aq) \rightleftharpoons H^+(aq) + NH_3(aq)$$

↗

Tends to make solutions **acidic.**

We will not study any + ions that are bases. Cations tend to repel, not accept, H^+ ions.

3. **Neutral Anions** = Negative ions that **come from strong acids** (when H^+ is removed) do not react with H_2O.

$$Cl^- + H_2O \not\rightarrow \text{No Reaction}$$

$$NO_3^- + H_2O \not\rightarrow \text{No Reaction}$$

Other examples: Br^- I^- ClO_4^-

4. **Basic Anions** = Negative ions that **come from weak acids** (when H^+ is removed) react with H_2O to produce OH^- because these ions are **weak bases**.

$$F^- + H_2O \rightleftharpoons HF + OH^-$$

Tend to make solutions **basic.**

$$CN^- + H_2O \rightleftharpoons HCN + OH^-$$

Other examples: $C_2H_3O_2^-$ ClO^- BrO^- NO_2^- CO_3^{2-} SO_3^{2-} PO_4^{3-}

Note: The −2 ions, such as CO_3^{2-} and SO_3^{2-}, that result from removing 2 H^+ from diprotic acids (see Table 2, p. 10) are weak bases. Also, PO_4^{3-}, which results from removing 3 H^+ from H_3PO_4, is a weak base.

Amphiprotic Ions and Molecules

The ions from diprotic and triprotic acids that still have some H^+'s attached can, in principle, act as **either acids or bases.** Such substances are called **amphiprotic** (can either donate or accept a proton).

Consider bicarbonate ion, HCO_3^-.

Acting as an acid: $HCO_3^- \rightleftharpoons H^+ + CO_3^{2-}$

Acting as a base: $HCO_3^- + H_2O \rightleftharpoons H_2CO_3 + OH^-$

Amphiprotic substances tend to behave as **acids when placed in a basic solution** and as **bases when placed in an acidic solution.**

Because the ion $\mathbf{HSO_4^-}$ comes from the strong acid H_2SO_4, it **cannot act as a base** in water:

$$HSO_4^- + H_2O \not\rightarrow H_2SO_4 + OH^- \quad \text{(Does not occur)}$$

It can, however, act as a **weak acid**:

$$HSO_4^- \rightleftharpoons H^+ + SO_4^{2-}$$

The most **important amphiprotic substance is $\mathbf{H_2O}$ itself:**

Acting as an acid: $H_2O \rightleftharpoons H^+ + OH^-$

Acting as a base: $H_2O + H^+ \rightleftharpoons H_3O^+$

Determining the Effect of Salts on pH

Four combinations of the types of ions discussed above are possible and produce **four different kinds of salts.**

I. Neutral Salt

Neutral Cation ***combined with*** **Neutral Anion**

Examples: $NaCl$ KNO_3 $CaBr_2$

Consider NaCl. When it dissolves in water, it produces 100 % ions:

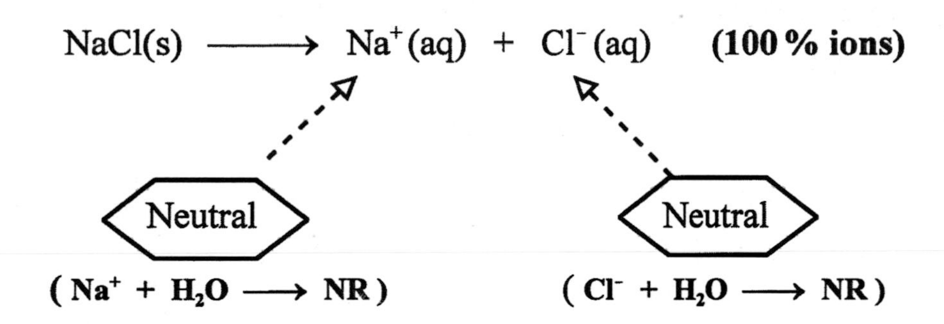

Overall: Neutral + Neutral = *Neutral*

II. Acidic Salt

Acidic Cation ***combined with*** **Neutral Anion**

Examples: NH_4Cl NH_4NO_3 NH_4Br

Consider NH_4NO_3. When it dissolves in water, it produces 100 % ions:

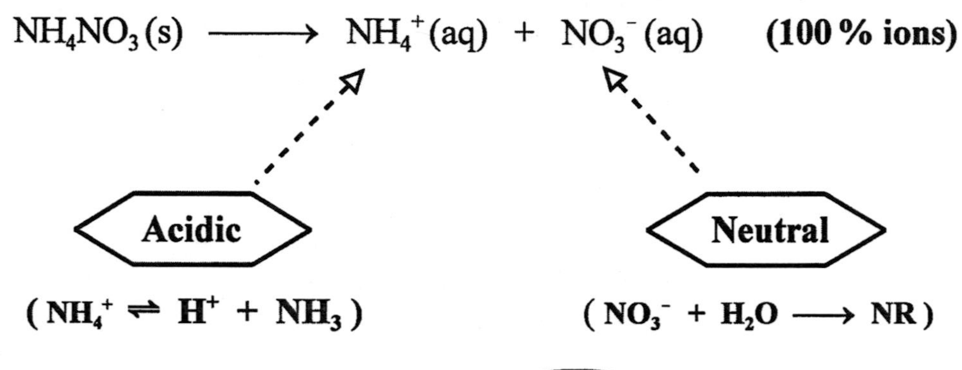

Overall: Acidic + Neutral = *Acidic*

III. Basic Salt

Neutral Cation ***combined with*** **Basic Anion**

Examples: KCN Li_2CO_3 $Ca(NO_2)_2$

Consider KCN. When it dissolves in water, it produces 100 % ions:

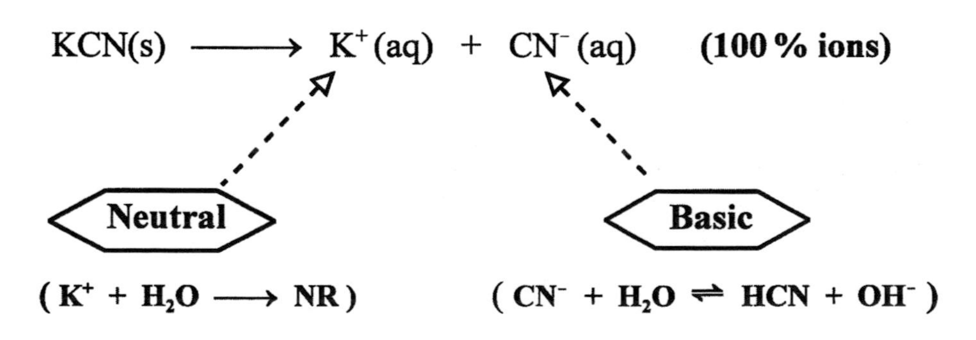

Overall: Neutral + Basic = *Basic*

IV. "Mixed" Salt

Acidic Cation ***combined with*** **Basic Anion**

Examples: $NH_4C_2H_3O_2$ $(NH_4)_2CO_3$ NH_4CN

Because NH_4^+ is acidic and the – ion is basic, the effects oppose each other. **We will not do this problem** because it involves two simultaneous equilibria.

<u>Problem</u>: Classify the following as a **neutral, acidic or basic salt.**

$CsClO_4$

Cs^+ = **Neutral** ClO_4^- = **Neutral**

Overall: Neutral + Neutral = *Neutral*

$KClO_2$

K^+ = **Neutral** ClO_2^- = **Basic** (on the **right side of the** $\rightleftharpoons$ **arrow** in Table 2)

Overall: Neutral + Basic = *Basic*

NH_4I

NH_4^+ = Acidic I^- = Neutral

Overall: Acidic + Neutral = *Acidic*

The pH of a salt solution can be calculated by the techniques used in our previous class.

Problem: Calculate the pH of .08 M KNO_2 (aq).

Solution: It is absolutely essential, before doing anything else, to classify this salt as acidic or basic.

K^+ = Neutral NO_2^- = Basic (on the **right side of the ⇌ arrow** in Table 2)

Overall: Neutral + Basic = *Basic*

Since K^+ is neutral, it is acting as a spectator, so the problem is really the same as asking: Calculate the pH of .08 M NO_2^- (aq). We did problems like this in class last time.

The equation for a weak base reacting with water always looks like the following:

	NO_2^- (aq)	+ $H_2O(\ell)$	⇌ HNO_2(aq)	+ OH^- (aq)
I	0.08	X	0	0
C	$-x$		$+x$	$+x$
E	$0.08 - x$		x	x

You must write a K_b because NO_2^- is a base, but that means you must calculate K_b from the K_a value for HNO_2.

$$K_b = \frac{[HNO_2]\,[OH^-]}{[NO_2^-]} = \frac{x \cdot x}{.08 - x} = \frac{x^2}{.08} = 2.2 \times 10^{-11}$$

Use the K_b value

$$K_b = \frac{1 \times 10^{-14}}{K_a} = \frac{1 \times 10^{-14}}{4.5 \times 10^{-4}} = 2.2 \times 10^{-11}$$

$$\frac{x^2}{.08} = 2.2 \times 10^{-11}$$

$$\cancel{0.08} \cdot \frac{x^2}{\cancel{0.08}} = 2.2 \times 10^{-11} \cdot 0.08$$

$$x^2 = 1.76 \times 10^{-12}$$

$$\sqrt{x^2} = \sqrt{1.76 \times 10^{-12}}$$

$$x = 1.3 \times 10^{-6} \text{M} = [OH^-]$$

Since NO_2^- is a base, pOH must be converted back to pH at the end.

$$\text{pOH} = -\log(1.3 \times 10^{-6}) = 5.9$$

$$\text{pH} = 14 - 5.9 = \boxed{8.1}$$

Problem: Calculate the pH of 0.08 M NH_4Br (aq).

Solution: It is absolutely essential, before doing anything else, to classify this salt as acidic or basic.

NH_4^+ = Acidic Br^- = Neutral

Overall: Acidic + Neutral = *Acidic*

Since Br^- is neutral, it is acting as a spectator, so the problem is really the same as asking: Calculate the pH of .08 M NH_4^+ (aq). We did problems like this in class last time.

Because NH_4^+ is a weak acid, this problem is done like any other weak acid problem:

	NH_4^+	$\rightleftharpoons$	H^+	+	NH_3
I	0.08		0		0
C	$-x$		$+x$		$+x$
E	$0.08 - x$		x		x

$$K_a = \frac{[H^+][NH_3]}{[NH_4^+]} = \frac{x \cdot x}{0.08 - x} = \frac{x^2}{0.08 - x} = 5.6 \times 10^{-10}$$

Value from <u>Table 2</u>, p. 9

$$\frac{x^2}{0.08 \cancel{- x}} = 5.6 \times 10^{-10}$$

$$\frac{x^2}{0.08} = 5.6 \times 10^{-10}$$

$$\cancel{0.08} \cdot \frac{x^2}{\cancel{0.08}} = 5.6 \times 10^{-10} \cdot 0.08$$

$$\sqrt{x^2} = \sqrt{4.48 \times 10^{-11}}$$

$$x = 6.7 \times 10^{-6} M = [H^+]$$

$$pH = -\log(6.7 \times 10^{-6}) = \boxed{5.17}$$

Molarity Review

The basic equation for molarity is:

$$M = \frac{\#\ \text{mol solute}}{\#\ \text{L solution}}$$

This equation can be rearranged into two other forms by algebraic manipulation:

$$\#\ \text{mol} = M \times \#\ L$$

$$\#\ L = \frac{\#\ \text{mol}}{M}$$

Some example problems follow.

Problem 1: What is the molarity when 7.31 g of $Al_2(SO_4)_3(s)$ **[Molar Mass = 342.17 g/mol]** is dissolved in enough water to make 750 mL of solution?

$$\#\ \text{mol}\ Al_2(SO_4)_3 = 7.31\ \cancel{g} \times \frac{1\ \text{mol}}{342.17\ \cancel{g}} = 0.0214\ \text{mol}$$

$$\#\ L\ \text{solution} = 750\ \cancel{mL} \times \frac{1\ L}{1000\ \cancel{mL}} = 0.750\ L$$

Use **form 1** of the molarity equation:

$$M = \frac{\#\ \text{mol}}{\#\ L} = \frac{0.0214\ \text{mol}}{0.750\ L} = \boxed{0.0285\ \text{mol/L}}$$

This answer can also be written **0.0285 M** or **0.0285 molar.**

Problem 2: How many grams of $Al_2(SO_4)_3(s)$ must be dissolved to make 350 mL of 0.15 M solution?

(Alternate wording: How many grams of $Al_2(SO_4)_3(s)$ are contained in 350 mL of 0.15 M solution?)

Use **form 2** of the molarity equation:

$$\# \text{mol} = M \times \# L = 0.15 \frac{\text{mol}}{\cancel{L}} \times 0.350\cancel{L} = 0.0525 \text{ mol } Al_2(SO_4)_3$$

$$0.0525 \text{ mol } \cancel{Al_2(SO_4)_3} \times \frac{342.17 \text{ g}}{1 \cancel{\text{mol}}} = \boxed{\mathbf{18.0 \text{ g } Al_2(SO_4)_3}}$$

Problem 3: How many mL of 0.071 M $Al_2(SO_4)_3(aq)$ solution can be made from 16.0 g of $Al_2(SO_4)_3(s)$?

(Alternate wording: How many mL of 0.071 M $Al_2(SO_4)_3(aq)$ solution contains 16.0 g of $Al_2(SO_4)_3$ (s)?)

$$\# \text{mol } Al_2(SO_4)_3 = 16.0\cancel{g} \times \frac{1 \text{ mol}}{342.17\cancel{g}} = 0.0468 \text{ mol}$$

Use **form 3** of the molarity equation:

$$\# L = \frac{\# \text{mol}}{M} = \frac{0.0468 \cancel{\text{mol}}}{0.071 \cancel{\text{mol}}/L} = .659 \text{ L} = \boxed{\mathbf{659 \text{ mL}}}$$

Classification of Electrolytes

Strong Electrolytes	Weak Electrolytes	Non-electrolytes
1. **Strong Acids**	1. **Weak Acids**	1. **Pure H_2O**
2. **Strong Bases**	2. **Neutral weak bases (NH_3)**	2. **Sugars**
3. **Soluble Salts** = ionic compounds that dissolve in H_2O		3. **Alcohols**

Problem: Classify the following as a **Strong, Weak or Non- Electrolyte**

$HClO_4$ **Strong** (Strong acid)

NH_3 **Weak** (Neutral weak base)

HF **Weak** (Weak acid)

CH_4O (Methyl Alcohol) **Non-** (covalent)

Sucrose (Table Sugar) **Non-** (covalent)

KCN **Strong** (Soluble salt)
[although CN^- is a weak base, KCN is a salt that produces 100 % ions and is, therefore, a strong electrolyte]

Na_2SO_4 **Strong** (Soluble salt)

NaOH **Strong** (Strong base)

$Sr(OH)_2$ **Strong** (Strong base)

$HCHO_2$ **Weak** (Weak acid)

Terminology used for Oxidation-Reduction (Redox) Reactions

Redox Reaction = a reaction in which electrons (e^-'s) are transferred from one substance to another. This transfer is always accompanied by a change in **oxidation numbers.**

Oxidation number = keeps track of the number of electrons lost or gained.
For **monatomic** ions, **same as charge**.

Oxidation = loss of e^-'s

Reduction = gain of electrons

LEO GER **OIL RIG**

Oxidizing agent = causes oxidation = causes loss of e^-

Oxidizing agents gain e^-'s

Reducing agent = causes reduction = causes gain of e^-

Reducing agents lose e^-'s

Example:

$$Na\cdot + Na\cdot + :\ddot{\underset{..}{Cl}}:\ddot{\underset{..}{Cl}}: \longrightarrow Na^+\ :\ddot{\underset{..}{Cl}}:^- \quad Na^+\ :\ddot{\underset{..}{Cl}}:^-$$

$$\overset{0}{2\,Na} + \overset{0}{Cl_2} \longrightarrow 2\,\overset{+1\ -1}{NaCl}$$

2 Na	Cl_2
↑ ox #	↓ ox #
lose e^-	gain e^-
oxidized	reduced
reducing agent	oxidizing agent

Calculating Oxidation Numbers

For **monatomic** ions, oxidation number is the **same as charge.**

For **covalent substances,** e^-'s are shared so there is **no complete transfer of e^-'s** from one substance to another.

Therefore, to assign ox #'s in covalent substances, the following "assignment" technique is used:

All the e^-'s in a bond are "assigned" to the **most electronegative atom.**

Electronegativity = measures how well an atom attracts the e^-'s in a bond.

Fluorine (F) is the "best" or "strongest" at attracting e^-, so it has the **largest electronegativity** (4.0)

Metals lose e^-'s rather than attracting them, so they have **small electronegativities** (around 1.0)

Even though ox # in covalent substances does not describe a "real" or "complete" charge, ox # assignment is useful for balancing redox equations and for keeping track of the movement of e^-**'s.**

Na_2SO_4

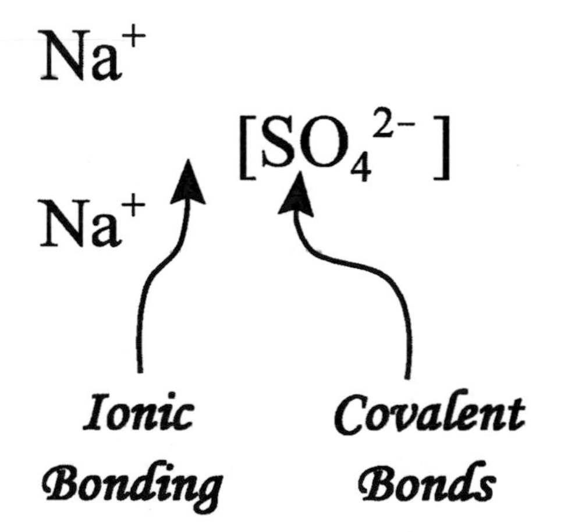

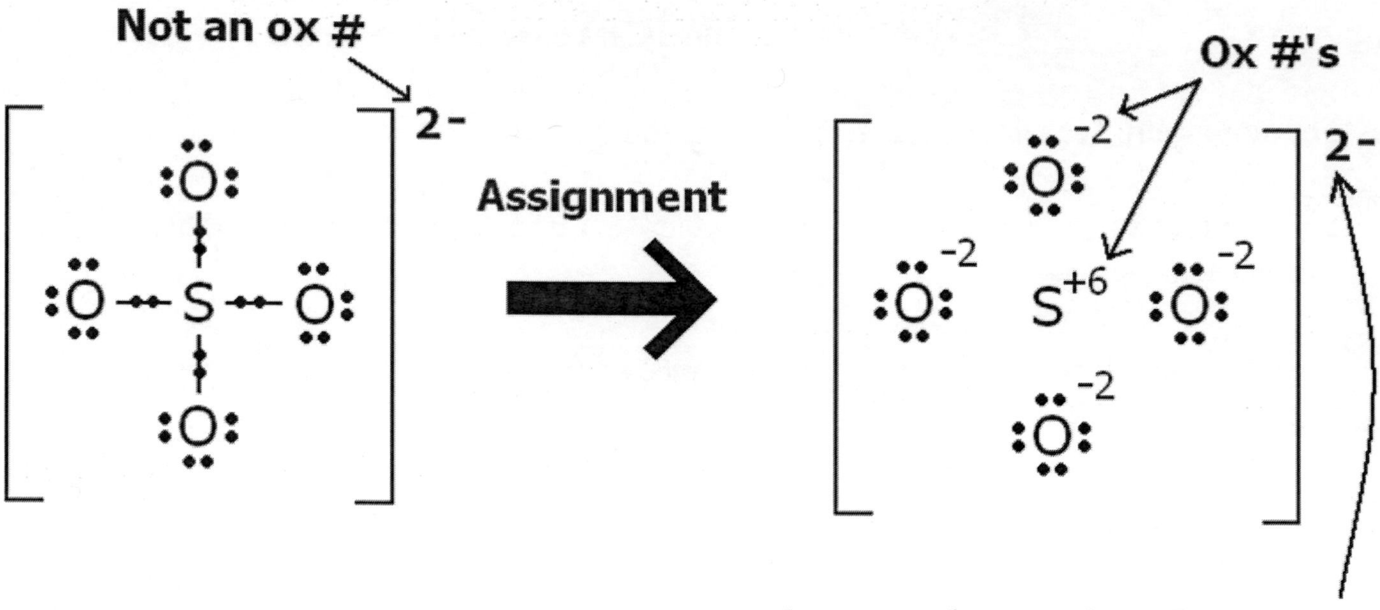

Not an ox #

$$\left[\begin{array}{c} :\ddot{O}: \\ | \\ :\ddot{O}-S-\ddot{O}: \\ | \\ :\ddot{O}: \end{array} \right]^{2-}$$

Assignment →

Ox #'s

$$\left[\begin{array}{ccc} & :\ddot{O}:^{-2} & \\ :\ddot{O}:^{-2} & S^{+6} & :\ddot{O}:^{-2} \\ & :\ddot{O}:^{-2} & \end{array} \right]^{2-}$$

$$(-2 \times 4) + (+6) = -2$$

$$\overset{+1}{Na}_2\overset{+6}{S}\overset{-2}{O}_4$$

$$2 \times (+1) + (+6) + 4 \times (-2) =$$

$$2 + 6 + (-8) = 0$$

Rules for Determining Oxidation Numbers

1. **Elements** are **zero.**

   Examples: Na Fe As F_2 O_2 H_2

2. **Metals** in compounds are always **positive.**

   Group I = **+1** Group II = **+2** Group III = **+3**

   Transition metals and metals at the **bottom** of Groups I – VIII have various charges.

3. **Nonmetals** and **metalloids** are

   a. **Negative** when combined **alone** with a metal or H.

      Group VII = **−1** Group VI = **−2** Group V = **−3**

   b. **Positive** when O or F is present in the compound.

4. **Special oxidation numbers.**

   a. O is almost always **−2** (except in $O_2(g)$, where it is **zero**).†

   b. H is almost always **+1** (except in $H_2(g)$, where it is **zero**).

   c. F is **−1** (except in $F_2(g)$, where it is **zero**).

5. The sum of oxidation numbers in an ion is equal to the **charge on the ion.**

6. The sum of oxidation numbers in a neutral compound is **zero.**

---

†**Note**: O in hydrogen peroxide (H_2O_2) and in peroxide ion (O_2^{2-}), is **−1**. The structure of H_2O_2 is:

$$\mathrm{H{-}\ddot{\underset{\cdot\cdot}{O}}{-}\ddot{\underset{\cdot\cdot}{O}}{-}H} \xrightarrow{\text{assignment}} \overset{+1}{\mathrm{H}}\ \ \overset{-1}{:\ddot{\underset{\cdot\cdot}{O}}\cdot}\ \ \overset{-1}{\cdot\ddot{\underset{\cdot\cdot}{O}}:}\ \ \overset{+1}{\mathrm{H}}$$

Calculate the Ox # of each atom in the following:

BiO_3^- $\quad$ $\overset{x\ \ -2}{(BiO_3)^-}$ $\quad$ $\overset{+5\ \ -2}{(BiO_3)^-}$

$$x + (3 \cdot (-2)) = -1$$
$$x + \quad -6 \quad = -1$$
$$x - 6 + 6 \quad = -1 + 6$$
$$x = +5$$

$Cr_2O_7^{2-}$ $\quad$ $\overset{x\ \ -2}{(Cr_2O_7)^{2-}}$ $\quad$ $\overset{+6\ \ -2}{(Cr_2O_7)^{2-}}$

$$2x + (7 \cdot (-2)) = -2$$
$$2x + \quad -14 \quad = -2$$
$$2x - 14 + 14 = -2 + 14$$
$$2x = 12$$
$$x = +6$$

HNO_3 $\quad$ $\overset{+1\ \ x\ \ -2}{HNO_3}$ $\quad$ $\overset{+1\ +5\ -2}{HNO_3}$

$$+1 + x + 3 \cdot (-2) = 0$$
$$+1 + x + \quad -6 \quad = 0$$
$$x - 5 = 0$$
$$x = +5$$

$Fe_2(CO_3)_3$ $\quad$ $\overset{+3\ \ \ x\ \ -2}{Fe_2(CO_3)_3}$ $\quad$ $\overset{+3\ \ \ +4\ -2}{Fe_2(CO_3)_3}$

Uncross to get the charge of Fe

$$(2 \cdot (+3)) + 3x + (9 \cdot (-2)) = 0$$
$$6 + 3x + -18 = 0$$
$$3x - 12 = 0$$
$$3x = 12$$
$$x = +4$$

CO_3^{2-} $\quad$ $\overset{x\ \ -2}{(CO_3)^{2-}}$ $\quad$ $\overset{+4\ \ -2}{(CO_3)^{2-}}$

$$x + (3 \cdot (-2)) = -2$$
$$x + \quad -6 \quad = -2$$
$$x - 6 + 6 \quad = -2 + 6$$
$$x = +4$$

The ox# of C in carbonate is +4 no matter what metal ion CO_3^{2-} is attached to.

Electrochemical Cells and Balancing Redox Reactions

(Homework #5)

Electrochemistry = using redox reactions to make batteries (Electrochemical Cells)

$$\overset{0}{Zn\,(s)} + \overset{+2}{Cu(NO_3)_2\,(aq)} \longrightarrow \overset{+2}{Zn(NO_3)_2\,(aq)} + \overset{0}{Cu\,(s)}$$

Zn (s)	$Cu(NO_3)_2$ (aq)
↑ ox #	↓ ox #
lost e^-	gained e^-
oxidized	reduced
reducing agent	oxidizing agent

NO_3^- is a spectator ion

$$Zn\,(s) + Cu^{2+} \longrightarrow Zn^{2+} + Cu(s)$$

Half-Reactions

Loss of electrons has e^- on **right**

$$Zn\,(s) \longrightarrow Zn^{2+} + \cancel{2e^-} \quad \textbf{(oxidation)}$$

$$Cu^{2+} + \cancel{2e^-} \longrightarrow Cu\,(s) \quad \textbf{(reduction)}$$

Gain of electrons has e^- on **left**

$$Zn\,(s) + Cu^{2+} \longrightarrow Zn^{2+} + Cu(s)$$

Electrons are lost

e⁻ e⁻ Zn^{2+} ➡ Zn^{2+} + $2e^-$

$$Zn\,(s) \longrightarrow Zn^{2+} + 2e^-$$

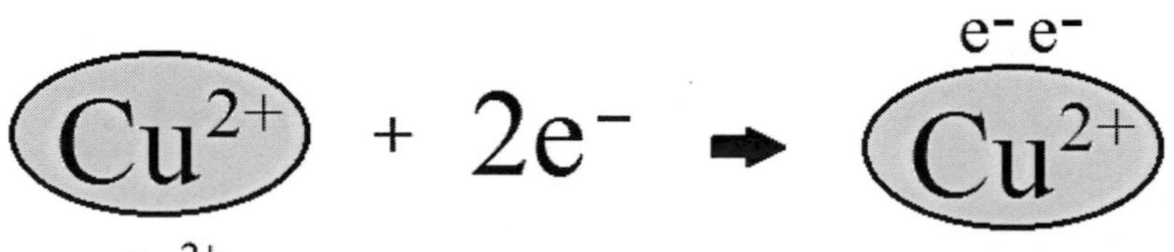

e⁻ e⁻

Cu^{2+} + $2e^-$ ➡ Cu^{2+}

$$Cu^{2+} + 2e^- \longrightarrow Cu\,(s)$$

Electrons are gained

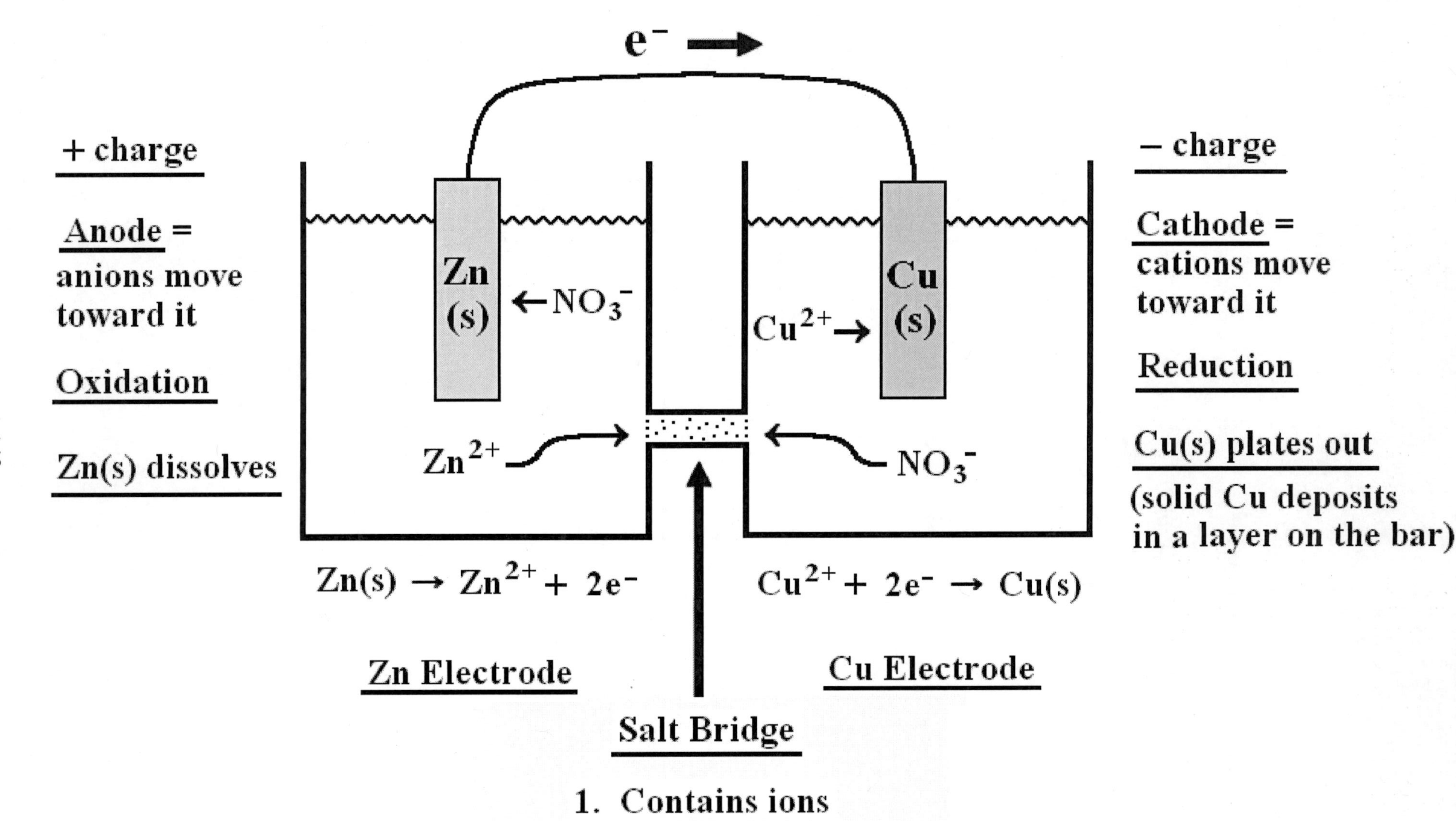
e⁻ →
+ charge
Anode = anions move toward it
Oxidation
Zn(s) dissolves
Zn (s)
← NO₃⁻
Zn²⁺
Cu²⁺ →
Cu (s)
NO₃⁻
– charge
Cathode = cations move toward it
Reduction
Cu(s) plates out
(solid Cu deposits in a layer on the bar)
Zn(s) → Zn²⁺ + 2e⁻
Cu²⁺ + 2e⁻ → Cu(s)
Zn Electrode
Cu Electrode
Salt Bridge
1. Contains ions
2. Keeps solutions from mixing

$$\overset{0}{Zn\,(s)} \quad + \quad 2\,\overset{+1}{H}NO_3\,(aq) \longrightarrow \overset{+2}{Zn}(NO_3)_2\,(aq) \quad + \quad \overset{0}{H_2}\,(g)$$

↑ ox #	↓ ox #
lost e^-	gained e^-
oxidized	reduced
reducing agent	oxidizing agent

NO_3^- is a spectator ion

$$Zn\,(s) \quad + \quad 2\,H^+ \longrightarrow Zn^{2+} \quad + \quad H_2\,(g)$$

Half-Reactions

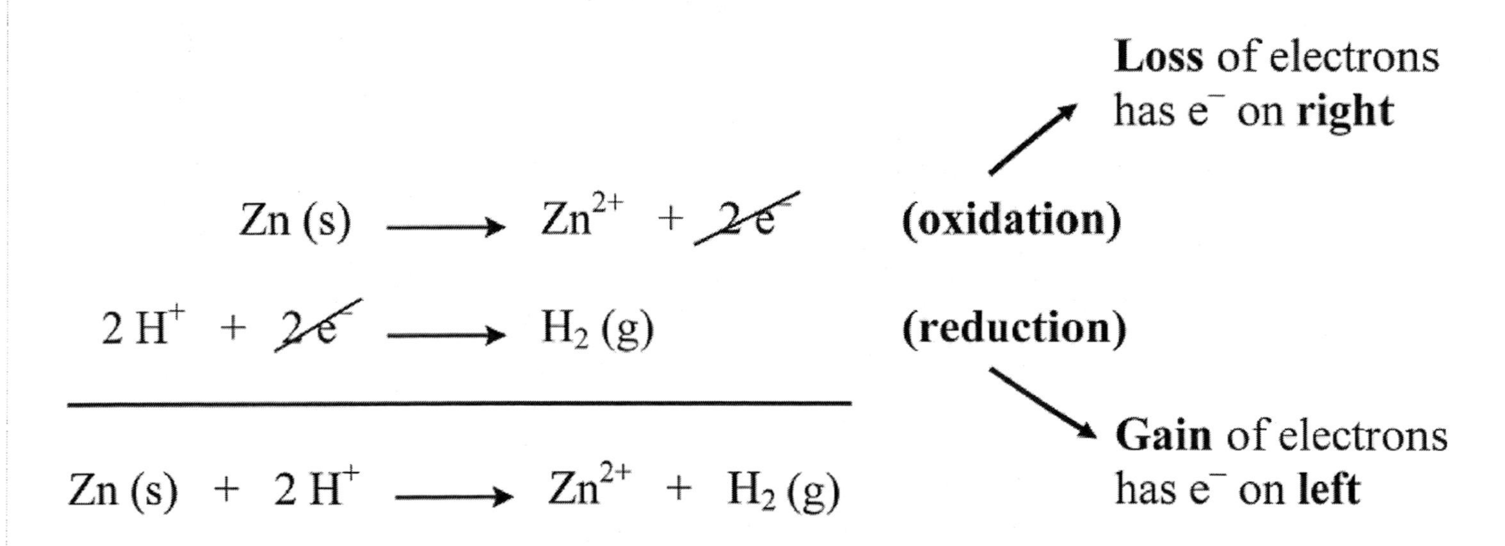

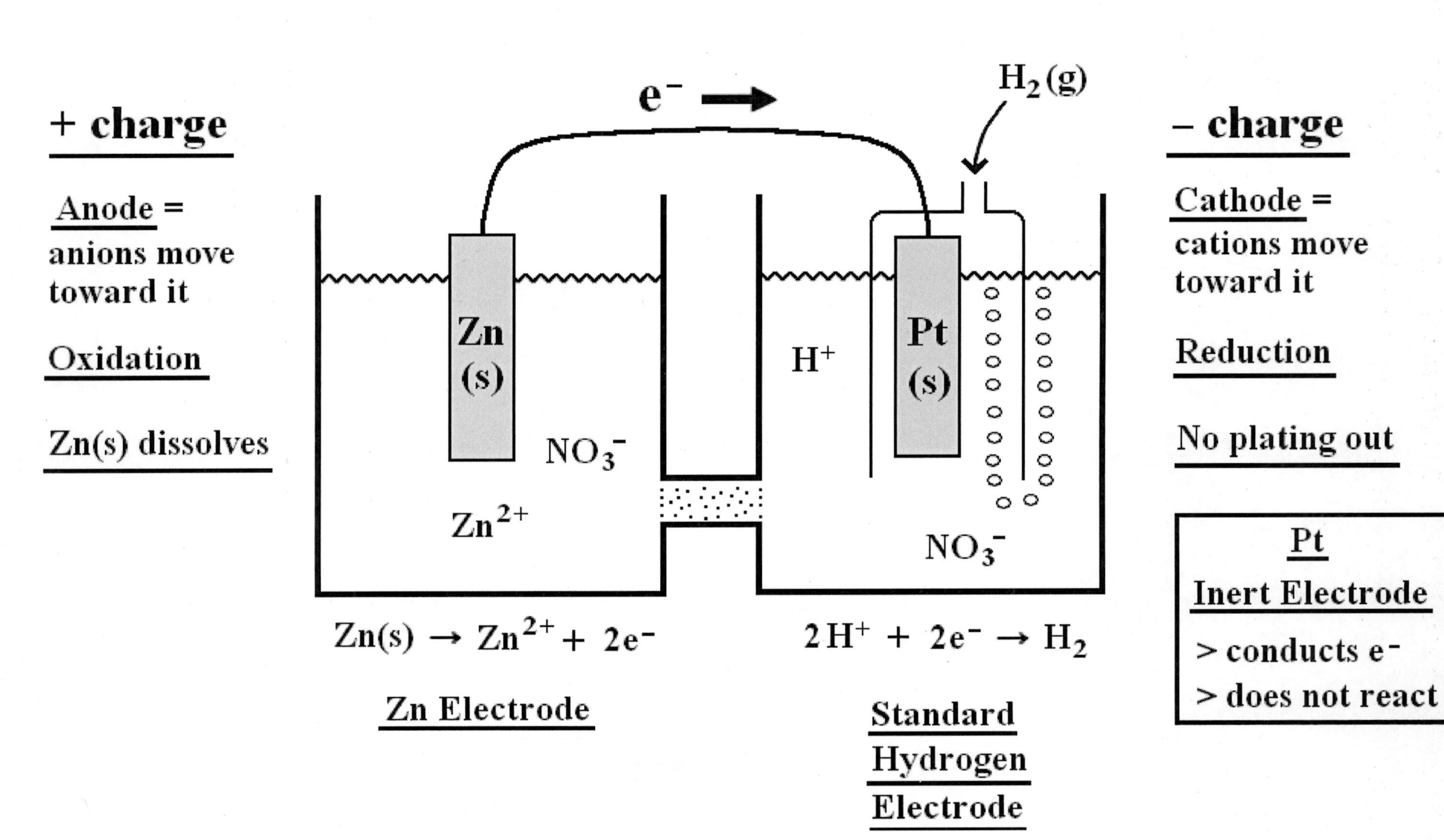
+ charge
Anode =
anions move
toward it
Oxidation
Zn(s) dissolves
e⁻
H₂(g)
Zn
(s)
Pt
(s)
H⁺
NO₃⁻
Zn²⁺
NO₃⁻
Zn(s) → Zn²⁺ + 2e⁻
Zn Electrode
2H⁺ + 2e⁻ → H₂
Standard
Hydrogen
Electrode
– charge
Cathode =
cations move
toward it
Reduction
No plating out
Pt
Inert Electrode
> conducts e⁻
> does not react

In order to construct a table of half-reactions, we first define one electrode as the "standard."

Chemists specify the **Standard Hydrogen Electrode** as 0.00 V and compare all the others to it:

$$2\,H^+ + 2\,e^- \longrightarrow H_2(g) \qquad 0.00\text{ V}$$

$$H_2(g) \longrightarrow 2\,H^+ + 2\,e^- \qquad 0.00\text{ V}$$

Attach the electrode to be tested to the SHE and measure the voltage and direction of electron flow.

Shorthand Notation for Cells

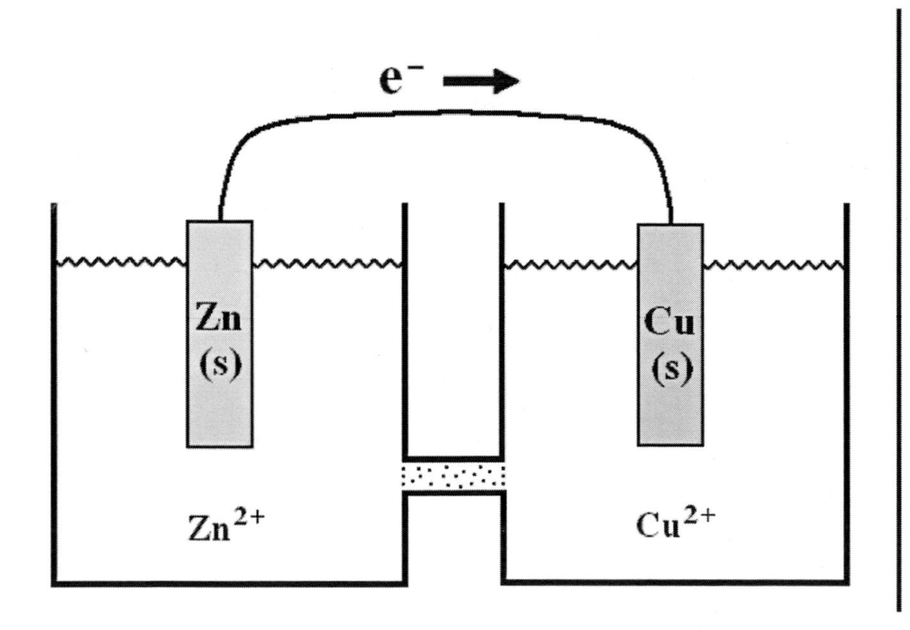

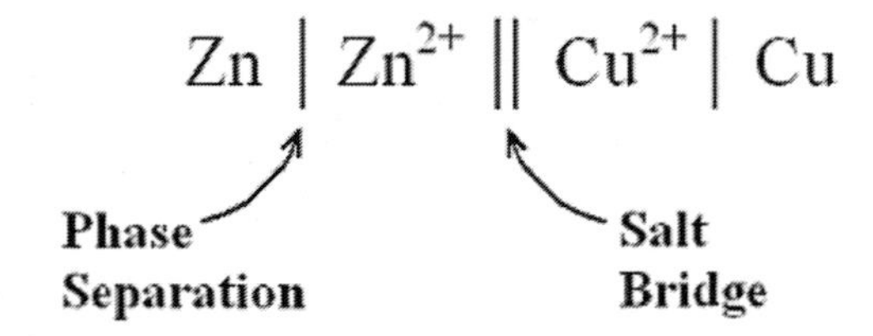

- **e^- move from left to right** $\longrightarrow \longrightarrow \longrightarrow$
- **Zn electrode loses e^-**
- **Cu electrode gains e^-**
- **Left side of $||$ is the anode**

Even if the picture is drawn the other way around, the shorthand notation is written the same way:

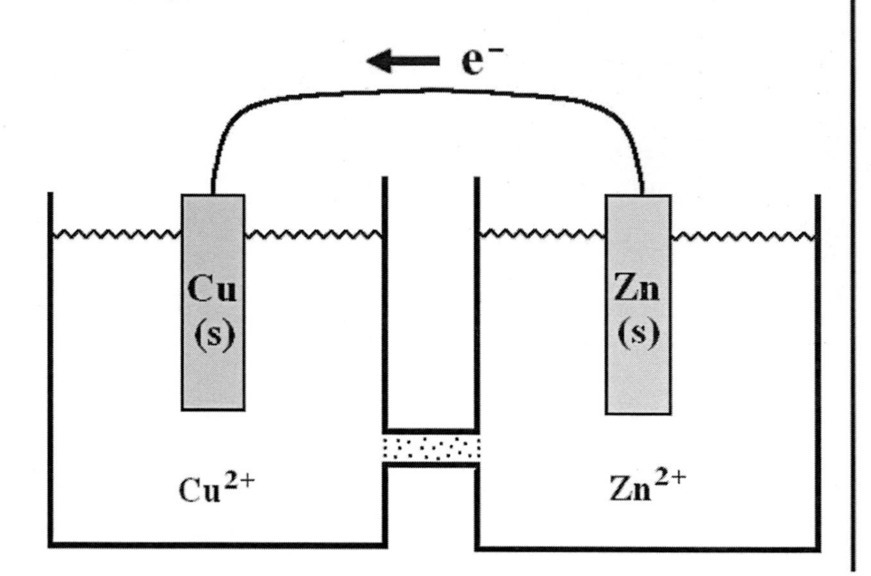

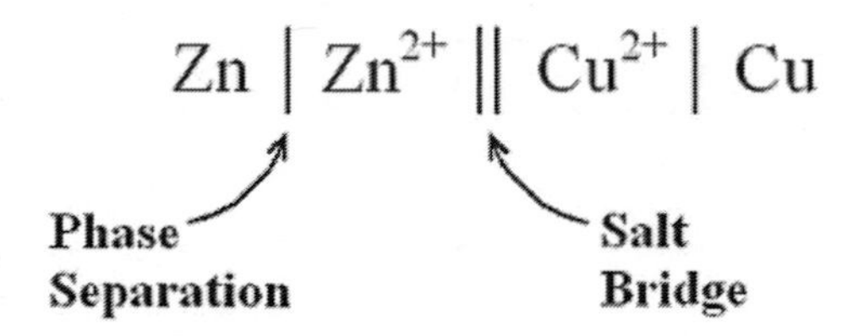

- **e^- move from left to right** ⟶ ⟶ ⟶
- **Zn electrode loses e^-**
- **Cu electrode gains e^-**
- **Left side of || is the anode**

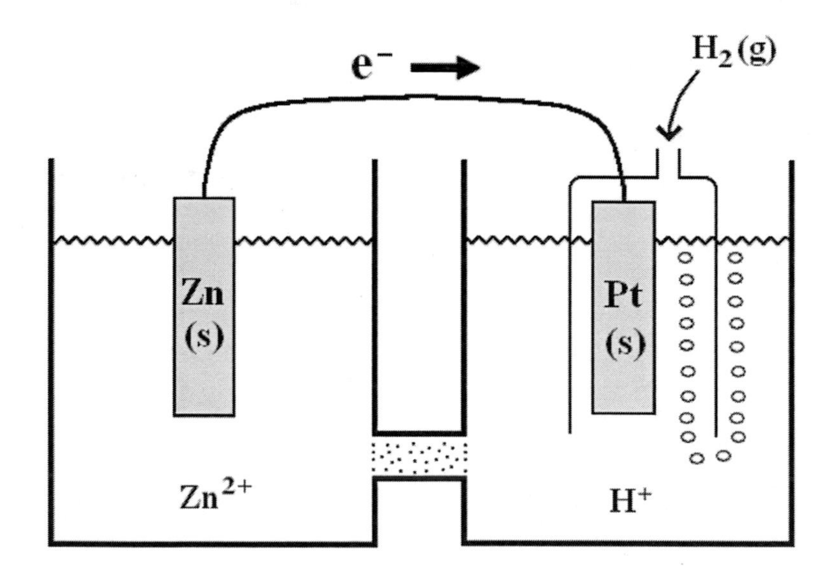

$Zn \mid Zn^{2+} \parallel H_2 \mid H^+ \mid Pt$

- **e^- move from left to right** ⟶ ⟶ ⟶
- **Zn electrode loses e^-**
- **H electrode gains e^-**
- **Left side of || is the anode**

If ions are in solution together:

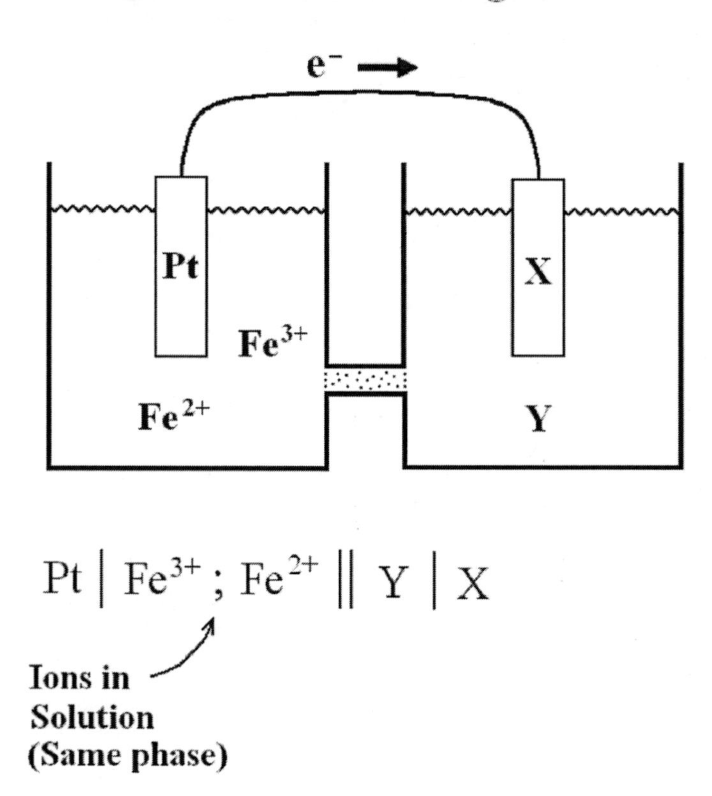

$$Pt \mid Fe^{3+} ; Fe^{2+} \parallel Y \mid X$$

Ions in Solution (Same phase)

Tables of Half-Reactions

Written as reductions, gain electrons, e^- on left in half-reactions.

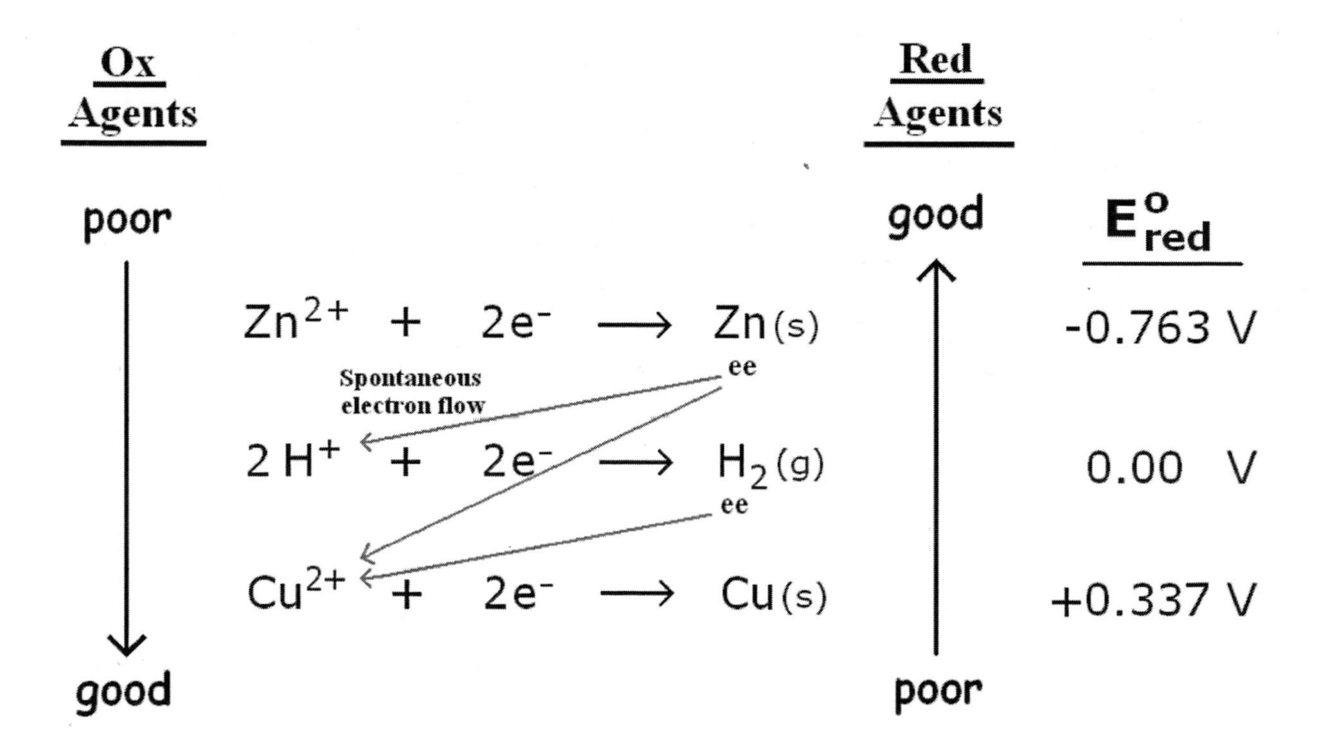

Spontaneous ("Good") Redox Reactions

A good redox reaction will have a substance that gains electrons well (good oxidizing agent) reacting with a substance that loses electrons well (good reducing agent):

Good Redox Reaction:

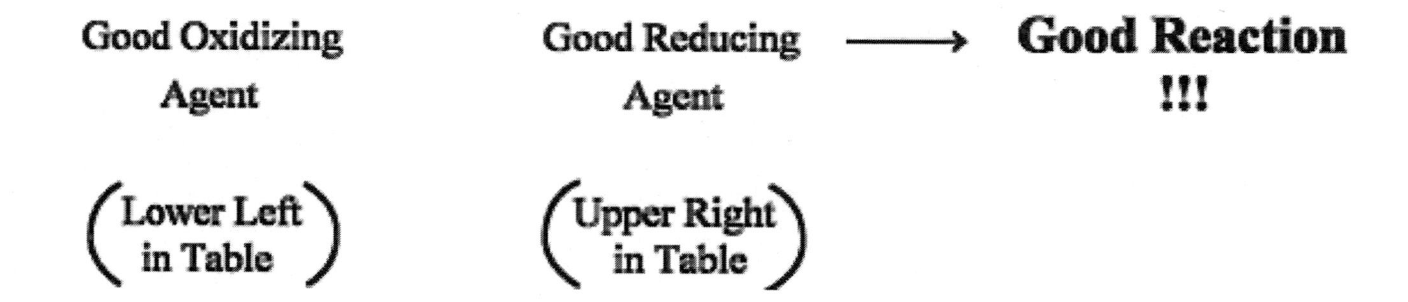

Spontaneous Direction of e^- Flow

Rule 1 = when an "above" electrode is attached to a "below" electrode, e^-'s flow spontaneously from "above" to "below." (**Down** the table)

Rule 2 = it must be the **reducing agent** (right side) of the "above" electrode that **loses e^-** and the **oxidizing agent** (left side) of the "below" electrode that **gains e^-**.

Summary

When half-reactions are written as reductions and arranged in order of voltage with the most negative E^o_{red} at the top, the **spontaneous direction** of e^- flow is **upper right to lower left**.

Principles for Balancing Redox Reactions

★ We will use the **half-reaction method** for balancing redox reactions.

★ The completed half-reactions to be used are found in **Table 3** (acidic and basic half-reactions are in separate places) and in **Table 4** (the same half-reactions as in **Table 3**, but in alphabetical order).

In order for a redox reaction to be correctly balanced, the following requirements must be fulfilled:

1. **Atoms** must balance.
2. **Charges** must balance.
3. **Electrons (e^-) cannot appear** in the final equation (all electrons must cancel).
4. Each substance can appear **on only one side** of the arrow (if a substance appears on both sides, the excess must be subtracted.)

Reactions can be run under **acidic or basic** conditions.

Acidic Reactions

1. Can contain H^+ and H_2O.
2. OH^- is not allowed.

Basic Reactions

1. Can contain OH^- and H_2O.
2. H^+ is not allowed.

Reactions that contain metal ions are sometimes classified as acidic even though they do not contain H^+. An example is:

$$Al^{3+} + 3\,e^- \longrightarrow Al(s)$$

This reaction is classified as acidic because Al^{3+} cannot exist in a basic solution. If Al^{3+} is placed in a basic environment, $Al(OH)_3\,(s)$ [$K_{sp} = 5 \times 10^{-33}$] forms.

Also, the reduction of elemental halogens (F_2, Cl_2, Br_2, and I_2) can occur under **either acidic or basic** conditions.

Balancing Redox Equations

Example #1. Balance the equation:

$$MnO_4^- + Ni(s) \longrightarrow Mn^{2+} + Ni^{2+} \qquad \textbf{(acidic)}$$

Step 1 = ***Find two half-reactions*** (in **Table 3** or **Table 4**) that contain **exactly** the same substances as in the given equation and **copy the reactions exactly** as they are written in the **Tables.** (In the present example, one half-reaction must contain MnO_4^- and Mn^{2+}, and the other must contain Ni(s) and Ni^{2+}).

$$MnO_4^- + 8H^+ + 5e^- \longrightarrow Mn^{2+} + 4H_2O$$

$$Ni^{2+} + 2e^- \longrightarrow Ni(s)$$

Step 2 = ***Turn one of the half-reactions around***, so that the substances in each reaction are on the **same side** of the arrow as given **in the original given equation**. (In the present example, the reaction containing **Ni** is the one that must be turned around.)

$$MnO_4^- + 8H^+ + 5e^- \longrightarrow Mn^{2+} + 4H_2O$$

$$Ni(s) \longrightarrow Ni^{2+} + 2e^-$$

Step 3 = ***Multiply the half-reactions by appropriate factors*** so as to get the **same number of e^-** in each equation. (In the present example, multiply the first equation by 2 and the second equation by 5.)

$$2MnO_4^- + 16H^+ + 10e^- \longrightarrow 2Mn^{2+} + 8H_2O$$

$$5Ni(s) \longrightarrow 5Ni^{2+} + 10e^-$$

Step 4 = ***Add equations***, cancelling the e^- and eliminating the excess of any other substances that appear on both sides of the arrows. (In the present example, only cancelling of e^- is necessary.)

$$2\,MnO_4^- + 16\,H^+ + \cancel{10\,e^-} \longrightarrow 2\,Mn^{2+} + 8\,H_2O$$

$$5\,Ni(s) \longrightarrow 5\,Ni^{2+} + \cancel{10\,e^-}$$

$$\overline{2\,MnO_4^- + 5\,Ni(s) + 16\,H^+ \longrightarrow 2\,Mn^{2+} + 5\,Ni^{2+} + 8\,H_2O}$$

Step 5 = ***Check*** that the atoms and charges both balance.

Atoms:

$$2\,Mn \quad 5\,Ni \quad 16\,H \quad 8\,O \longrightarrow 2\,Mn \quad 5\,Ni \quad 16\,H \quad 8\,O$$

Charges:

$$2\,MnO_4^- + 5\,Ni(s) + 16\,H^+ \longrightarrow 2\,Mn^{2+} + 5\,Ni^{2+} + 8\,H_2O$$

$$(-2) + 0 + (+16) \longrightarrow (+4) + (+10) + 0$$

$$+14 \longrightarrow +14$$

Oxidizing agent: MnO_4^-

Mn (+7) → Mn (+2)

↓ ox #

e^- on **left** in half-rxn

Reducing agent: Ni(s)

Ni (0) → Ni (+2)

↑ ox #

e^- on **right** in half-rxn

Example #2. Balance the equation:

$$ClO_3^- + MnO_4^- \longrightarrow ClO_4^- + MnO_2(s) \quad \textbf{(basic)}$$

Step 1 = ***Find two half–reactions*** (in **Table 3** or **Table 4**) that contain **exactly** the same substances as in the given equation and **copy the reactions exactly** as they are written in the **Tables.** (In the present example, one half-reaction must contain ClO_3^- and ClO_4^-, and the other must contain MnO_4^- and $MnO_2(s)$.)

$$ClO_4^- + H_2O + 2e^- \longrightarrow ClO_3^- + 2OH^-$$

$$MnO_4^- + 2H_2O + 3e^- \longrightarrow MnO_2(s) + 4OH^-$$

Step 2 = ***Turn one of the half–reactions around,*** so that the substances in each reaction are on the **same side** of the arrow as given **in the original given equation.** (In the present example, the reaction containing **Cl** is the one that must be turned around.)

$$ClO_3^- + 2OH^- \longrightarrow ClO_4^- + H_2O + 2e^-$$

$$MnO_4^- + 2H_2O + 3e^- \longrightarrow MnO_2(s) + 4OH^-$$

Step 3 = ***Multiply the half–reactions by appropriate factors*** so as to get the **same number of e⁻** in each equation. (In the present example, multiply the first equation by 3 and the second equation by 2.)

$$3ClO_3^- + 6OH^- \longrightarrow 3ClO_4^- + 3H_2O + 6e^-$$

$$2MnO_4^- + 4H_2O + 6e^- \longrightarrow 2MnO_2(s) + 8OH^-$$

Step 4 = ***Add equations***, cancelling the e^- and eliminating the excess of any other substances that appear on both sides. (In the present example, 6 OH^- and 3 H_2O must be subtracted from each side.)

$$3\,ClO_3^- + \cancel{6\,OH^-} \longrightarrow 3\,ClO_4^- + \cancel{3\,H_2O} + \cancel{6e^-}$$

$$2\,MnO_4^- + \overset{1}{\cancel{4}}H_2O + \cancel{6e^-} \longrightarrow 2\,MnO_2 + \overset{2}{\cancel{8}}OH^-$$

$$3\,ClO_3^- + 2\,MnO_4^- + H_2O \longrightarrow 3\,ClO_4^- + 2\,MnO_2(s) + 2\,OH^-$$

Step 5 = ***Check*** that the atoms and charges both balance.

Atoms:

3 Cl 2 Mn 2 H 18 O $\longrightarrow$ 3 Cl 2 Mn 2 H 18 O

Charges:

$$3\,ClO_3^- + 2\,MnO_4^- + H_2O \longrightarrow 3\,ClO_4^- + 2\,MnO_2(s) + 2\,OH^-$$

$$(-3) + (-2) + 0 \longrightarrow (-3) + 0 + (-2)$$

$$-5 \longrightarrow -5$$

Oxidizing agent: MnO_4^-

Mn (+7) → Mn (+4)

↓ ox #

e^- on **left** in half-rxn

Reducing agent: ClO_3^-

Cl (+5) → Cl (+7)

↑ ox #

e^- on **right** in half-rxn

Example #3. Balance the equation:

$$AuCl_4^- + Ag(s) + I^- \longrightarrow Au(s) + Cl^- + AgI(s) \quad \textbf{(acidic)}$$

Step 1 = ***Find two half–reactions*** (in **Table 3** or **Table 4**) that contain **exactly** the same substances as in the given equation and **copy the reactions exactly** as they are written in the **Tables.** (In the present example, one half-reaction must contain $AuCl_4^-$, Au(s) and Cl^- and the other must contain Ag(s), I^- and AgI(s).)

$$AuCl_4^- + 3\,e^- \longrightarrow Au(s) + 4\,Cl^-$$

$$AgI(s) + e^- \longrightarrow Ag(s) + I^-$$

Step 2 = ***Turn one of the half–reactions around***, so that the substances in each reaction are on the **same side** of the arrow as given **in the original given equation**. (In the present example, the reaction containing **Ag** is the one that must be turned around.)

$$AuCl_4^- + 3\,e^- \longrightarrow Au(s) + 4\,Cl^-$$

$$Ag(s) + I^- \longrightarrow AgI(s) + e^-$$

Step 3 = ***Multiply the half–reactions by appropriate factors*** so as to get the **same number of e^-** in each equation. (In the present example, multiply the second equation by 3.)

$$AuCl_4^- + 3\,e^- \longrightarrow Au(s) + 4\,Cl^-$$

$$3\,Ag(s) + 3\,I^- \longrightarrow 3\,AgI(s) + 3\,e^-$$

Step 4 = ***Add equations***, cancelling the e^- and eliminating the excess of any other substances that appear on both sides. (In the present example, only cancelling of e^- is necessary.)

$$AuCl_4^- + \cancel{3e^-} \longrightarrow Au(s) + 4\,Cl^-$$

$$3\,Ag(s) + 3\,I^- \longrightarrow 3\,AgI(s) + \cancel{3e^-}$$

$$\overline{AuCl_4^- + 3\,Ag(s) + 3\,I^- \longrightarrow Au(s) + 3\,AgI(s) + 4\,Cl^-}$$

Step 5 = ***Check*** that the atoms and charges both balance.

Atoms:

1 Au   3 Ag   4 Cl   3 I $\longrightarrow$ 1 Au   3 Ag   4 Cl   3 I

Charges:

$$AuCl_4^- + 3\,Ag(s) + 3\,I^- \longrightarrow Au(s) + 3\,AgI(s) + 4\,Cl^-$$

$$(-1) + 0 + (-3) \longrightarrow 0 + 0 + (-4)$$

$$-4 \longrightarrow -4$$

Oxidizing agent: $AuCl_4^-$

Au (+3) → Au (0)

↓ ox #

e^- on **left** in half-rxn

Reducing agent: Ag(s)

Ag (0) → Ag (+1)

↑ ox #

e^- on **right** in half-rxn

Example #4. Write a balanced equation for the following shorthand diagram of an electrochemical cell:

$$Al \mid Al^{3+} \parallel Cr_2O_7^{2-}; Cr^{3+}; H^+ \mid Pt$$

Step 1 = ***Find two half-reactions*** (in **Table 3** or **Table 4**), one that contains **exactly** the same substances as on the left side of the || and another that contains **exactly** the same substances as on the right side (except **Pt**). Copy the reactions **exactly as they are written in the Tables** and **<u>DO NOT</u>** take into account the "order" the substances are written in the shorthand diagram. (In the present example, one half-reaction must contain Al(s) and Al^{3+} and the other must contain $Cr_2O_7^{2-}$, Cr^{3+} and H^+.)

$$Al^{3+} + 3\,e^- \longrightarrow Al(s)$$

$$Cr_2O_7^{2-} + 14\,H^+ + 6\,e^- \longrightarrow 2\,Cr^{3+} + 7\,H_2O$$

Step 2 = ***Turn one of the half-reactions around.*** For a shorthand diagram, ALWAYS turn around the equation containing the substances to the **LEFT** of the ||. (In the present example, the reaction containing **Al** is the one that must be turned around.)

$$Al(s) \longrightarrow Al^{3+} + 3\,e^-$$

$$Cr_2O_7^{2-} + 14\,H^+ + 6\,e^- \longrightarrow 2\,Cr^{3+} + 7\,H_2O$$

Step 3 = ***Multiply the half-reactions by appropriate factors*** so as to get the **same number of e^-** in each equation. (In the present example, multiply the first equation by 2.)

$$2\,Al(s) \longrightarrow 2\,Al^{3+} + 6\,e^-$$

$$Cr_2O_7^{2-} + 14\,H^+ + 6\,e^- \longrightarrow 2\,Cr^{3+} + 7\,H_2O$$

Step 4 = ***Add equations***, cancelling the e^- and eliminating the excess of any other substances that appear on both sides. (In the present example, only cancelling of e^- is necessary.)

$$2\,Al(s) \longrightarrow 2\,Al^{3+} + \cancel{6e^-}$$

$$Cr_2O_7^{2-} + 14\,H^+ + \cancel{6e^-} \longrightarrow 2\,Cr^{3+} + 7\,H_2O$$

$$Cr_2O_7^{2-} + 2\,Al(s) + 14\,H^+ \longrightarrow 2\,Cr^{3+} + 2\,Al^{3+} + 7\,H_2O$$

Step 5 = ***Check*** that the atoms and charges both balance.

Atoms:

$$2\,Cr \quad 2\,Al \quad 14\,H \quad 7\,O \longrightarrow 2\,Cr \quad 2\,Al \quad 14\,H \quad 7\,O$$

Charges:

$$Cr_2O_7^{2-} + 2\,Al(s) + 14\,H^+ \longrightarrow 2\,Cr^{3+} + 2\,Al^{3+} + 7\,H_2O$$

$$(-2) + 0 + (+14) \longrightarrow (+6) + (+6) + 0$$

$$+12 \longrightarrow +12$$

Oxidizing agent: $Cr_2O_7^{2-}$

Cr (+6) → Cr (+3)

↓ ox #

e^- on **left** in half-rxn

Reducing agent: Al(s)

Al (0) → Al (+3)

↑ ox #

e^- on **right** in half-rxn

Example #5. Write a balanced equation for the following electrochemical cell:

$$Fe \mid Fe(OH)_2(s) \mid OH^- \parallel OH^- \mid O_2(g) \mid Pt$$

Step 1 = ***Find two half–reactions*** (in **Table 3** or **Table 4**), one that contain **exactly** the same substances as on the left side of the || and the another that contains **exactly** the same substances as on the right side (except **Pt**). Copy the reactions **exactly as they are written in the Tables** and **<u>DO NOT</u>** take into account the "order" the substances are written in the shorthand diagram. (In the present example, one half-reaction must contain Fe(s), $Fe(OH)_2(s)$ and OH^- and the other must contain OH^- and $O_2(g)$.)

$$Fe(OH)_2 + 2e^- \longrightarrow Fe(s) + 2OH^-$$

$$O_2(g) + 2H_2O + 4e^- \longrightarrow 4OH^-$$

Step 2 = ***Turn one of the half–reactions around.*** For a shorthand diagram, ALWAYS turn around the equation containing the substances to the **LEFT** of the ||. (In the present example, the reaction containing **Fe** is the one that must be turned around.)

$$Fe(s) + 2OH^- \longrightarrow Fe(OH)_2 + 2e^-$$

$$O_2(g) + 2H_2O + 4e^- \longrightarrow 4OH^-$$

Step 3 = ***Multiply the half–reactions by appropriate factors*** so as to get the **same number of e⁻** in each equation. (In the present example, multiply the first equation by 2.)

$$2Fe(s) + 4OH^- \longrightarrow 2Fe(OH)_2 + 4e^-$$

$$O_2(g) + 2H_2O + 4e^- \longrightarrow 4OH^-$$

Step 4 = ***Add equations***, cancelling the e^- and eliminating the excess of any other substances that appear on both sides. (In the present example, even though the reaction is basic, all the OH^- ions cancel, so no OH^- appears in the final balanced equation.)

$$2\,Fe(s) + \cancel{4\,OH^-} \longrightarrow 2\,Fe(OH)_2 + \cancel{4\,e^-}$$

$$O_2(g) + 2\,H_2O + \cancel{4\,e^-} \longrightarrow \cancel{4\,OH^-}$$

$$\overline{2\,Fe(s) + O_2(g) + 2\,H_2O \longrightarrow 2\,Fe(OH)_2}$$

Step 5 = ***Check*** that the atoms and charges both balance.

Atoms:

$$2\,Fe \quad 4\,H \quad 4\,O \longrightarrow 2\,Fe \quad 4\,H \quad 4\,O$$

Charges:

$$2\,Fe(s) + O_2(g) + 2\,H_2O \longrightarrow 2\,Fe(OH)_2$$

$$0 + 0 + 0 \longrightarrow 0$$

$$0 \longrightarrow 0$$

Oxidizing agent: $O_2(g)$	**Reducing agent:** $Fe(s)$
$O\,(0) \rightarrow O\,(-2)$	$Fe\,(0) \rightarrow Fe\,(+2)$
↓ ox #	↑ ox #
e^- on **left** in half-rxn	e^- on **right** in half-rxn

Hydrogen Peroxide

- H_2O_2 is a weak acid and is included in **Table 2.**

- The equilibrium below shifts to the left under acidic conditions (large $[H^+]$), and H_2O_2 is the predominant form.

- The equilibrium shifts to the right under basic conditions (OH^- "eliminates" H^+), and HO_2^- is the predominant form.

Predominant form under acidic conditions

Written this way in acidic reactions

Predominant form under basic conditions

Written this way in basic reactions

Neutralization Reactions and Introduction to Buffers

(Homework #6)

Buffers

Solution that contains substances that resist large pH changes upon addition of strong acid or strong base to the solution.

The buffer resists pH changes by neutralizing the added acid or base.

In order to discuss buffers in detail, we must first describe the different types of neutralizations possible.

Differences exist between types of neutralizations based on whether the acids and bases involved are strong or weak.

Types of Neutralization Reactions

(I) Strong Acid/Strong Base

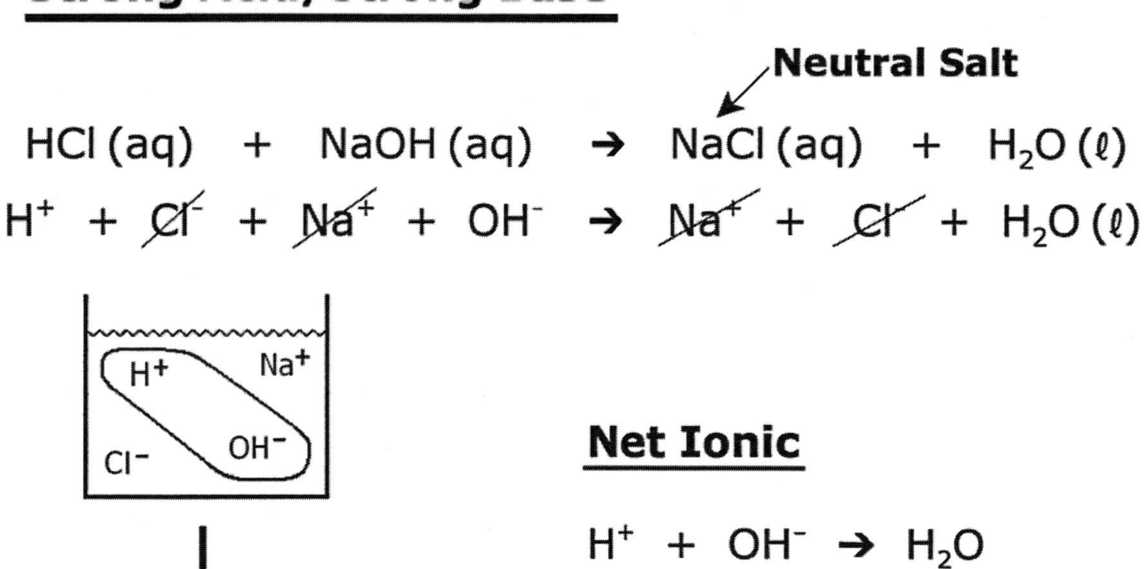

Na⁺

H_2O

Cl^-

Neutral Salt

$$HNO_3\,(aq) + KOH\,(aq) \rightarrow KNO_3\,(aq) + H_2O\,(\ell)$$

$$H^+ + \cancel{NO_3^-} + \cancel{K^+} + OH^- \rightarrow \cancel{K^+} + \cancel{NO_3^-} + H_2O\,(\ell)$$

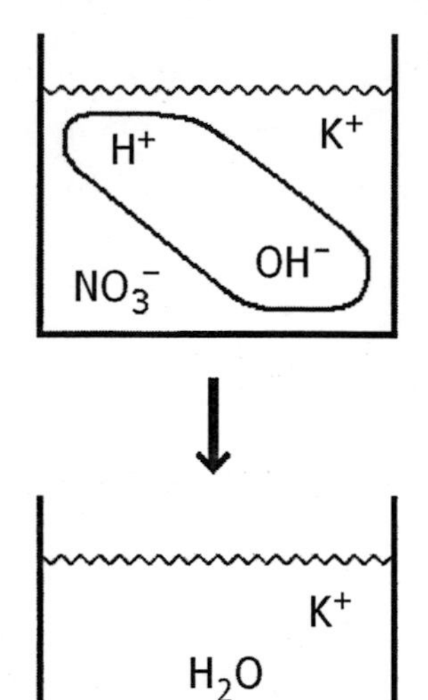

Net Ionic

$$H^+ + OH^- \rightarrow H_2O$$

Neutral Salt

$$2\,HCl\,(aq) + Ba(OH)_2\,(aq) \rightarrow BaCl_2\,(aq) + 2\,H_2O\,(\ell)$$

$$2\,H^+ + \cancel{2\,Cl^-} + \cancel{Ba^{2+}} + 2\,OH^- \rightarrow \cancel{Ba^{2+}} + \cancel{2\,Cl^-} + 2\,H_2O\,(\ell)$$

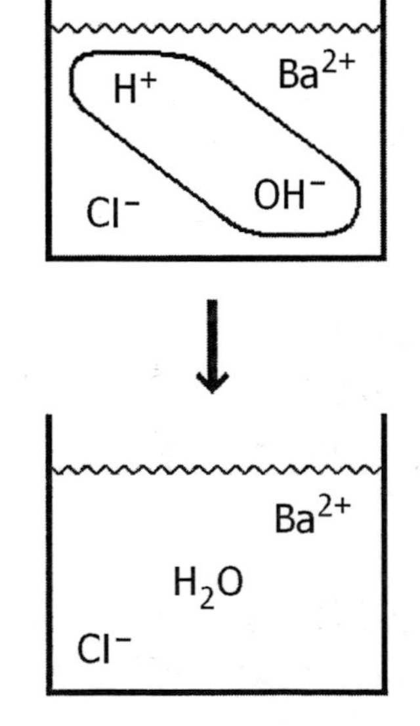

Net Ionic

$$H^+ + OH^- \rightarrow H_2O$$

(II) Weak Acid/Strong Base

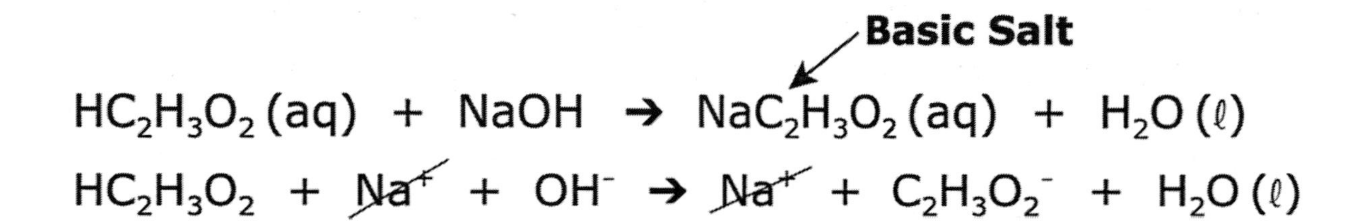

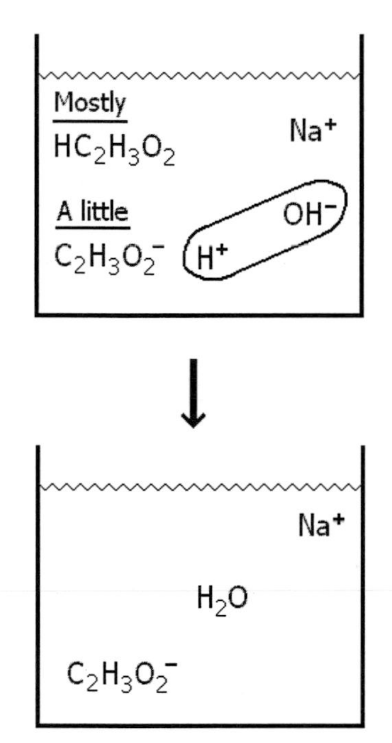

1) OH^- neutralizes H^+
2) More $HC_2H_3O_2$ ionizes to form more H^+:

$$HC_2H_3O_2 \rightleftharpoons H^+ + C_2H_3O_2^-$$

$HC_2H_3O_2$ gone

Net Ionic

$$HC_2H_3O_2 + OH^- \rightarrow C_2H_3O_2^- + H_2O$$

Type II: $HC_2H_3O_2 + OH^- \rightarrow C_2H_3O_2^- + H_2O$

Type I: $H^+ + OH^- \rightarrow H_2O$

- H attached to $HC_2H_3O_2$ **cannot change the pH.**
- H^+ in the **Type I** reaction **changes the pH dramatically** because it is "free."
- The **weak acid** $HC_2H_3O_2$ **can be part of a buffer** because it serves as a "storage form" of H^+ ready to be released in the presence of OH^-.
- **Strong acids** (like HCl) **cannot be part of a buffer** because H^+ is not "stored" but is 100 % "free."

Net ionic equations for **Type II** WA/SB neutralizations always have the following form (where A^- is a weak base):

General Form: $HA + OH^- \rightarrow A^- + H_2O$

Specific Examples:

$HF + OH^- \rightarrow F^- + H_2O$

$HClO_2 + OH^- \rightarrow ClO_2^- + H_2O$

$HCN + OH^- \rightarrow CN^- + H_2O$

$NH_4^+ + OH^- \rightarrow NH_3 + H_2O$

Effect: It appears as if OH^- "pulls" H^+ directly off the acid, but we know that, actually, the two-step process discussed previously occurs.

(III) Strong Acid/Weak Base → **Neutral (NH_3) (III-a)** / **Anion (III-b)**

(III-a) Strong Acid/Weak Base

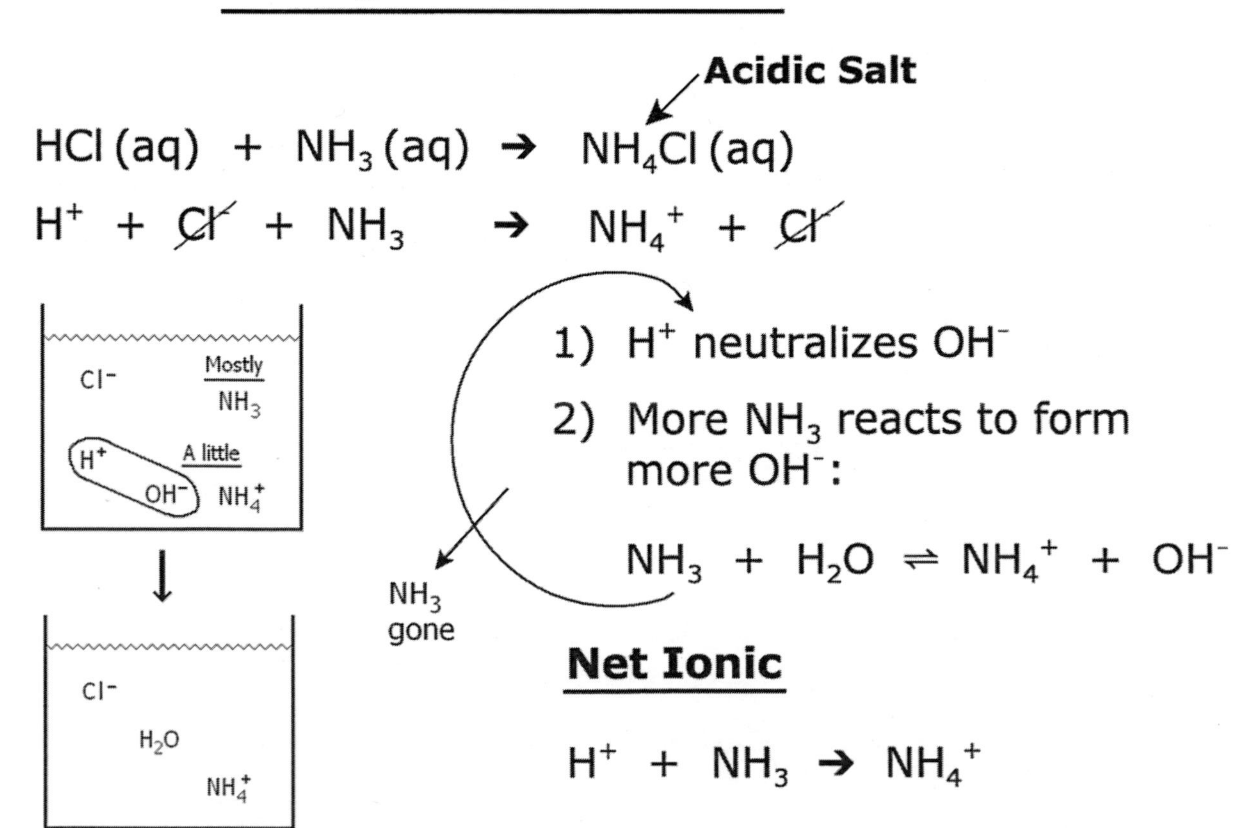

(III-b) Strong Acid/Weak Base Anion

$$HCl\,(aq) + KCN\,(aq) \rightarrow KCl\,(aq) + HCN\,(aq)$$

$$H^+ + \cancel{Cl^-} + \cancel{K^+} + CN^- \rightarrow \cancel{K^+} + \cancel{Cl^-} + HCN$$

Extra Spectator (K⁺)   **Do not split apart because weak** (HCN)

Net Ionic: $H^+ + CN^- \rightarrow HCN$

Net ionic equations for **Type III** SA/WB neutralizations always have the following form (where NH_3 and A^- are weak bases).

General Form: $H^+ + NH_3 \rightarrow NH_4^+$ **(III-a)**

$H^+ + A^- \rightarrow HA$ **(III-b)**

Specific Examples: $H^+ + C_7H_5O_2^- \rightarrow HC_7H_5O_2$

$H^+ + BrO^- \rightarrow HBrO$

Effect: It appears that H^+ directly combines with the weak base, but actually, the two-step process discussed previously occurs.

"(IV)" Weak Acid/Weak Base

This combination does not produce a true neutralization reaction.

The weak acid does not "want" to lose H^+, and the weak base does not "want" to accept H^+.

$HCN + F^- \rightarrow$ almost no reaction

$HC_2H_3O_2 + NO_2^- \rightarrow$ almost no reaction

A true neutralization occurs only if either the acid, the base, or both is (are) strong.

This **Type "IV"** neutralization corresponds to the kind of salt we called a "mixed" salt, because NH_4^+ is a weak, acid and the anion is a weak base. **Almost no reaction occurs** between the two ions.

Examples: $NH_4C_2H_3O_2$ NH_4F

When writing the net ionic equation for a neutralization, you can apply these principles:

1) Write **strong acids as H^+** and **strong bases as OH^-.** Do not show the spectator.

2) Write **weak acids and weak bases as is,** without showing them forming any ions. (Don't "split up" weak acids or bases.)

Summary of Neutralizations

Type	Net Ionic	Salt
(I) SA/SB	$H^+ + OH^- \rightarrow H_2O$	Neutral
(II) WA/SB	$HA + OH^- \rightarrow A^- + H_2O$	Basic
	$NH_4^+ + OH^- \rightarrow NH_3 + H_2O$	--------
(III-a) SA/NH_3	$H^+ + NH_3 \rightarrow NH_4^+$	Acidic
(III-b) SA/WB	$H^+ + A^- \rightarrow HA$	--------

Note: "A" in the above equations represents any anion from a weak acid.

Problem: Write the net ionic equation for the neutralization reaction between:

Reactants	Net ionic equation	Type
$HClO_4$ (SA) and $Sr(OH)_2$ (SB)	$H^+ + OH^- \rightarrow H_2O$	**(I)**
HBr (SA) and KF (WB (salt))	$H^+ + F^- \rightarrow HF$	**(III-b)**
NH_3 (WB) and HNO_3 (SA)	$NH_3 + H^+ \rightarrow NH_4^+$	**(III-a)**
$NaOH$ (SB) and $HCHO_2$ (WA)	$OH^- + HCHO_2 \rightarrow CHO_2^- + H_2O$	**(II)**
NH_4Br (WA (salt)) and KOH (SB)	$NH_4^+ + OH^- \rightarrow NH_3 + H_2O$	**(II)**
$HClO_2$ (WA) and $Ba(OH)_2$ (SB)	$HClO_2 + OH^- \rightarrow ClO_2^- + H_2O$	**(II)**

Buffers – Acetate Buffer as an Example

Suppose a solution contains both aqueous $HC_2H_3O_2$ and $NaC_2H_3O_2$: (Na^+ is a spectator)

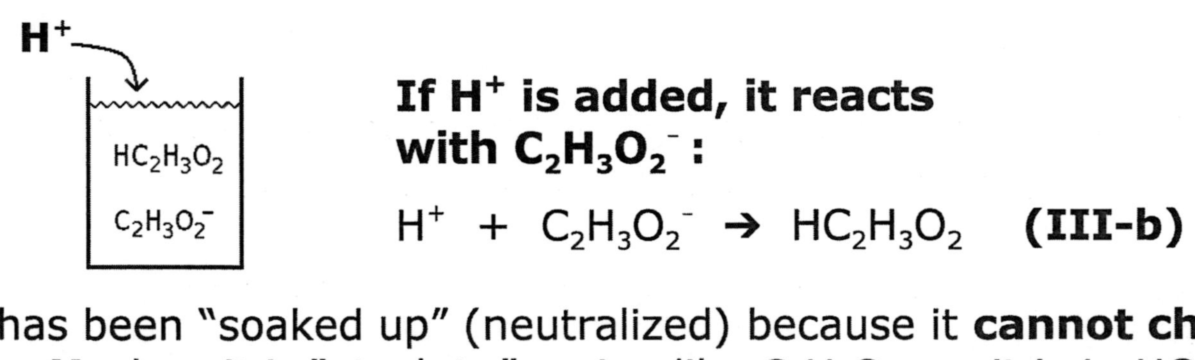

If H^+ is added, it reacts with $C_2H_3O_2^-$:

$H^+ + C_2H_3O_2^- \rightarrow HC_2H_3O_2$ **(III-b)**

H^+ has been "soaked up" (neutralized) because it **cannot change the pH** when it is "stuck to" an ion like $C_2H_3O_2^-$ as it is in $HC_2H_3O_2$.

Also notice that, when $C_2H_3O_2^-$ neutralizes H^+, the reaction forms the other substance **already present**: $HC_2H_3O_2$

All adding H^+ did was change the **ratio** of $HC_2H_3O_2$ to $C_2H_3O_2^-$.

OH$^-$

HC$_2$H$_3$O$_2$

$C_2H_3O_2^-$

If OH^- is added, it reacts with $HC_2H_3O_2$:

$$OH^- + HC_2H_3O_2 \rightarrow C_2H_3O_2^- + H_2O \quad \textbf{(II)}$$

OH^- has been "soaked up" (neutralized) because it cannot change the pH after reacting with H^+ to form H_2O.

Notice that, when $HC_2H_3O_2$ neutralizes OH^-, the reaction forms the other substance already present: $C_2H_3O_2^-$

All adding OH^- did was change the ratio of $HC_2H_3O_2$ to $C_2H_3O_2^-$.

Buffers always have 2 components: a **weak acid** and the **conjugate base of that acid.**

When H^+ or OH^- is added to a buffer, it changes the **ratio** of weak acid to conjugate base without changing the pH much.

pH of a Buffer

Each buffer "works" only within a small range of pH values. Outside this range, there is no buffering action.

The following discussion shows how to determine the pH "range" of a specific buffer.

We start with a solution of weak acid, then add to it the other component of the buffer.

Problem: Calculate the pH of 0.1 M $HC_2H_3O_2$ (aq) mixed with NO $NaC_2H_3O_2$ (aq).

Solution:

$$HC_2H_3O_2 \rightleftharpoons H^+ + C_2H_3O_2^-$$

	$HC_2H_3O_2$	H^+	$C_2H_3O_2^-$
I	.1	0	0
C	$-x$	$+x$	$+x$
E	$.1 \not{-} \not{x}$	x	x

$$K_a = \frac{[H^+][C_2H_3O_2]}{[HC_2H_3O_2]} = \frac{(x)(x)}{.1} = \frac{x^2}{.1} = 1.8 \times 10^{-5}$$

$$x^2 = 1.8 \times 10^{-5} \times .1$$

$$x^2 = 1.8 \times 10^{-6}$$

$$\sqrt{x^2} = \sqrt{1.8 \times 10^{-6}}$$

$$x = 1.34 \times 10^{-3}\text{ M} = [H^+]$$

$$\text{pH} = -\log(1.34 \times 10^{-3}) = \boxed{2.87}$$

Problem: Calculate the pH of 0.1 M $HC_2H_3O_2$ (aq) mixed with 0.1 M $NaC_2H_3O_2$ (aq).
(Na ↖ spectator)

Solution:

$$HC_2H_3O_2 \rightleftharpoons H^+ + C_2H_3O_2^-$$

	$HC_2H_3O_2$	H^+	$C_2H_3O_2^-$
I	.1	0	.1
C	$-x$	$+x$	$+x$
E	$.1 \not{-} \not{x}$	x	$.1 \not{+} \not{x}$

$$K_a = \frac{[H^+][C_2H_3O_2]}{[HC_2H_3O_2]} = \frac{(x)(\not{.1})}{\not{.1}} = 1.8 \times 10^{-5}$$

$$x = [H^+] = 1.8 \times 10^{-5}$$

$$\text{pH} = -\log(1.8 \times 10^{-5}) = \boxed{4.74}$$

↑pH because added $C_2H_3O_2^-$ is a **base**.

For a buffer where [weak acid] = [weak base], also called an **Equimolar buffer:**

$$[H^+] = K_a$$

$$-\log [H^+] = -\log K_a$$

$$\boxed{pH = pK_a}$$

In **Table 2**, pK_a gives the pH of an equimolar buffer containing the weak acid on the left and the conjugate weak base on the right.

Buffers have a range of about ± 1 pH unit around the pK_a. (For $HC_2H_3O_2/C_2H_3O_2^-$, this range is 3.74 - 5.74). Outside this range, there is little or no buffering ability.

Summary of Acetate Buffer

weak acid: $HC_2H_3O_2$ ⟵ **Source:** Pure "Glacial" Acetic Acid

weak base: $C_2H_3O_2^-$ ⟵ **Source:** $NaC_2H_3O_2$ (s) or $KC_2H_3O_2$ (s)

Net Ionic for the buffer neutralizing ("soaking up") **added acid (H^+):**

$$H^+ + C_2H_3O_2^- \rightarrow HC_2H_3O_2$$

Net Ionic for the buffer neutralizing ("soaking up") **added base (OH^-):**

$$OH^- + HC_2H_3O_2 \rightarrow C_2H_3O_2^- + H_2O$$

Equimolar pH: 4.74

Buffering Range: 3.74 - 5.74 (Acidic Buffer)

Ammonia Buffer

Weak Acid: NH_4^+ ⟵ **Source:** NH_4Cl (s) or NH_4NO_3 (s)

Weak Base: NH_3 ⟵ **Source:** Saturated "Ammonium Hydroxide" ("NH_4OH"). Actually NH_3 (aq) [saturated is about 15 M]

pH when equimolar

9.25 (pK_a in Table 2)

Buffering Range

8.25 - 10.25 (Basic Buffer)

Net Ionic for buffer neutralizing added acid (H^+)

$H^+ + NH_3 \rightarrow NH_4^+$

Net Ionic for buffer neutralizing added base (OH^-)

$OH^- + NH_4^+ \rightarrow NH_3 + H_2O$

Sulfate Buffer

Weak Acid: HSO_4^- ⟵ **Source:** $NaHSO_4$ (s) or $KHSO_4$ (s)

Weak Base: SO_4^{2-} ⟵ **Source:** Na_2SO_4 (s) or K_2SO_4 (s)

Note: HSO_4^- cannot act as a base in water:

$HSO_4^- + H^+ \not\rightarrow \cancel{H_2SO_4}$ Does not occur

pH when equimolar

1.89 (pK_a in **Table 2**)

Buffering Range

0.89 - 2.89 (Very Acidic Buffer)

Net Ionic for buffer neutralizing added acid (H^+)

$H^+ + SO_4^{2-} \rightarrow HSO_4^-$ **(III-b)**

Net Ionic for buffer neutralizing added base (OH^-)

$OH^- + HSO_4^- \rightarrow SO_4^{2-} + H_2O$ **(II)**

Problem: For a buffer of 0.31 M HNO_2 combined with 0.31 M KNO_2:

a) What is the pH?

b) What is the buffering range?

c) What is the net ionic for the buffer neutralizing added acid (H^+)?

d) What is the net ionic for the buffer neutralizing added base (OH^-)?

Solution: a) 3.35 (pK_a in **Table 2**) $\Longrightarrow$ no calculating because equimolar

b) 2.35 - 4.35

c) $H^+ + NO_2^- \rightarrow HNO_2$ **(III-b)**

d) $OH^- + HNO_2 \rightarrow NO_2^- + H_2O$ **(II)**

Which of the following pairs of substances will form a buffer?

$HC_2H_3O_2$ and HF	*WA*	*WA*	**NO**
NH_3 and KCN	*WB*	*WB*	**NO**
NaClO and $NaClO_2$	*WB*	*WB*	**NO**
HCN and NaCN	*WA*	*WB*	**YES**
NH_4NO_3 and NH_3	*WA*	*WB*	**YES**
H_2CO_3 and $NaHCO_3$	*WA*	*WB*	**YES**
$NaHCO_3$ and Na_2CO_3	*WA*	*WB*	**YES**
HCl and NaCl	*SA*	*unreactive*	**NO**
HNO_2 and KNO_2	*WA*	*WB*	**YES**

H_2CO_3 and pH

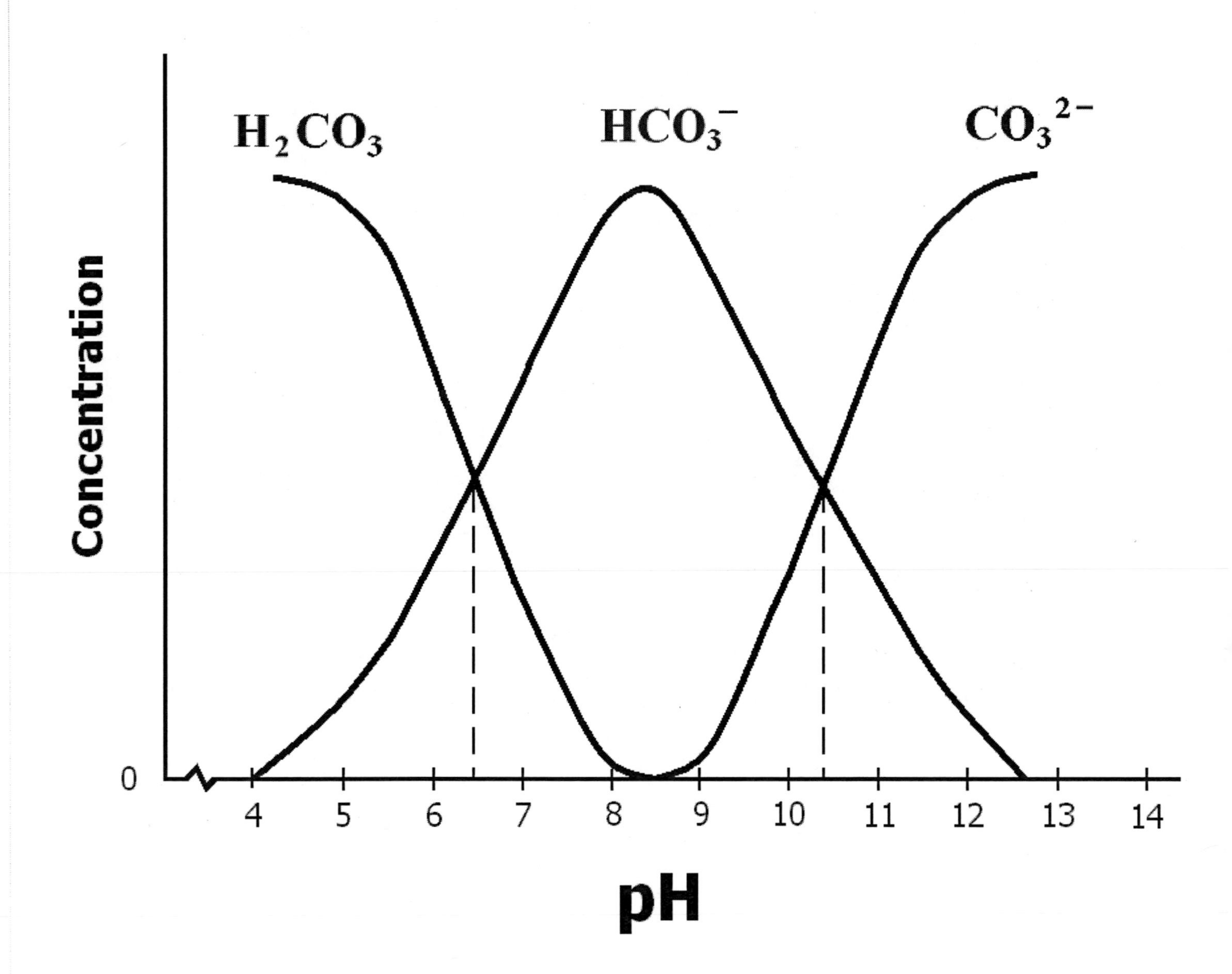

What would you mix with the following to make a buffer?

NaBrO **Ans:** HBrO

$HClO_2$ **Ans:** $NaClO_2$ (could use other spectators besides Na)

$H_2C_2O_4$ **Ans:** $NaHC_2O_4$ (choose an ion that differs by only 1 H^+)

NaH_2PO_4 (2 choices) **Ans:** H_3PO_4 or Na_2HPO_4

Equimolar pH of $H_3PO_4/H_2PO_4^-$ = 2.12

Equimolar pH of $H_2PO_4^-/HPO_4^{2-}$ = 7.21

Suppose you wish to make a buffer of pH 8.0 Choose an appropriate pair of substances.

Possibilities

- HBrO NaBrO
- HClO NaClO
- H_2S NaHS
- $H_2PO_4^-$ HPO_4^{2-} ⇒ (NaH_2PO_4 Na_2HPO_4)

[**Not** $H_3PO_4/H_2PO_4^-$ because H_3PO_4 would be the acid part and the buffer would have a pH around 2.12 (pK_{a1})]

- HSO_3^- SO_3^{2-} ⇒ ($NaHSO_3$ Na_2SO_3)

Mathematics of Buffers

(Homework #7)

Problem: Calculate the pH of 0.1 M $HC_2H_3O_2$ (aq) mixed with 0.5 M $NaC_2H_3O_2$ (aq).

↖spectator

Solution:

$$HC_2H_3O_2 \rightleftharpoons H^+ + C_2H_3O_2^-$$

	$HC_2H_3O_2$	H^+	$C_2H_3O_2^-$
I	.1	0	.5
C	$-x$	$+x$	$+x$
E	$.1 \not{+} \not{x}$	x	$.5 \not{+} \not{x}$

$$K_a = \frac{[H^+][C_2H_3O_2^-]}{[HC_2H_3O_2]} = \frac{(x)(.5)}{.1} = 1.8 \times 10^{-5}$$

$$\frac{\not{.1}}{\not{.5}} \cdot \frac{(x)(\not{.5})}{\not{.1}} = 1.8 \times 10^{-5} \cdot \frac{.1}{.5}$$

$$x = 3.6 \times 10^{-6}\ M = [H^+]$$

$$pH = -\log(3.6 \times 10^{-6}\ M) = \boxed{5.44}$$

Use the general form for acid dissociation:

$$HA \rightleftharpoons H^+ + A^-$$

$$K_a = \frac{[H^+][A^-]}{[HA]}$$

$$\log K_a = \log\left(\frac{[H^+][A^-]}{[HA]}\right)$$

$$\log K_a = \log\left([H^+] \cdot \frac{[A^-]}{[HA]}\right)$$

Property of logs

$\log(a \cdot b) = \log a + \log b$

$$\log K_a = \log[H^+] + \log\left(\frac{[A^-]}{[HA]}\right)$$

$$-\log K_a = -\log[H^+] - \log\left(\frac{[A^-]}{[HA]}\right)$$

$$pK_a = pH - \log\left(\frac{[A^-]}{[HA]}\right)$$

$$pH = pK_a + \log\left(\frac{[A^-]}{[HA]}\right)$$

Henderson-Hasselbach Equation (Buffer Equation)

$$pH = pK_a + \log\left(\frac{[A^-]}{[HA]}\right)$$

Base ($[A^-]$)

Acid ($[HA]$)

* For equimolar $[A^-] = [HA]$, $\frac{[A^-]}{[HA]} = 1$

$$pH = pK_a + \log 1$$
$$= pK_a + 0$$
$$pH = pK_a$$

* When $[A^-] > [HA]$ (more base than acid), $\frac{[A^-]}{[HA]} > 1$

$$pH = pK_a + \log(>1)$$
$$= pK_a + (+)$$
$$pH > pK_a$$

* When $[HA] > [A^-]$ (more acid than base), $\frac{[A^-]}{[HA]} < 1$

$$pH = pK_a + \log(<1)$$
$$= pK_a + (-)$$
$$pH < pK_a$$

Problem: Use the buffer equation to calculate the pH of the 0.1 M $HC_2H_3O_2$ / 0.5 M $NaC_2H_3O_2$ buffer.

WA ($HC_2H_3O_2$), WB ($NaC_2H_3O_2$)

$$pH = pK_a + \log\left(\frac{[C_2H_3O_2^-]}{[HC_2H_3O_2]}\right)$$
$$= 4.74 + \log\left(\frac{.5}{.1}\right)$$
$$= 4.74 + (0.7)$$
$$= 5.44$$

Problem: Calculate the pH of a buffer made by dissolving .0741 M $NH_4Cl_{(aq)}$ with .132 M $NH_{3(aq)}$

WA ↗ (on NH_4), ↖ spectator (on Cl), ↖ WB (on NH_3)

$$pH = pK_a + \log\left(\frac{[NH_3]}{[NH_4^+]}\right) = 9.25 + \log\left(\frac{.132}{.0741}\right)$$

$$= 9.25 + (.25) = \boxed{9.50}$$

(More base than acid, $pH > pK_a$)

Problem: Calculate the pH of a buffer made by dissolving .045 M $Na_2SO_{4(aq)}$ with .15 M $NaHSO_{4(aq)}$

spectator ↗ (on Na_2), ↖ WB (on SO_4), spectator ↗ (on Na), ↖ WA (on HSO_4)

$$pH = pK_a + \log\left(\frac{[SO_4^{2-}]}{[HSO_4^-]}\right) = 1.89 + \log\left(\frac{.045}{.15}\right)$$

$$= 1.89 + (-.52) = \boxed{1.37}$$

(More acid than base, $pH < pK_a$)

Adding a Strong Acid or a Strong Base to a Buffer

The purpose of a buffer is to resist pH changes.

In order to show how effective buffers are, we will:

1) Construct two solutions that have the same pH, one of which is a buffer and one of which is not.
2) Add the same # mol of strong acid to each solution.
3) Calculate the change in pH of each solution.

In the process, you will see how to calculate the pH change when a strong acid is added to a buffer.

Solution 1 (not a buffer)

1.8×10^{-5} M HCl(aq)

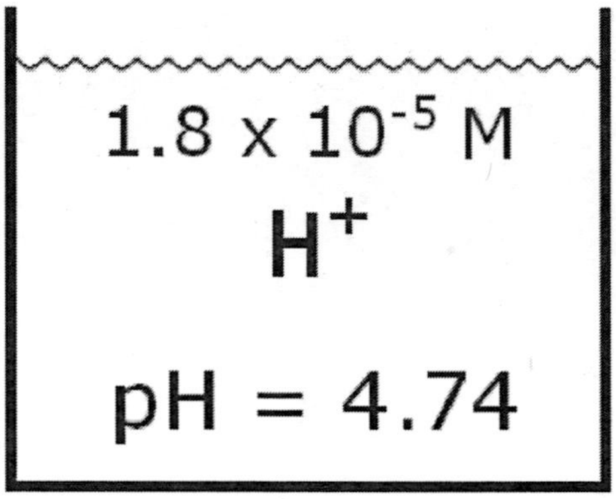

1.8×10^{-5} M

H^+

pH = 4.74

1.0 L

Starting pH $= -\log\left(1.8 \times 10^{-5}\right)$

$= 4.74$

Solution 2 (Acetate Buffer)

0.1 M $HC_2H_3O_2$ / 0.1 M $NaC_2H_3O_2$

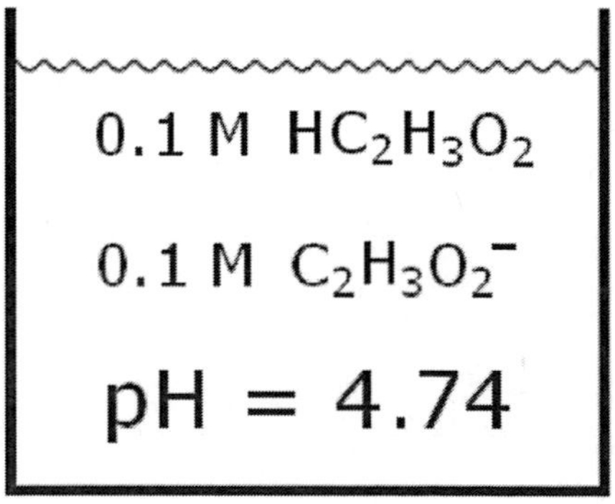

0.1 M $HC_2H_3O_2$

0.1 M $C_2H_3O_2^-$

pH = 4.74

1.0 L

Starting pH = pK_a of $HC_2H_3O_2$

$= 4.74$

What is the new pH if 1.0 mL of 12 M HCl (aq) is added to each solution?

$$\# \text{ mol } H^+ \text{ added} = M_{HCl} \times L_{HCl}$$

$$= 12 \frac{\text{mol}}{\text{L}} \times .001 \text{ L}$$

$$= .012 \text{ mol } H^+ \text{ added}$$

(1 mL is too small an amount to change significantly the 1.0 L volume of each solution.)

Solution 1 (not a buffer)

1.8×10^{-5} M HCl(aq)

If the volume is restricted to 1.0 L, #mol and M are interchangable:

#mol = M x #L = M x 1.0

#mol = M

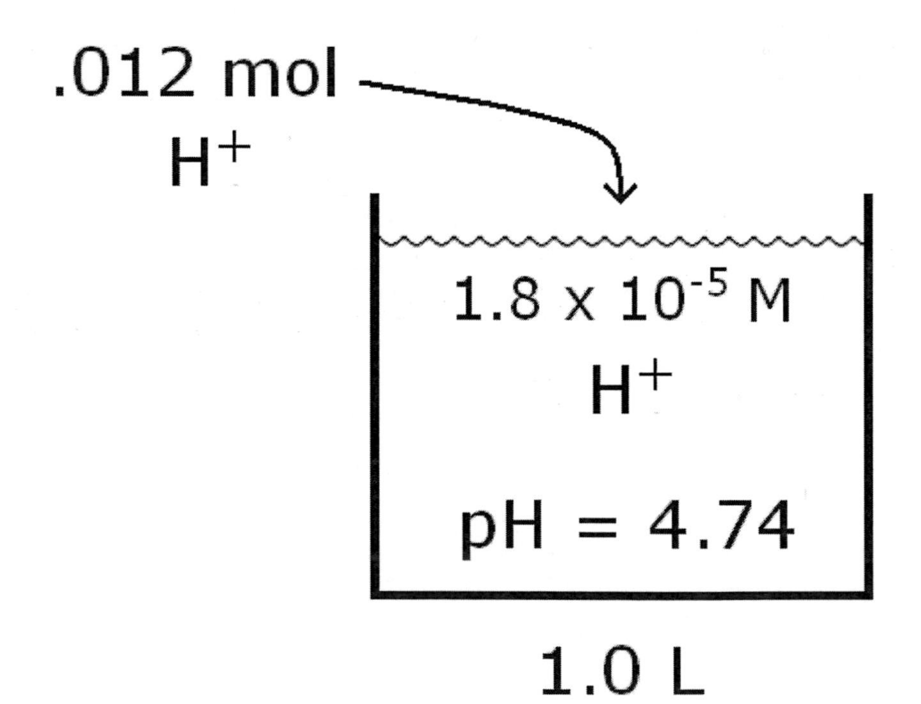

Starting pH = $-\log\left(1.8 \times 10^{-5}\right)$

= 4.74

$\#$mol H^+ after adding $= 1.8 \times 10^{-5} + .012$

$= .012018$ mol H^+

pH after adding = -log (.012018) = **1.92**

pH before	:	4.74
pH after	:	1.92
Change	:	2.82 units

$H^+ \uparrow$ almost 10^3 (1000) x

pH $\downarrow$ almost 3 units

Effect: Since there was no buffer to "soak up" H^+, adding the HCl just added more H^+.

Solution 2 (Acetate Buffer)

$0.1\ M\ HC_2H_3O_2 / 0.1\ M\ NaC_2H_3O_2$

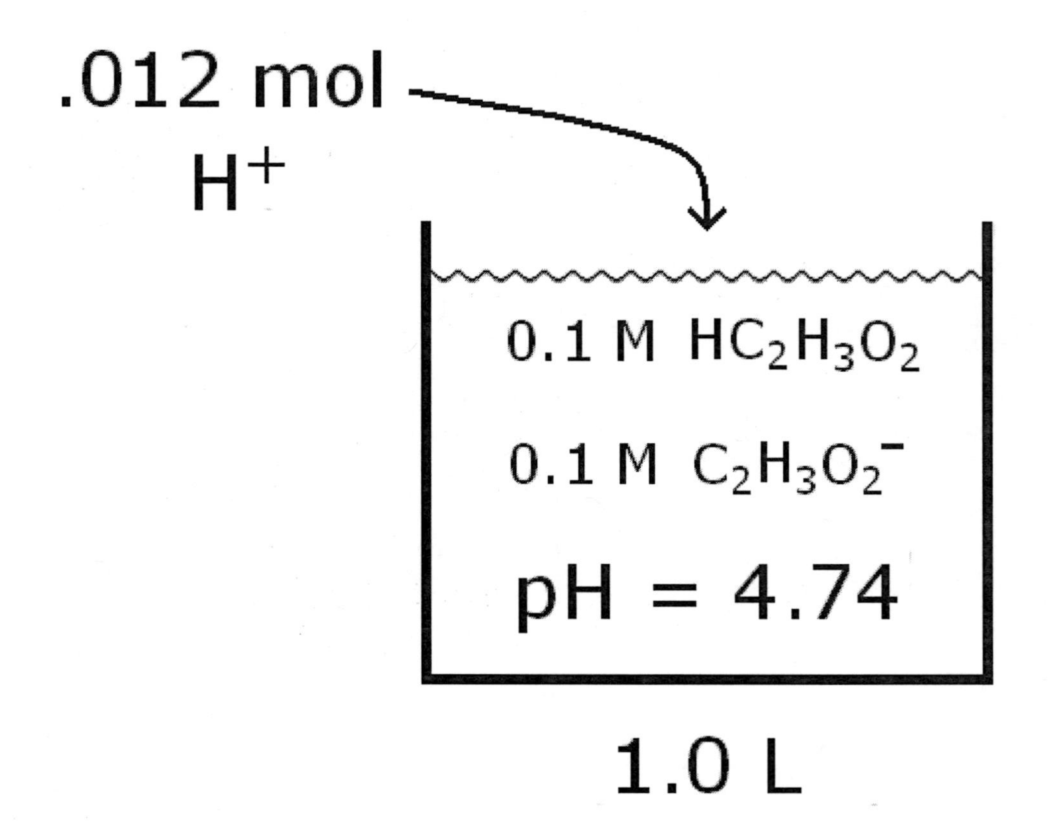

Starting pH = pK_a of $HC_2H_3O_2$

= 4.74

Net Ionic for the Buffer Neutralizing H^+

$$H^+ + C_2H_3O_2^- \longrightarrow HC_2H_3O_2$$

	H^+	$C_2H_3O_2^-$	$HC_2H_3O_2$
start		0.1	0.1
add	.012		
end		$0.1 - .012 = .088$ mol	$0.1 + .012 = .112$ mol

$$pH = pK_a + \log\left(\frac{[C_2H_3O_2^-]}{[HC_2H_3O_2]}\right)$$

$$= 4.74 + \log\left(\frac{.088}{.112}\right)$$

$$= 4.74 + (-.10) = 4.64$$

pH before: 4.74

pH after : 4.64

Change : 0.10 unit

Effect: The buffer "soaked up" the added H^+, so the pH hardly changed.

When adding H^+ (strong acid) to a buffer

1) Add to the acid, subtract from the base.
2) Plug into the Buffer Equation.

When adding OH^- (strong base) to a buffer

1) Add to the base, subtract from the acid.
2) Plug into the Buffer Equation.

Problem: A buffer contains 0.25 M $NH_4Cl(aq)$ and 0.12 M $NH_3(aq)$ in a volume of 1.0 L. Calculate the original pH; then calculate the new pH after 2.0 g of NaOH(s) is dissolved in the buffer.

Solution: original pH $= pK_a + \log\left(\frac{[NH_3]}{[NH_4^+]}\right)$

$$= 9.25 + \log\left(\frac{.12}{.25}\right)$$

$$= 9.25 + (-.32) = \boxed{8.93}$$

$$2.0\ \cancel{g}\ NaOH \times \frac{1\ mol}{40.0\ \cancel{g}} = \boxed{.05\ mol\ OH^-}$$

40.0 g ← **MM of NaOH**

Na^+ is a spectator in the reaction, but it contributes to the mass of the solid.

.25 mol NH_4^+

.12 mol NH_3

Net Ionic for the Buffer Neutralizing OH^-

$$OH^- + NH_4^+ \longrightarrow NH_3 + H_2O$$

	OH^-	NH_4^+	NH_3
start		.25	.12
add	.05		
end		.25 − .05 = (.20 mol)	0.12 + .05 = (.17 mol)

$$pH = pK_a + \log\left(\frac{[NH_3]}{[NH_4^+]}\right)$$

$$= 9.25 + \log\left(\frac{.17}{.20}\right)$$

$$= 9.25 + (-.07) = \boxed{9.18}$$

pH before : 8.93
pH after : 9.18

Change : 0.25 unit

If you start with a pH 8.93 solution that is not a buffer ($[OH^-] = 8.5 \times 10^{-6}$ M) and add .05 mol OH^-, the final concentration of OH^- is $8.5 \times 10^{-6} + .05 = .0500085$ M

pOH = −log (.00500085) = 1.3, pH = 12.7

change of pH = 12.7 − 8.93 = (3.77)

* .05 mol OH^- is enough to change the pH almost 4 units.

* pH only changes .25 unit with buffer.

Constructing a Buffer of a Given pH

Suppose an experiment requires a pH 10.0 buffer.
If a buffer of NH_4Cl/NH_3 is used:

a) What $\frac{\text{base}}{\text{acid}}$ ratio will give pH 10.0?

b) What $[NH_4^+]$ (that is, NH_4Cl), is needed to give a pH 10.0 buffer when mixed with 0.15 M $NH_3(aq)$?

Solution:

a) $$pH = pK_a + \log\left(\frac{\text{base}}{\text{acid}}\right)$$

$$10.0 = 9.25 + \log\left(\frac{[NH_3]}{[NH_4^+]}\right)$$
$$-9.25 \qquad -9.25$$

$$\log\left(\frac{[NH_3]}{[NH_4^+]}\right) = .75$$

$$\cancel{\text{INV log}}\left[\cancel{\log}\left(\frac{[NH_3]}{[NH_4^+]}\right)\right] = \text{INV log}\ (.75)$$

$$\frac{[NH_3]}{[NH_4^+]} = \boxed{5.62}$$

Any time the concentrations are in this ratio, the pH will be 10.0

b) $$\frac{.15}{[NH_4^+]} = 5.62$$

$$\cancel{[NH_4^+]} \times \frac{.15}{\cancel{[NH_4^+]}} = 5.62 \times [NH_4^+]$$

$$5.62 \times [NH_4^+] = .15 \Rightarrow \frac{\cancel{5.62} \times [NH_4^+]}{\cancel{5.62}} = \frac{.15}{5.62}$$

$$[NH_4^+] = \boxed{.027\ M}$$

A buffer made by dissolving .15 M $NH_3(aq)$ and .027 M $NH_4Cl(aq)$ should have a pH of 10.0

- Usually, the pH will come out slightly lower.
- Possibly because, when $CO_2(g)$ dissolves in water, it forms the weak acid $H_2CO_3(aq)$.

$$CO_2(g) + H_2O(\ell) \rightleftharpoons H_2CO_3(aq)$$

Alternate Way of Making Buffers

- Start with a solution of the weak acid or weak base.
- Monitor pH with a pH meter.
- Add strong acid (such as HCl) if you start with the weak base, or add a strong base (such as NaOH) if you start with the weak acid.
- Stop when the pH reaches the desired value.

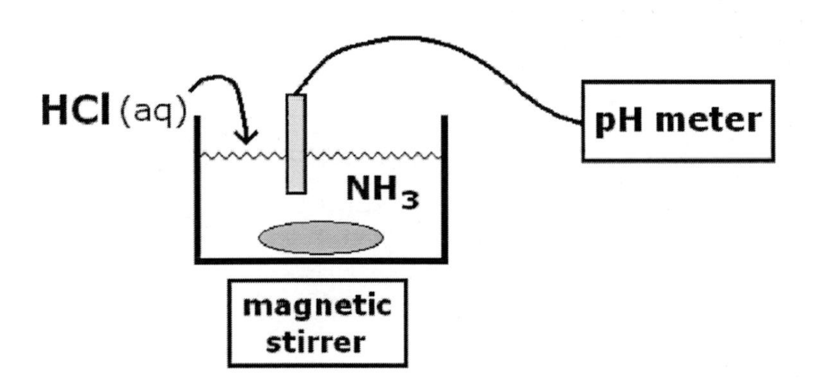

1) Start with only NH_3 (aq) $\longrightarrow$ pH reads $\approx$ 11.
2) Slowly add HCl. This lowers the pH and produces NH_4^+

$$H^+ + NH_3 \longrightarrow NH_4^+$$

3) Stop at pH 10.0

I call this process

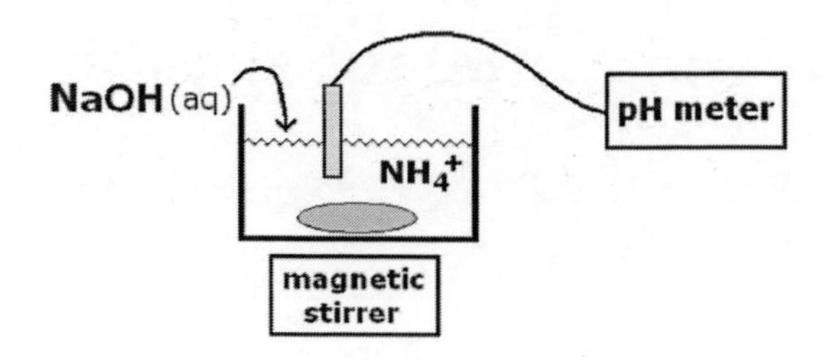

1) Start with only $NH_4^+(aq) \longrightarrow$ pH reads ≈ 5.
2) Slowly add NaOH. This raises the pH and produces NH_3.

$$OH^- + NH_4^+ \longrightarrow NH_3 + H_2O$$

3) Stop at pH 10.0

I call this process

NH_4^+ with slowly added NaOH

Combinations that work for making buffers

WB with slowly added SA (HCl)

WA with slowly added SB (NaOH)

Problem:

Suppose an experiment requires a pH 3.0 buffer. If a buffer of $HCHO_2$ / $NaCHO_2$ is used:

a) What $\frac{\text{base}}{\text{acid}}$ ratio will give pH 3.0?

b) What $[CHO_2^-]$ (that is, $NaCHO_2$) is needed to give a pH 3.0 buffer when mixed with 0.6 M $HCHO_2(aq)$?

Solution:

$$pH = pK_a + \log\left(\frac{\text{base}}{\text{acid}}\right)$$

$$\begin{array}{l} 3.0 \\ -3.77 \end{array} = \begin{array}{l} \cancel{3.77} \\ \cancel{-3.77} \end{array} + \log\left(\frac{[CHO_2^-]}{[HCHO_2]}\right)$$

$$\log\left(\frac{[CHO_2^-]}{[HCHO_2]}\right) = -.77$$

$$\cancel{\underset{\log}{\text{INV}}}\left[\cancel{\log}\left(\frac{[CHO_2^-]}{[HCHO_2]}\right)\right] = \underset{\log}{\text{INV}}(-.77)$$

$$\frac{[CHO_2^-]}{[HCHO_2]} = \textcircled{.17}$$

Any time the concentrations are in this ratio, the pH will be 3.0

b) $$\frac{[CHO_2^-]}{.6} = .17$$

$$\cancel{.6} \cdot \frac{[CHO_2^-]}{\cancel{.6}} = .17 \cdot .6$$

$$[CHO_2^-] = \boxed{0.10\ M}$$

A buffer made by dissolving 0.6 M $HCHO_2(aq)$ and 0.10 M $NaCHO_2(aq)$ should have pH 3.0

Alternates:

Buffer could be made from:

$NaCHO_2$ with slowly added HCl

$HCHO_2$ with slowly added NaOH

Will the following produce a buffer?

a) $HClO_2$ with slowly added HCl **NO.** *WA* *SA*

b) NaCN with slowly added NaOH **NO.** *WB* *SB*

c) NH_3 with slowly added NaOH **NO.** *WB* *SB*

d) $HC_2H_3O_2$ with slowly added NaOH **YES.** *WA* *SB*

e) NaClO with slowly added HCl **YES.** *WB* *SA*

Buffer Capacity = the amount of strong acid or strong base that can be added to a buffer without destroying the buffering ability.

Suppose you start with a buffer containing 0.1 mol $HC_2H_3O_2(aq)$ and 0.1 mol $NaC_2H_3O_2(aq)$ in 1.0 L. The net ionics for neutralizing H^+ and OH^- are:

$$H^+ + C_2H_3O_2^- \longrightarrow HC_2H_3O_2$$

$$OH^- + HC_2H_3O_2 \longrightarrow C_2H_3O_2^- + H_2O$$

If you add .3 mol of H^+, you destroy all buffering ability because you use up all the $C_2H_3O_2^-$, and there is none left to neutralize the excess .2 mol H^+.

The change in pH as H^+ or OH^- is added can be graphed.

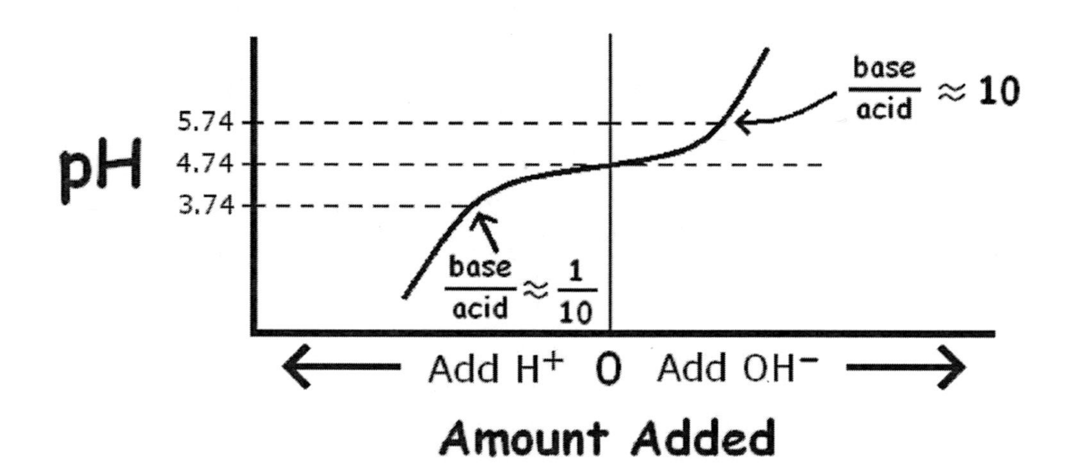

Buffering Range

$\frac{\text{base}}{\text{acid}} = 10 \qquad pH = pK_a + \log 10 = pK_a + 1$

$\frac{\text{base}}{\text{acid}} = \frac{1}{10} \qquad pH = pK_a + \log .1 = pK_a - 1$

$$\boxed{pH = pK_a \pm 1}$$

How To Increase Buffer Capacity

1) Use higher [weak acid] and [weak base]
   More H^+ and OH^- can be neutralized.

2) Stay as close to equimolar as possible.
   pH changes least on the graph at
   the point where [acid] = [conj. base]
   Choose an acid with a pK_a as close to
   the desired pH as possible.

Problems Involving K_{sp} Part 1

(Homework #8)

Review of K_{sp} Problems

Writing K_{sp} Expressions

$$Ag_2CO_3(s) \rightleftharpoons 2\ Ag^+(aq) + CO_3^{2-}(aq)$$

$$K_{sp} = [Ag^+]^2\,[CO_3^{2-}] = 8.2 \times 10^{-12}$$

$$Ag_2SO_4(s) \rightleftharpoons 2\ Ag^+(aq) + SO_4^{2-}(aq)$$

$$K_{sp} = [Ag^+]^2\,[SO_4^{2-}] = 1.6 \times 10^{-5}$$

$Ag_2SO_4(s)$ is more soluble than $Ag_2CO_3(s)$.

Larger K_{sp} = more soluble
(If exponents in the K_{sp} expression are identical.)

"Will a ppt form?" problems

Given: concentrations of the two ions.

Asked: Will a ppt form?

Solved: by calculating **Q** and comparing it to K_{sp}
(**Q** has same math expression as K_{sp}, but with ***initial*** concentrations plugged in)

$Q < K_{sp}$ no ppt

$Q > K_{sp}$ ppt forms

Solubility Problems

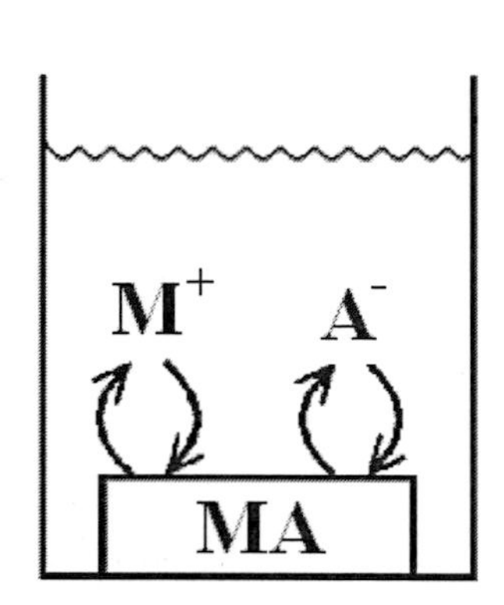

(I) Calculate K_{sp} from Solubility

(II) Calculate Solubility from K_{sp}

Salt "puts ions in" by dissolving.

Multiply by coefficients

Precipitation Problems

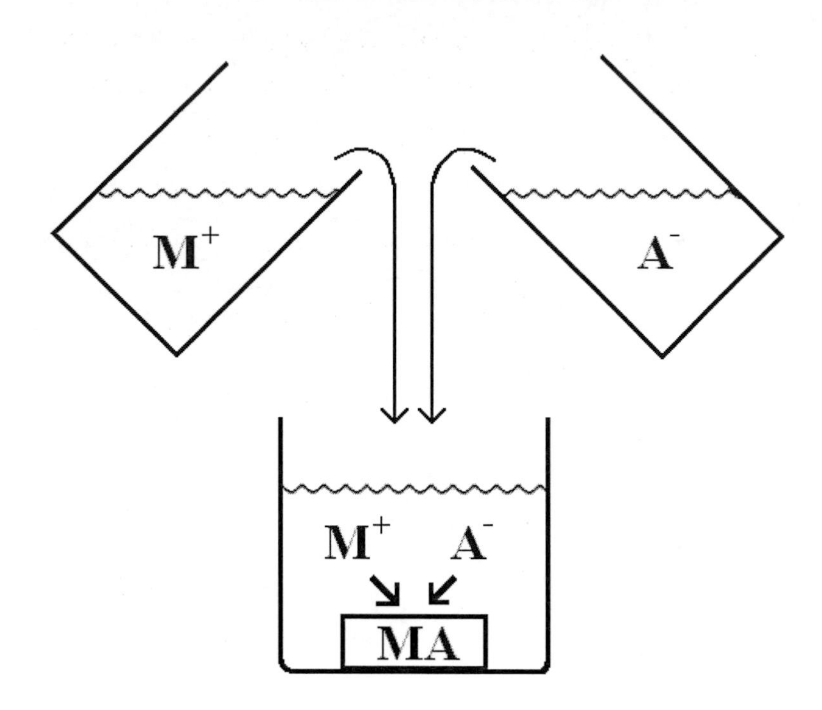

(III) Will a ppt form?

(IV) Minimum concentration of an ion needed to just start precipitation

(V) Fractional Precipitation

Experimenter "puts ions in" and chooses concentrations

Do Not Multiply by coefficients

(I) Calculate K_{sp} from solubility

Solubility = amount that will dissolve in a given volume of water.

$$\left(\frac{g}{L}\ ;\ \frac{mol}{L}\ \text{or}\ M\right)$$

The solubility of $Ag_2CrO_4(s)$ is $2.59 \times 10^{-2}\ \frac{g}{L}$. What is the value of K_{sp}?

$$Ag_2CrO_4(s) \rightleftharpoons 2\,Ag^+(aq) + CrO_4^{2-}(aq)$$

	$Ag_2CrO_4(s)$	$2\,Ag^+(aq)$	$CrO_4^{2-}(aq)$
I	solid	0	0
C	$-x$	$+2x$	$+x$
E	less	$2x$	x

x is the solubility in $\frac{mol}{L}$

$$K_{sp} = [Ag^+]^2[CrO_4^{2-}]$$

must be in mol/L (M)

$$2.59 \times 10^{-2}\ \frac{g}{L} \times \frac{1\ mol}{331.74\ g} = 7.81 \times 10^{-5}\ \frac{mol}{L}$$

MM of Ag_2CrO_4

$$[Ag^+] = 2x = 2 \times 7.81 \times 10^{-5}\ M = 1.56 \times 10^{-4}\ M$$

$$[CrO_4^{2-}] = x = 7.81 \times 10^{-5}\ M$$

plug these into the K_{sp} expression

$$K_{sp} = [Ag^+]^2[CrO_4^{2-}]$$
$$= (1.56 \times 10^{-4})^2 \times (7.81 \times 10^{-5})$$
$$= 1.9 \times 10^{-12}$$

Final answer
Same as in **Table 1**

Multiply $[Ag^+]$ by 2 because every **one** Ag_2CrO_4 dissolves to give **two** Ag^+.

Square $[Ag^+]$ because the exponent is part of the "definition" of K_{sp}.

(II) Calculate solubility from K_{sp}

The K_{sp} of $Ca_3(PO_4)_2$ is 1×10^{-33}.
What is the solubility $\left(\text{in } \frac{\text{mol}}{\text{L}} \text{ and } \frac{\text{g}}{\text{L}}\right)$?

$$Ca_3(PO_4)_2\,(s) \rightleftharpoons 3\,Ca^{2+}(aq) + 2\,PO_4^{3-}(aq)$$

	$Ca_3(PO_4)_2\,(s)$	$3\,Ca^{2+}(aq)$	$2\,PO_4^{3-}(aq)$
I	solid	0	0
C	$-x$	$+3x$	$+2x$
E	less	$3x$	$2x$

$$K_{sp} = [Ca^{2+}]^3[PO_4^{3-}]^2$$

$$1 \times 10^{-33} = (3x)^3(2x)^2$$

$$1 \times 10^{-33} = 3^3 \cdot x^3 \cdot 2^2 \cdot x^2$$

$$1 \times 10^{-33} = 27 \cdot x^3 \cdot 4 \cdot x^2$$

$$\frac{1 \times 10^{-33}}{108} = \frac{\cancel{108} \cdot x^5}{\cancel{108}}$$

$$\sqrt[5]{x^5} = \sqrt[5]{9.26 \times 10^{-36}}$$

MM of $Ca_3(PO_4)_2$

$$x = 9.85 \times 10^{-8} \frac{\cancel{mol}}{L} \times \frac{310.18 \text{ g}}{1 \cancel{mol}}$$

$$= 3.06 \times 10^{-5} \frac{g}{L} = 30.6 \times 10^{-6} \frac{g}{L} \text{ or } 30.6 \frac{\mu g}{L}$$

How to determine roots

Graphing calculator

5 MATH $\sqrt[x]{\ }$ ENTER 9.26 EE (–) 36 ENTER

OR

$$\sqrt{x} = x^{\frac{1}{2}} = x^{.5}$$

$$\sqrt[3]{x} = x^{\frac{1}{3}} = x^{.3333...}$$

$$\sqrt[4]{x} = x^{\frac{1}{4}} = x^{.25}$$

$$\sqrt[5]{x} = x^{\frac{1}{5}} = x^{.2}$$

9.26 EE (–) 36 ^ (1/5) *or* 9.26 EE (–) 36 ^ .2

Regular Calculator

9.26 EE **or** EXP 36 +/– y^x *or* x^y .2 =

(May have $\sqrt[x]{y}$ key, but check whether to enter the root or the number itself first.)

Review of "Will a ppt form?" problems

(Lecture 2, HW 2, Quiz 2)

Will a ppt of $Ag_3PO_4(s)$ form if you mix 1.3×10^{-4} M $AgNO_3(aq)$ with 9.7×10^{-3} M $K_3PO_4(aq)$?

spectator (NO_3) spectator (K_3)

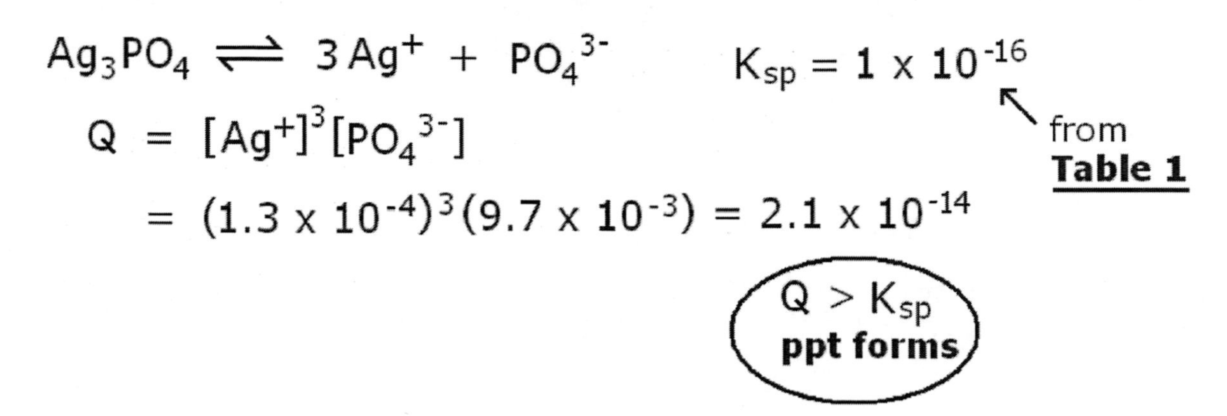

Why is 1.3×10^{-4} M for Ag^+ not multiplied by 3 before plugging into Q?

Answer: The experimenter **chose the amount** of $AgNO_3(aq)$. Any amount that is soluble could have been used. The person has **control** over how much is added.

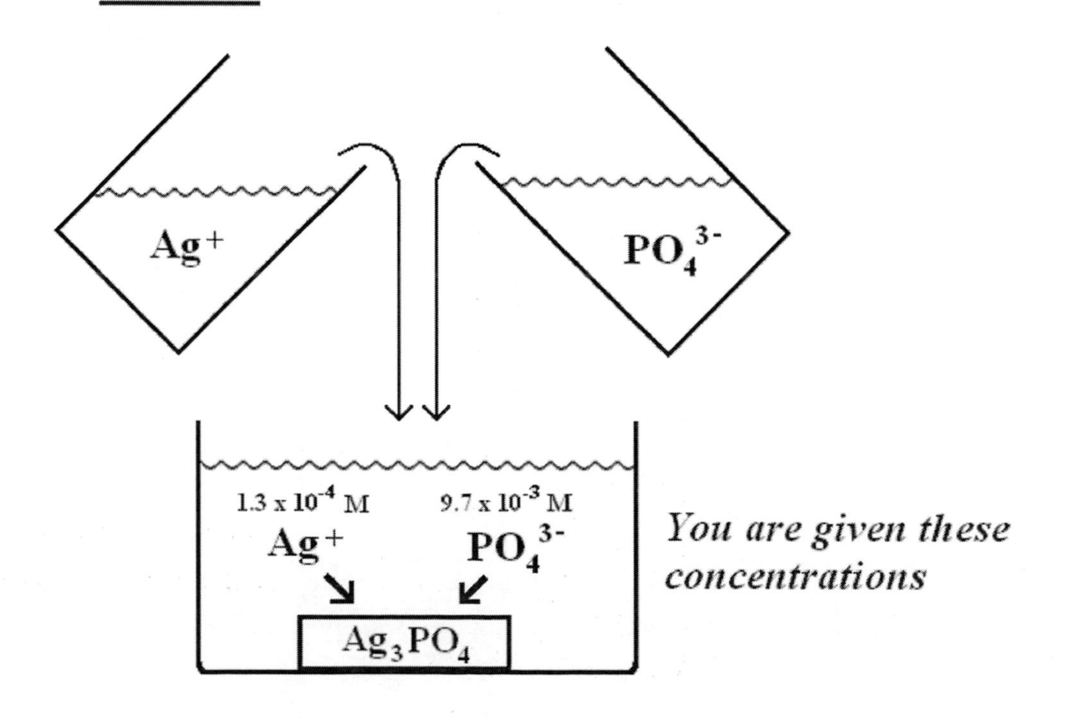

"Will a ppt form?" problems can involve pH if the ppt has OH^- in it.

Will a ppt of $Fe(OH)_3(s)$ form in a 0.1 M $Fe(NO_3)_3(aq)$ solution at pH 5.4?

$$Fe(OH)_3(s) \rightleftharpoons Fe^{3+} + 3\,OH^- \qquad K_{sp} = 6 \times 10^{-38}$$

$$Q = [Fe^{3+}][OH^-]^3$$

$[Fe^{3+}]$: Given in problem (.1 M)

$[OH^-]$: $pOH = 14 - 5.4 = 8.6$

$[OH^-] = \text{2nd log}(-8.6)$

$= 2.51 \times 10^{-9}$ M

PLUG THESE IN:

$$Q = (.1)(2.51 \times 10^{-9})^3$$

$$= 1.58 \times 10^{-27}$$

(Do not multiply by 3; experimenter adjusts pH)

$Q > K_{sp}$ **ppt forms**

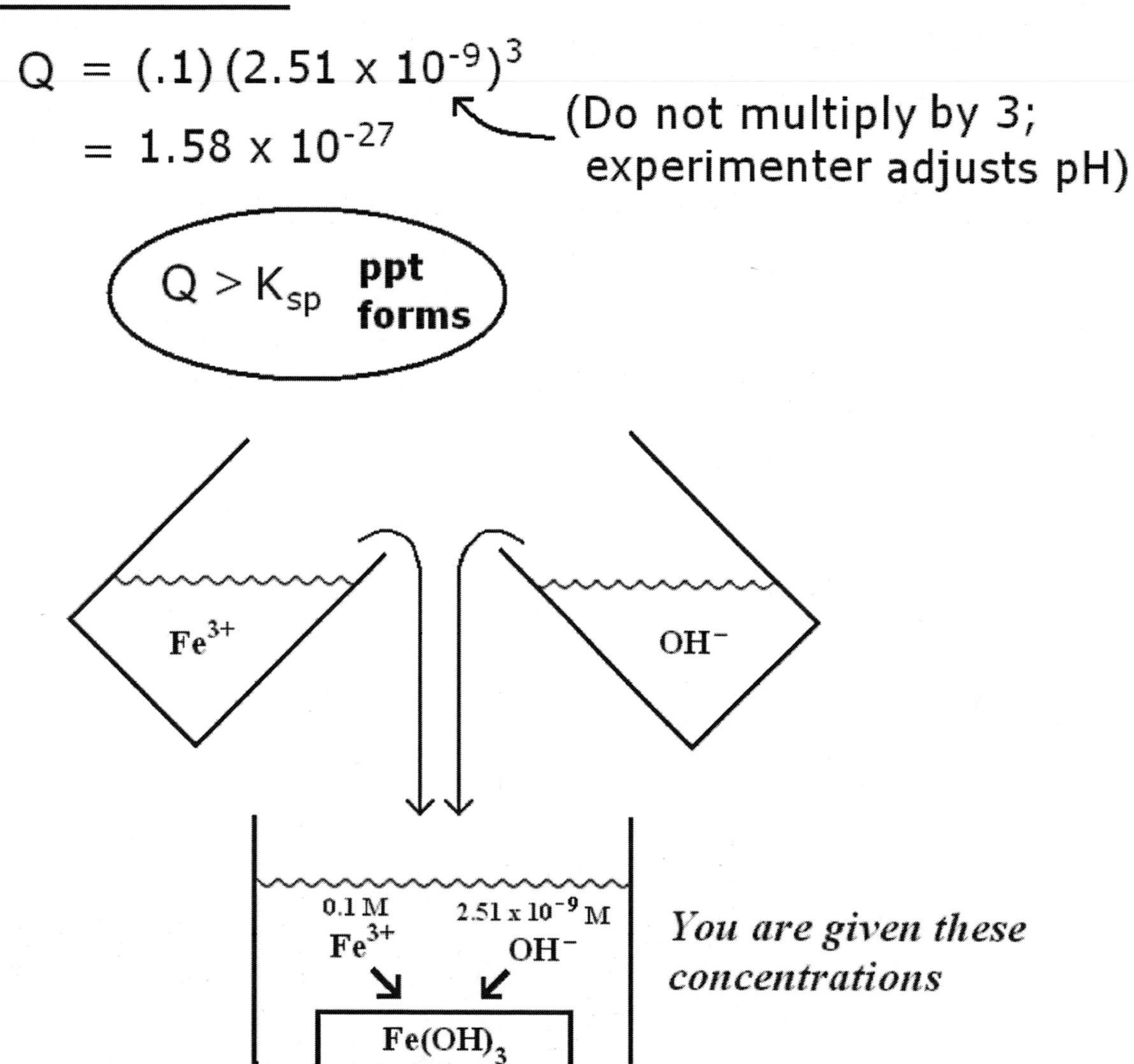

You are given these concentrations

(III) Will a ppt form? (with dilution)

Will a ppt of $CaCO_3(s)$ form if you mix 25 mL of 0.1 M $Ca(NO_3)_2(aq)$ with 75 mL of 3.4×10^{-3} M $Na_2CO_3(aq)$?

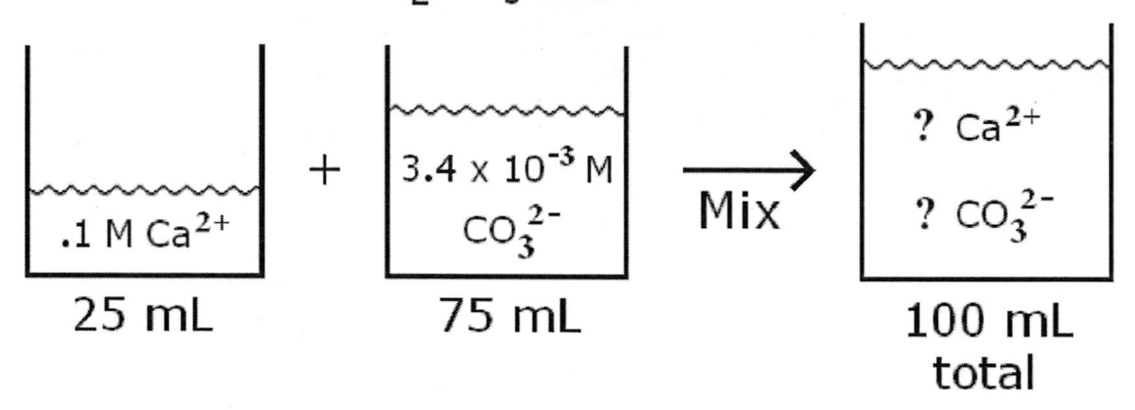

$$CaCO_3(s) \rightleftharpoons Ca^{2+}(aq) + CO_3^{2-}(aq) \quad K_{sp} = 1.7 \times 10^{-8}$$

$$Q = [Ca^{2+}][CO_3^{2-}]$$

Neither ion has the same concentration as before mixing – they are diluted.

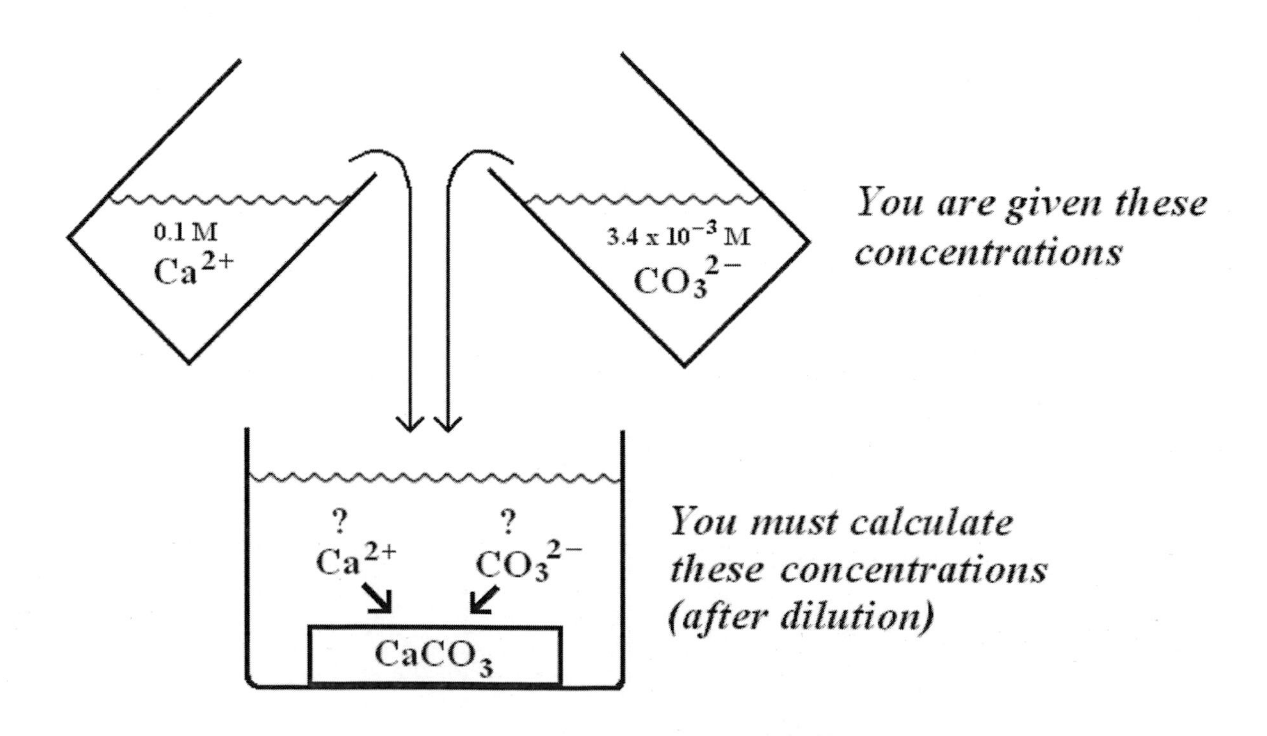

The Dilution Equation

What is the new concentration of NaCl(aq) if 1 L of 0.6 M solution is diluted by adding 4 L of water?

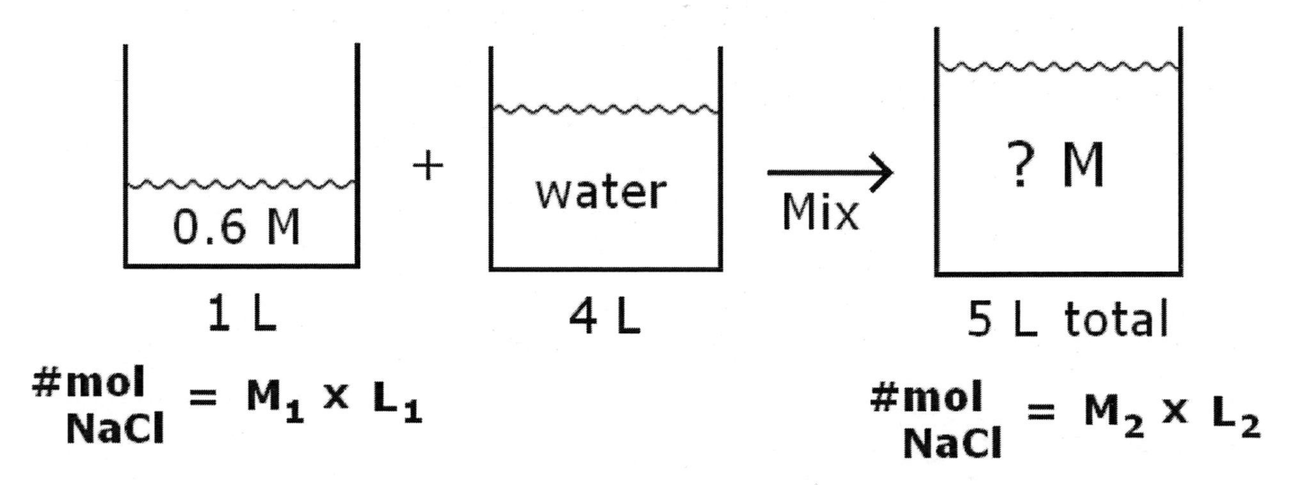

#mol NaCl $= M_1 \times L_1$

#mol NaCl $= M_2 \times L_2$

Since #mol NaCl does not change when water is added,

$$M_1 \times L_1 = M_2 \times L_2$$

$$\frac{.6\ M \times 1\ L}{5\ L} = \frac{M_2 \times 5\ L}{5\ L}$$

Use the **total** volume, not just the amount of water added.

$$.12\ M = M_2$$

Since volumes cancel, you can use any volume units, as long as they are the same. For example, you do not have to convert mL to L.

Final form of the dilution equation: $M_1V_1 = M_2V_2$

Back to the Original Problem

Before plugging in values for $[Ca^{2+}]$ and $[CO_3^{2-}]$, apply the dilution equation to each ion separately.

Ca^{2+}

$$M_1V_1 = M_2V_2$$

$$\frac{.1\ M \times 25\ \cancel{mL}}{100\ \cancel{mL}} = \frac{M_{Ca^{2+}} \times \cancel{100\ mL}}{\cancel{100\ mL}}$$

$$.025\ M = M_{Ca^{2+}}$$

CO_3^{2-}

$$M_1V_1 = M_2V_2$$

$$\frac{3.4 \times 10^{-3}\ M \times 75\ \cancel{mL}}{100\ \cancel{mL}} = \frac{M_{CO_3^{2-}} \times \cancel{100\ mL}}{\cancel{100\ mL}}$$

$$2.55 \times 10^{-3}\ M = M_{CO_3^{2-}}$$

$$CaCO_3(s) \rightleftharpoons Ca^{2+}(aq) + CO_3^{2-}(aq) \qquad K_{sp} = 1.7 \times 10^{-8}$$

$$Q = [Ca^{2+}][CO_3^{2-}]$$

$$= (.025)(2.55 \times 10^{-3}) = 6.4 \times 10^{-5}$$

$Q > K_{sp}$ ppt forms

Additional problem including dilution

Will a ppt of $Ag_2C_2O_4$(s) form if you mix 1.5 mL of 1.48×10^{-2} M $AgNO_3$ (aq) with 10.7 mL of 4.61×10^{-4} M $Na_2C_2O_4$(aq)?

$$Ag_2C_2O_4(s) \rightleftharpoons 2Ag^+(aq) + C_2O_4^{2-}(aq) \qquad K_{sp} = 3.5 \times 10^{-11}$$

$$Q = [Ag^+]^2[C_2O_4^{2-}]$$

1.48×10^{-2} M Ag^+

1.5 mL

+

4.61×10^{-4} M $C_2O_4^{2-}$

10.7 mL

Mix

? Ag^+

? $C_2O_4^{2-}$

12.2 mL total

Ag^+

$$M_1V_1 = M_2V_2$$

$$\frac{1.48 \times 10^{-2}\ M \times 1.5\ mL}{12.2\ mL} = \frac{M_{Ag+} \times 12.2\ mL}{12.2\ mL}$$

$$1.82 \times 10^{-3}\ M = M_{Ag+}$$

$C_2O_4^{2-}$

$$M_1V_1 = M_2V_2$$

$$\frac{4.61 \times 10^{-4}\ M \times 10.7\ mL}{12.2\ mL} = \frac{M_{C_2O_4^{2-}} \times 12.2\ mL}{12.2\ mL}$$

$$4.04 \times 10^{-4}\ M = M_{C_2O_4^{2-}}$$

$$Ag_2C_2O_4(s) \rightleftharpoons 2\,Ag^+(aq) + C_2O_4^{2-}(aq) \qquad K_{sp} = 3.5 \times 10^{-11}$$

$$Q = [Ag^+]^2[C_2O_4^{2-}]$$

$$= (1.82 \times 10^{-3})^2(4.04 \times 10^{-4}) = 1.34 \times 10^{-9}$$

$Q > K_{sp}$ ppt forms

(IV) Minimum conc. of an ion needed to just start precipitation

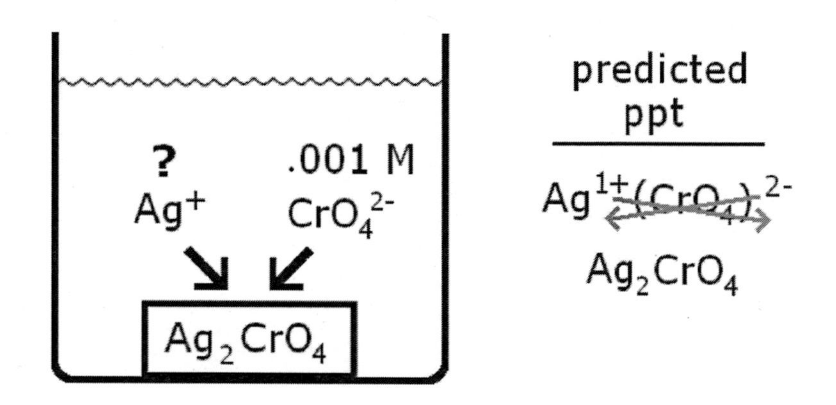

Even "insoluble" salts have a little solubility. In order for a ppt to form, the conc. of ions must still be larger than the "cutoff" value.

$Q < K_{sp}$ **no ppt**

$Q > K_{sp}$ **ppt forms**

We want to determine when $Q = K_{sp}$ and then use a larger amount than this minimum value.

Since this is a "mixing" problem (the experimenter adds the ions), the ions **DO NOT** come from a salt dissolving, so **DO NOT** multiply conc. by coefficients.

Problem: What is the minimum $[Ag^+]$ needed to just begin precipitating $Ag_2CrO_4(s)$ from a .001 M $CrO_4^{2-}(aq)$ solution?

$$Ag_2CrO_4(s) \rightleftharpoons 2Ag^+(aq) + CrO_4^{2-}(aq)$$

$$Q = [Ag^+]^2[CrO_4^{2-}]$$

set $Q = K_{sp}$

$$\frac{1.9 \times 10^{-12}}{.001} = \frac{[Ag^+]^2 \cancel{(.001)}}{\cancel{.001}}$$

$$\sqrt{[Ag^+]^2} = \sqrt{1.9 \times 10^{-9}}$$

$$[Ag^+] = 4.36 \times 10^{-5}\ M$$

A question that determines whether you really understand what this number means (<u>without</u> doing any further calculating) is:

Will a ppt form if you use .02 M (2×10^{-2} M) $Ag^+(aq)$?

Answer: **Yes.** 2×10^{-2} M is **larger** than the **minimum** amount (4.36×10^{-5} M) needed.

Minimum concentration problem including pH

What pH is needed to just begin precipitating $Cu(OH)_2(s)$ from a 0.02 M $Cu^{2+}(aq)$ solution?

Solution:

Since pH and $[OH^-]$ are interchangable, first calculate $[OH^-]$ required and then convert it to pH.

$$Cu(OH)_2(s) \rightleftharpoons Cu^{2+}(aq) + 2\,OH^-(aq)$$

$$Q = [Cu^{2+}][OH^-]^2$$

set $Q = K_{sp}$ →

$$1.6 \times 10^{-19} = (0.02)[OH^-]^2$$

$$\frac{1.6 \times 10^{-19}}{0.02} = \frac{\cancel{(0.02)}[OH^-]^2}{\cancel{0.02}}$$

$$[OH^-]^2 = 8 \times 10^{-18}$$

$$\sqrt{[OH^-]^2} = \sqrt{8 \times 10^{-18}}$$

$$[OH^-] = 2.83 \times 10^{-9}\text{ M}$$

$$pOH = -\log(2.83 \times 10^{-9}) = 8.55$$

$$pH = 14 - 8.55 = \boxed{5.45}$$

0.02 M Cu^{2+} ↘ $Cu(OH)_2$ ↙ ? OH^-

Will a ppt form at pH 6?

Answer: **Yes.** At pH 6, $[OH^-]$ is larger (more basic) than at pH 5.45

Problems Involving K_{sp} Part 2

(Homework #9)

(V) Fractional Precipitation

This technique allows separation of one "fraction" of a sample from another based on differences in solubility.

Suppose you have a solution containing 0.1 M $Ba^{2+}(aq)$ and 0.1 M $Sr^{2+}(aq)$. You wish to separate these ions by adding CrO_4^{2-}, which forms ppts of $BaCrO_4(s)$ **[K_{sp} = 8.5 x 10^{-11}]** and $SrCrO_4(s)$ **[K_{sp} = 3.6 x 10^{-5}]**.

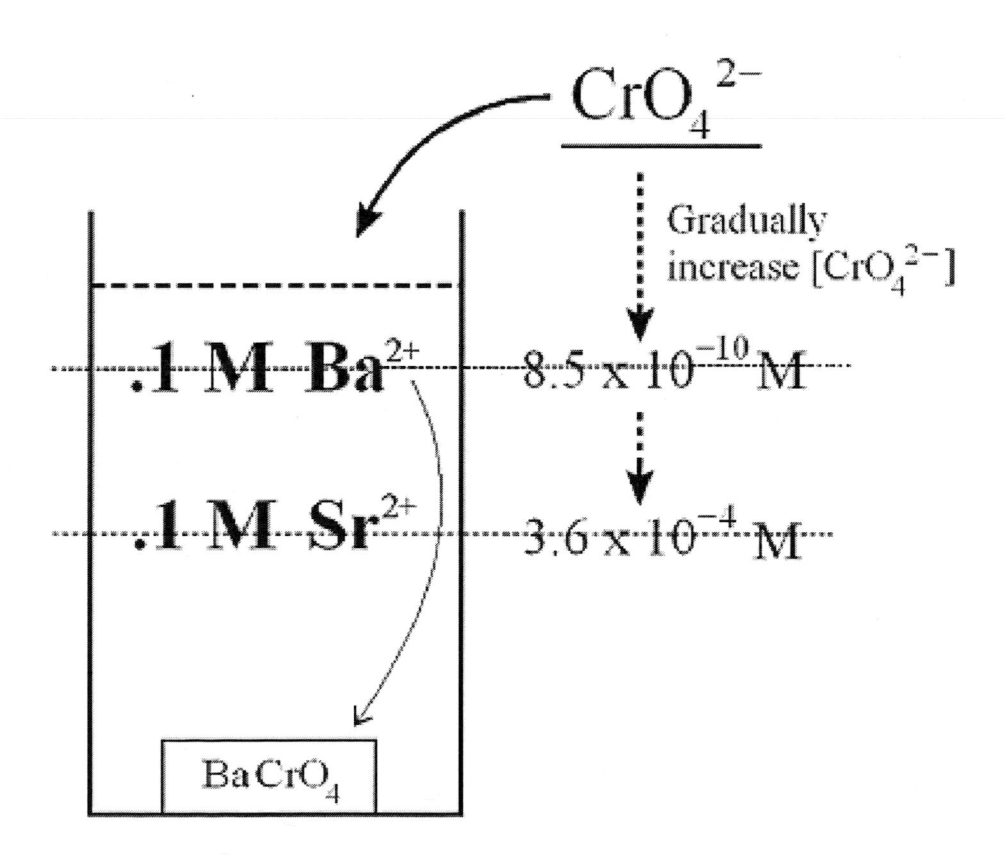

a) What $[CrO_4^{2-}]$ is needed to start precipitating Ba^{2+} as $BaCrO_4(s)$?

$$BaCrO_4(s) \rightleftharpoons Ba^{2+}(aq) + CrO_4^{2-} \quad K_{sp} = 8.5 \times 10^{-11}$$

$$Q = [Ba^{2+}][CrO_4^{2-}] \quad \Rightarrow \quad \textbf{set } \mathbf{Q = K_{sp}}$$

$$8.5 \times 10^{-11} = (.1) \cdot [CrO_4^{2-}]$$

$$\frac{8.5 \times 10^{-11}}{\cancel{.1}} = \frac{\cancel{(.1)} \cdot [CrO_4^{2-}]}{\cancel{.1}}$$

$$[CrO_4^{2-}] = \boxed{8.5 \times 10^{-10}\ M}$$

b) What $[CrO_4^{2-}]$ is needed to start precipitating Sr^{2+} as $SrCrO_4(s)$?

$$SrCrO_4(s) \rightleftharpoons Sr^{2+}(aq) + CrO_4^{2-} \quad K_{sp} = 3.6 \times 10^{-5}$$

$$Q = [Sr^{2+}][CrO_4^{2-}] \quad \Rightarrow \quad \textbf{set } \mathbf{Q = K_{sp}}$$

$$3.6 \times 10^{-5} = (.1) \cdot [CrO_4^{2-}]$$

$$\frac{3.6 \times 10^{-5}}{\cancel{.1}} = \frac{\cancel{(.1)} \cdot [CrO_4^{2-}]}{\cancel{.1}}$$

$$[CrO_4^{2-}] = \boxed{3.6 \times 10^{-4}\ M}$$

c) Which ion ppts first? **Ans:** Ba^{2+}

d) What is the concentration of $[Ba^{2+}]$ left in solution when Sr^{2+} starts to precipitate? (Occurs at $[CrO_4^{2-}] = 3.6 \times 10^{-4}$ M)

$$BaCrO_4(s) \rightleftharpoons Ba^{2+}(aq) + CrO_4^{2-} \qquad K_{sp} = 8.5 \times 10^{-11}$$

$Q = [Ba^{2+}][CrO_4^{2-}]$ ➡ **set $Q = K_{sp}$**

$$8.5 \times 10^{-11} = [Ba^{2+}] \cdot (3.6 \times 10^{-4})$$

$$\frac{8.5 \times 10^{-11}}{(3.6 \times 10^{-4})} = \frac{[Ba^{2+}] \cdot \cancel{(3.6 \times 10^{-4})}}{\cancel{(3.6 \times 10^{-4})}}$$

$$[Ba^{2+}] = \boxed{2.36 \times 10^{-7}\ M}$$

e) What % of the original $[Ba^{2+}]$ is left in solution when Sr^{2+} starts to precipitate?

$$\%\ left = \frac{[Ba^{2+}]\ left}{[Ba^{2+}]\ originally} \times 100$$

$$\%\ left = \frac{2.36 \times 10^{-7}\ M}{.1\ M} \times 100 = \boxed{.000236\ \%}$$

If you won \$1,000,000.00 ➡ .000236 % left is \$2.36

Further Example of Fractional Precipitation

Suppose you have a solution containing 0.04 M $Mg^{2+}(aq)$ and 0.2 M $Pb^{2+}(aq)$. You wish to separate these ions by adding F^-, which forms ppts of $MgF_2(s)$ [$\mathbf{K_{sp} = 7 \times 10^{-11}}$] and $PbF_2(s)$ [$\mathbf{K_{sp} = 7.1 \times 10^{-7}}$].

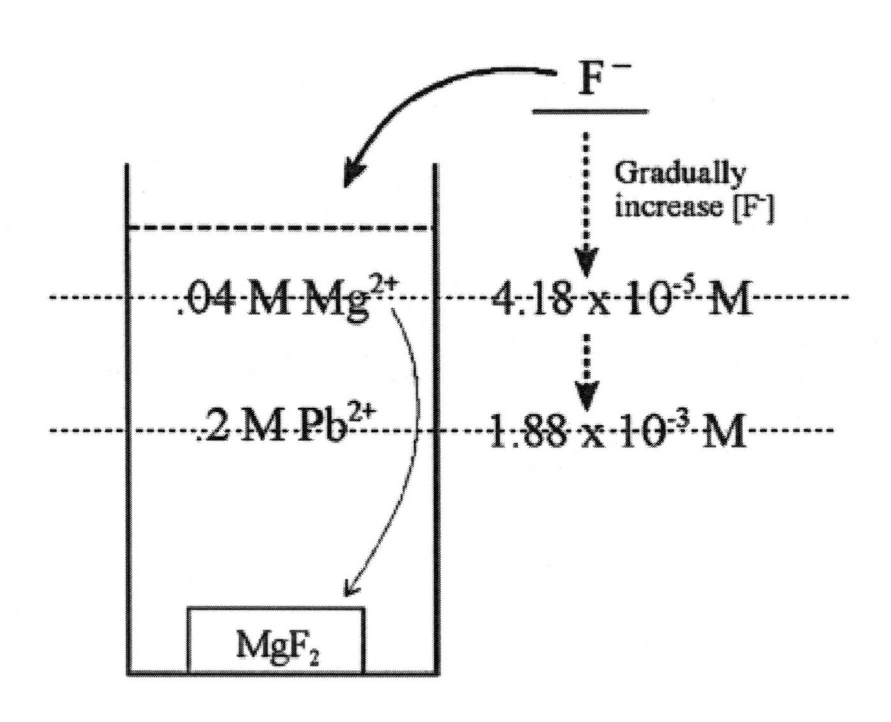

$$MgF_2(s) \rightleftharpoons Mg^{2+}(aq) + 2F^- \quad K_{sp} = 7 \times 10^{-11}$$

$$Q = [Mg^{2+}][F^-]^2$$ ➡ **set Q = K_{sp}**

$$7 \times 10^{-11} = (.04) \cdot [F^-]^2$$

$$\frac{7 \times 10^{-11}}{\cancel{.04}} = \frac{\cancel{(.04)} \cdot [F^-]^2}{\cancel{.04}}$$

$$[F^-]^2 = 1.75 \times 10^{-9}$$

$$\sqrt{[F^-]^2} = \sqrt{1.75 \times 10^{-9}}$$

$$[F^-] = \boxed{4.18 \times 10^{-5}\ M}$$

b) What $[F^-]$ is needed to start precipitating Pb^{2+} as $PbF_2(s)$?

$$PbF_2(s) \rightleftharpoons Pb^{2+}(aq) + 2F^- \quad K_{sp} = 7.1 \times 10^{-7}$$

$$Q = [Pb^{2+}][F^-]^2$$ ➡ **set Q = K_{sp}**

$$7.1 \times 10^{-7} = (.2) \cdot [F^-]^2$$

$$\frac{7.1 \times 10^{-7}}{\cancel{.2}} = \frac{\cancel{(.2)} \cdot [F^-]^2}{\cancel{.2}}$$

$$[F^-]^2 = 3.55 \times 10^{-6}$$

$$\sqrt{[F^-]^2} = \sqrt{3.55 \times 10^{-6}}$$

$$[F^-] = \boxed{1.88 \times 10^{-3}\ M}$$

c) Which ion ppts first? **Ans:** Mg^{2+}

d) What is the concentration of $[Mg^{2+}]$ left in solution when Pb^{2+} starts to precipitate? (Occurs at $[F^-] = 1.88 \times 10^{-3}$ M)

$$MgF_2(s) \rightleftharpoons Mg^{2+}(aq) + 2F^- \qquad K_{sp} = 7 \times 10^{-11}$$

$$Q = [Mg^{2+}][F^-]^2 \quad \Rightarrow \quad \textbf{set } Q = K_{sp}$$

$$7 \times 10^{-11} = [Mg^{2+}] \cdot (1.88 \times 10^{-3})^2$$

$$\frac{7 \times 10^{-11}}{(1.88 \times 10^{-3})^2} = \frac{[Mg^{2+}] \cdot \cancel{(1.88 \times 10^{-3})^2}}{\cancel{(1.88 \times 10^{-3})^2}}$$

$$[Mg^{2+}] = \boxed{2.0 \times 10^{-5} \text{ M}}$$

e) What % of the original $[Mg^{2+}]$ is left in solution when Pb^{2+} starts to precipitate?

$$\% \text{ left} = \frac{[Mg^{2+}] \text{ left}}{[Mg^{2+}] \text{ originally}} \times 100$$

$$\% \text{ left} = \frac{2.0 \times 10^{-5} \text{ M}}{.04 \text{ M}} \times 100 = \boxed{.05\ \%}$$

If you won \$1,000,000 ➡ .05 % left is \$500

Altering the Solubility of Insoluble Salts and Bases

1) Solubility decreases (↓) in the presence of a "**common ion**".
2) Solubility **sometimes** increases (↑) in the presence of a **strong acid (H^+)**.
3) Solubility increases (↑) in the presence of a "**ligand**" which forms a "**metal ion complex**" with the metal ion.

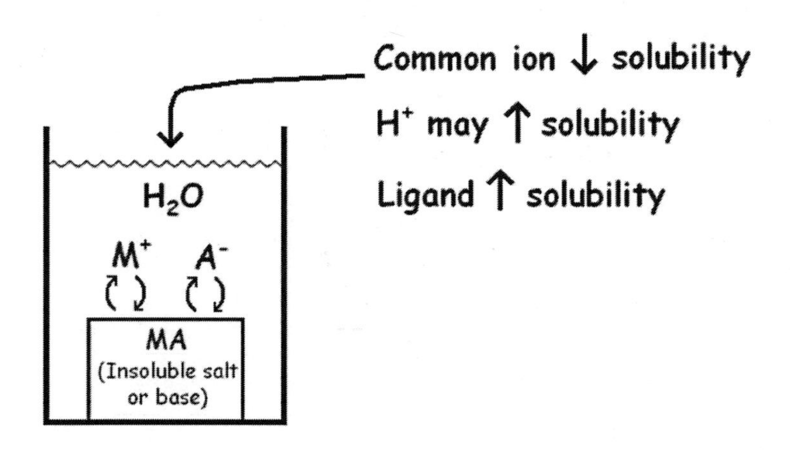

(VI) Common Ion Problems

Compare the solubility of PbF_2(s) in pure water and in a solution of a common ion.

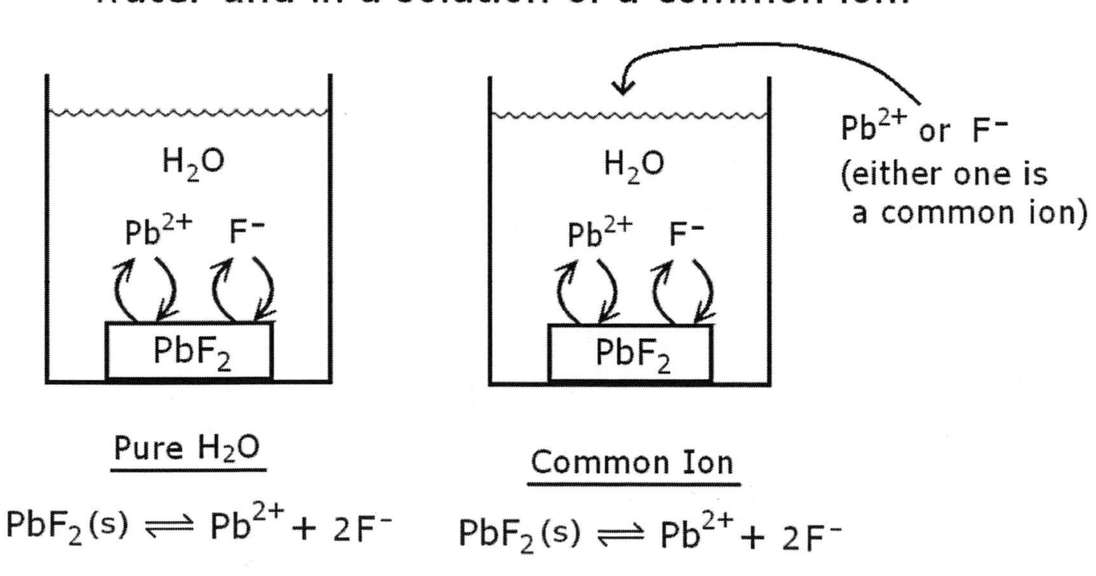

Pure water problem (Type II)

Calculate the solubility of PbF_2 (s) in $\frac{mol}{L}$ and $\frac{g}{L}$ in pure water.

	$PbF_2(s)$	$\rightleftharpoons$	Pb^{2+}	+	$2F^-$
I	*solid*		0		0
C	$-x$		$+x$		$+2x$
E	*less*		x		$2x$

$$K_{sp} = [Pb^{2+}][F^-]^2$$

$$7.1 \times 10^{-7} = (x)(2x)^2$$

$$7.1 \times 10^{-7} = 4x^3$$

$$\frac{7.1 \times 10^{-7}}{4} = \frac{\cancel{4}x^3}{\cancel{4}}$$

$$\sqrt[3]{x^3} = \sqrt[3]{1.78 \times 10^{-7}}$$

MM of PbF_2

$$x = 5.63 \times 10^{-3} \frac{\cancel{mol}}{L} \times \frac{245.2\ g}{\cancel{mol}}$$

$$= 1.38 \frac{g}{L}$$

Common Ion Problem (New One, Type VI)

Calculate the solubility of PbF_2 (s) in a 0.1 M NaF (aq) solution.

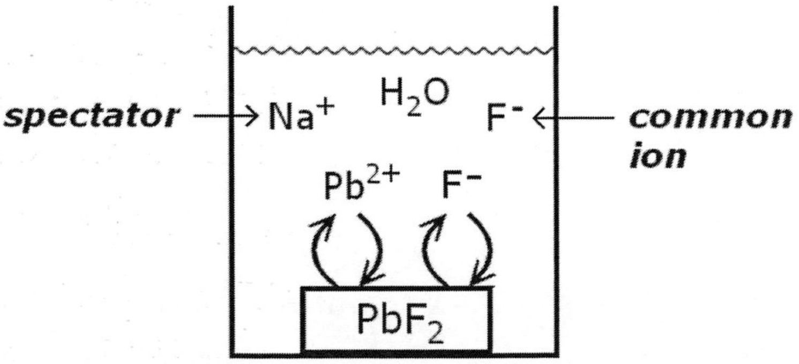

spectator → Na^+ H_2O F^- ← *common ion*

Pb^{2+} F^-

PbF_2

	$PbF_2(s)$	$\rightleftharpoons$	Pb^{2+}	+	$2F^-$
I	*solid*		0		.1 ← **DO NOT multiply by 2**
C	$-x$		$+x$		$+2x$
E	*less*		x		$.1 \cancel{+2x}$

$$K_{sp} = [Pb^{2+}][F^-]^2$$

$$7.1 \times 10^{-7} = (x)(.1)^2$$

$$\frac{7.1 \times 10^{-7}}{(.1)^2} = \frac{(x)\cancel{(.1)^2}}{\cancel{(.1)^2}}$$

$$x = 7.1 \times 10^{-5} \frac{\cancel{mol}}{L} \times \frac{245.2 \text{ g}}{\cancel{mol}}$$

$$= \boxed{.0174 \frac{g}{L}}$$ *less soluble*

$$\frac{1.38}{.0174} = \mathbf{79x}$$ less soluble in the solution of the common ion

Comparison with the pure water problem

Pure water: $7.1 \times 10^{-7} = (x)(2x)^2$

.1 M $F^-(aq)$: $7.1 \times 10^{-7} = (x)(.1)^2$

Replace whatever was in the ( ) with the given conc. of the common ion

* (DO NOT multiply by 2)
* (The experimenter chose the conc. 0.1 M)

Another Example (common ion problems)

Calculate the solubility of Ag_2CO_3 in:

a) pure water

b) 0.2 M $Na_2CO_3\,(aq)$

c) 0.5 M $AgNO_3\,(aq)$

	$Ag_2CO_3\,(s)$	$\rightleftharpoons$ $2\,Ag^+$	$+\;CO_3^{2-}$	
I	solid	0	0	Pure H_2O
C	$-x$	$+2x$	$+x$	
E	less	$2x$	x	

Ag⁺
Ag⁺ CO_3^{2-}
Ag_2CO_3

	$Ag_2CO_3\,(s)$	$\rightleftharpoons$ $2\,Ag^+$	$+\;CO_3^{2-}$	
I	solid	0	.2	in 0.2 M $Na_2CO_3(aq)$
C	$-x$	$+2x$	$+x$	
E	less	$2x$	.2 ~~$+x$~~	

0.2 M CO_3^{2-}
Ag^+
Ag^+ CO_3^{2-}
Ag_2CO_3

	$Ag_2CO_3\,(s)$	$\rightleftharpoons$ $2\,Ag^+$	$+\;CO_3^{2-}$	
I	solid	.5	0	in 0.5 M $AgNO_3(aq)$
C	$-x$	$+2x$	$+x$	
E	less	.5 ~~$+2x$~~	x	

0.5 M Ag^+
Ag^+
Ag^+ CO_3^{2-}
Ag_2CO_3

Pure H_2O

$$K_{sp} = [Ag^+]^2[CO_3^{2-}]$$

$$8.2 \times 10^{-12} = (2x)^2(x)$$

$$\frac{8.2 \times 10^{-12}}{4} = \frac{\cancel{4}x^3}{\cancel{4}}$$

$$\sqrt[3]{x^3} = \sqrt[3]{2.05 \times 10^{-12}}$$

$$x = \boxed{1.27 \times 10^{-4}\ \frac{mol}{L}}$$

0.2 M Na_2CO_3 (aq)

Start with the pure H_2O equation above, then replace what is in the CO_3^{2-} parenthesis with .2

$$[8.2 \times 10^{-12} = (2x)^2(\cancel{x}) \leftarrow \text{From above}]$$

$$8.2 \times 10^{-12} = (2x)^2(.2)$$

$$8.2 \times 10^{-12} = 4x^2(.2)$$

$$\frac{8.2 \times 10^{-12}}{.8} = \frac{\cancel{.8}x^2}{\cancel{.8}}$$

$$\sqrt{x^2} = \sqrt{1.03 \times 10^{-11}}$$

$$x = \boxed{3.2 \times 10^{-6}\ \frac{mol}{L}}$$

$$\frac{1.27 \times 10^{-4}}{3.2 \times 10^{-6}} =$$ **40 x** less soluble in 0.2 M Na_2CO_3 (aq) than in pure water

0.5 M $AgNO_3$ (aq)

Start with the pure H_2O equation above, then replace what is in the Ag^+ parenthesis with .5

$$\left[8.2 \times 10^{-12} = (2x)^2(x) \leftarrow \text{From above}\right]$$

$$8.2 \times 10^{-12} = (.5)^2(x)$$

$$\frac{8.2 \times 10^{-12}}{(.5)^2} = \frac{(.5)^2(x)}{(.5)^2}$$

$$x = 3.28 \times 10^{-11} \frac{\text{mol}}{\text{L}}$$

$$\frac{1.27 \times 10^{-4}}{3.28 \times 10^{-11}} =$$ 3.9 million x less soluble in 0.5 M $AgNO_3$ than in pure water

Summary of the Setups

$$K_{sp} = [Ag^+]^2[CO_3^{2-}]$$

Pure H_2O : $8.2 \times 10^{-12} = (2x)^2(x)$

0.2 M Na_2CO_3 : $8.2 \times 10^{-12} = (2x)^2(.2)$

0.5 M $AgNO_3$: $8.2 \times 10^{-12} = (.5)^2(x)$

Altering the Solubility of Insoluble Salts and Metal Hydroxides (Strong Bases)

1) Common Ion – **Discussed**
2) Adding Strong Acid (H^+) – **Next Topic**

[3) Adding a Ligand – **Next Class**]

Effect of Strong Acid (H^+)

Trying to Dissolve PbF_2 and *AgCl* with H^+

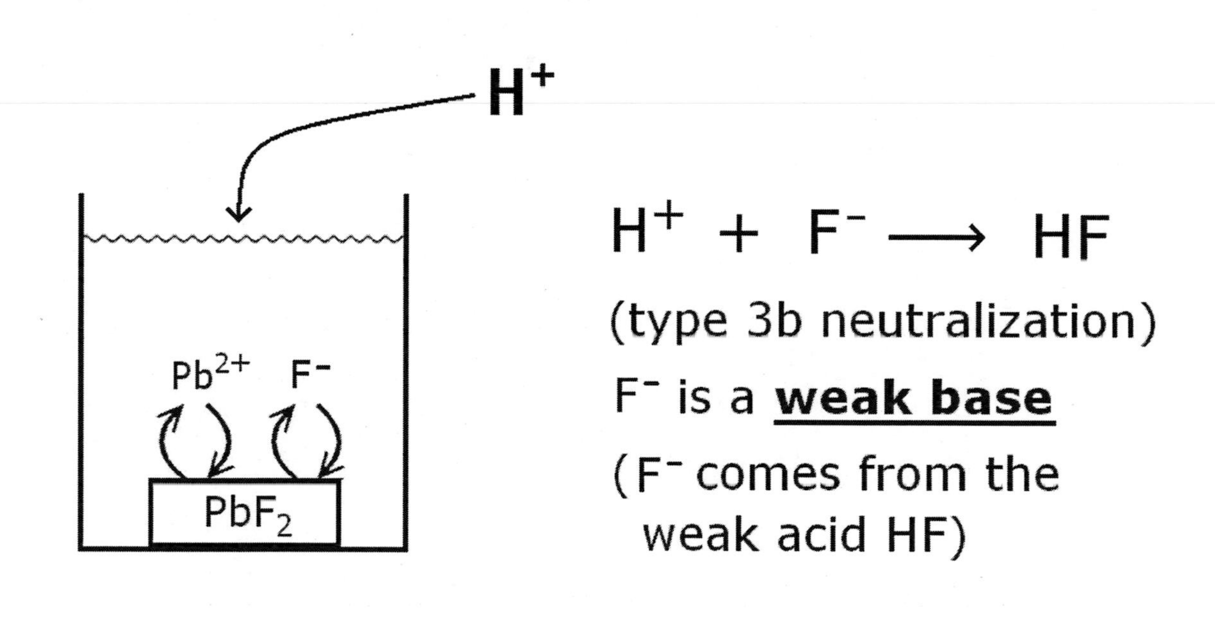

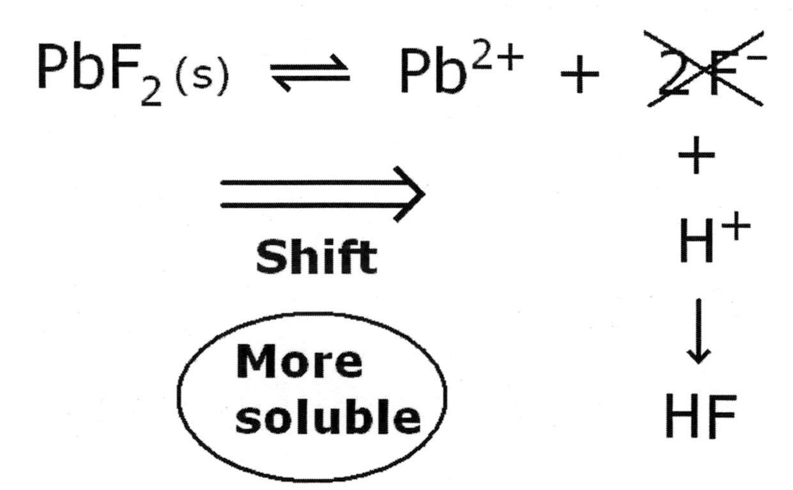

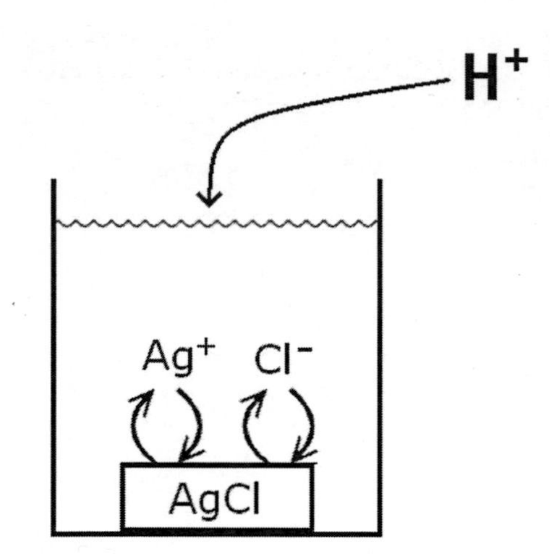

No effect on solubility of AgCl

$H^+ + Cl^- \not\rightarrow$ **NR**

Cl^- is a **"neutral anion"** = will not accept H^+ in water

Cl^- comes from the **Strong acid** HCl

Principle: The solubility of an insoluble salt ↑ in strong acid (H^+)

ONLY IF

the – ion (anion) in the salt is a **base** (that is, the conjugate base of a weak acid)

Insoluble metal hydroxides usually dissolve in H^+ because OH^- reacts with H^+ to form H_2O

Will the following be more soluble in strong acid (H^+) than in pure water?

BiI_3

I^- is from the strong acid HI, so **NO**.

FeS

S^{2-} is from the weak acid HS^- or H_2S, so it is a base. Therefore, **YES.**

$Al(OH)_3$

Metal hydroxides usually dissolve in H^+ because the H^+ reacts with the OH^- to form H_2O. Therefore, **YES.**

$Ca_3(PO_4)_2$

PO_4^{3-} is from the weak acid HPO_4^{2-} (or H_3PO_4), so it is a weak base. Therefore, **YES.**

Metal Ion Complexes and Introduction to Kinetics

(Homework #10)

Metal Ion Complexes

(“Coordination Compounds”)

$FeSCN^{2+}$	blood red solution
$Ni(DMG)_2$	strawberry red ppt
$Cu(NH_3)_4^{2+}$	deep blue solution

Example of a Specific Complex

- Put Sn^{4+} and Cl^- together, you **expect** the following **ionic** compound from crossing:

$$Sn^{+4}\ Cl^{-1} \longrightarrow \mathbf{SnCl_4}$$

- This compound exists, but is a liquid with a BP just a little above water’s. Therefore, it must be **covalent**.

- If you put Sn^{4+} and Cl^- together in **aqueous solution**, you don’t get $SnCl_4$. You get a **metal ion complex**:

$$Sn^{4+}(aq) + 6\ Cl^-(aq) \longrightarrow SnCl_6^{2-}(aq)$$

- You do not have to predict whether a complex forms or its formula. Once given the formula, you will be asked questions about it.

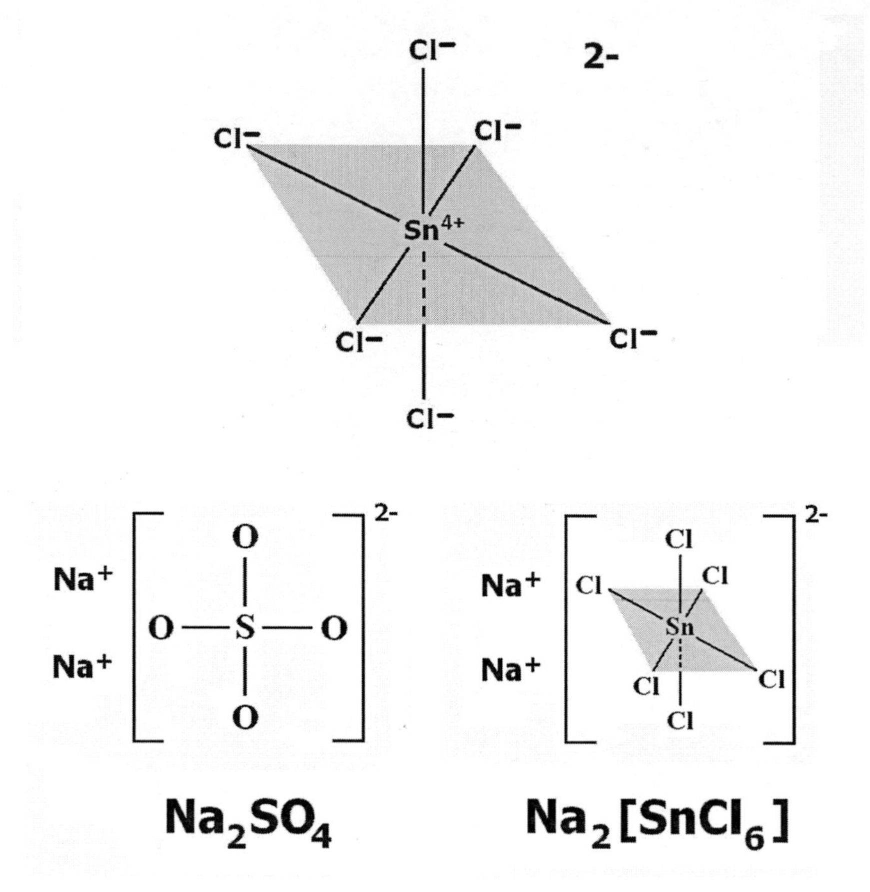

The metal ion is called the **central metal ion**.

Whatever substances are attached to it are called **ligands**.

Metal ion complexes are also called **"coordination compounds"** because the bonding between the metal ion and ligands is essentially a **"coordinate covalent bond"** (both electrons come from the ligand):

Sn^{4+} $:\ddot{\underset{\cdot\cdot}{Cl}}:^{-}$

Sn^{4+} —••— $\ddot{\underset{\cdot\cdot}{Cl}}:^{-}$

Ammonia (NH_3), even though it is neutral, can also be a ligand because it has an unshared pair of electrons:

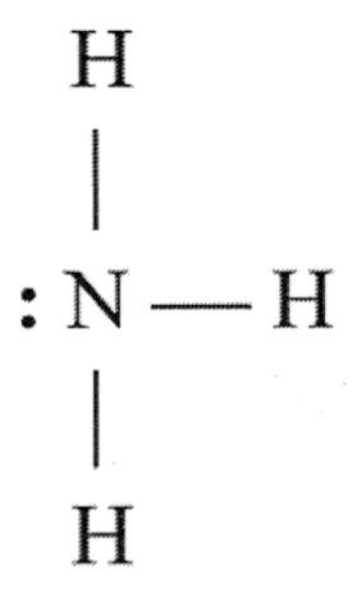

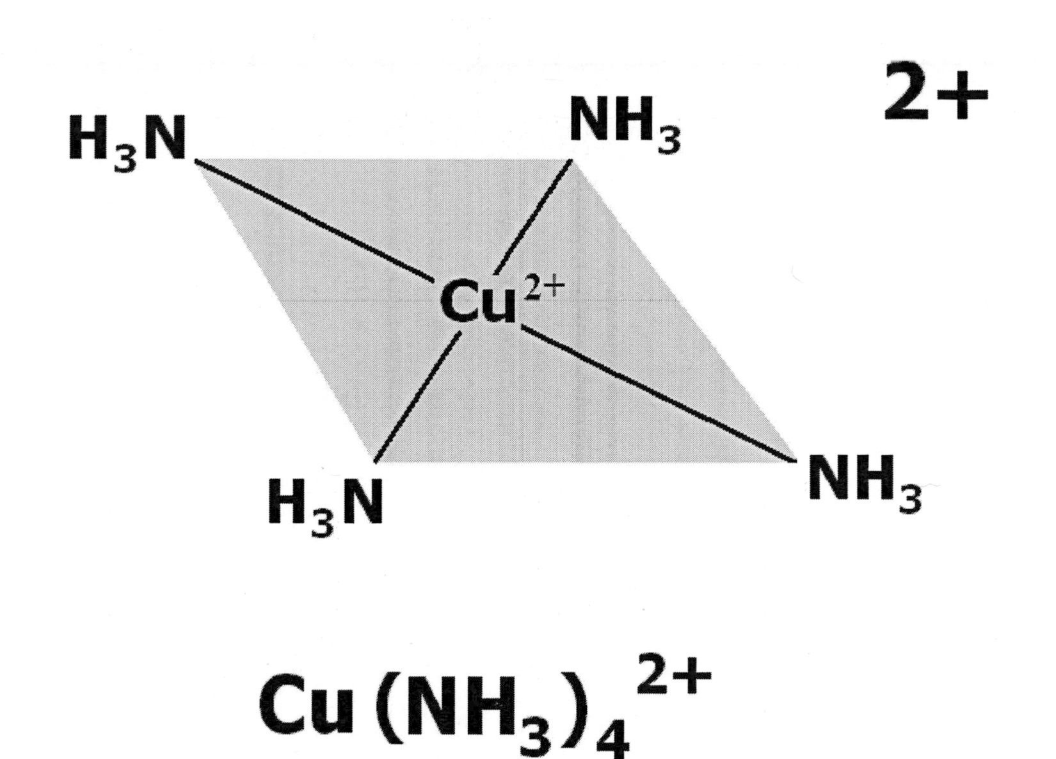

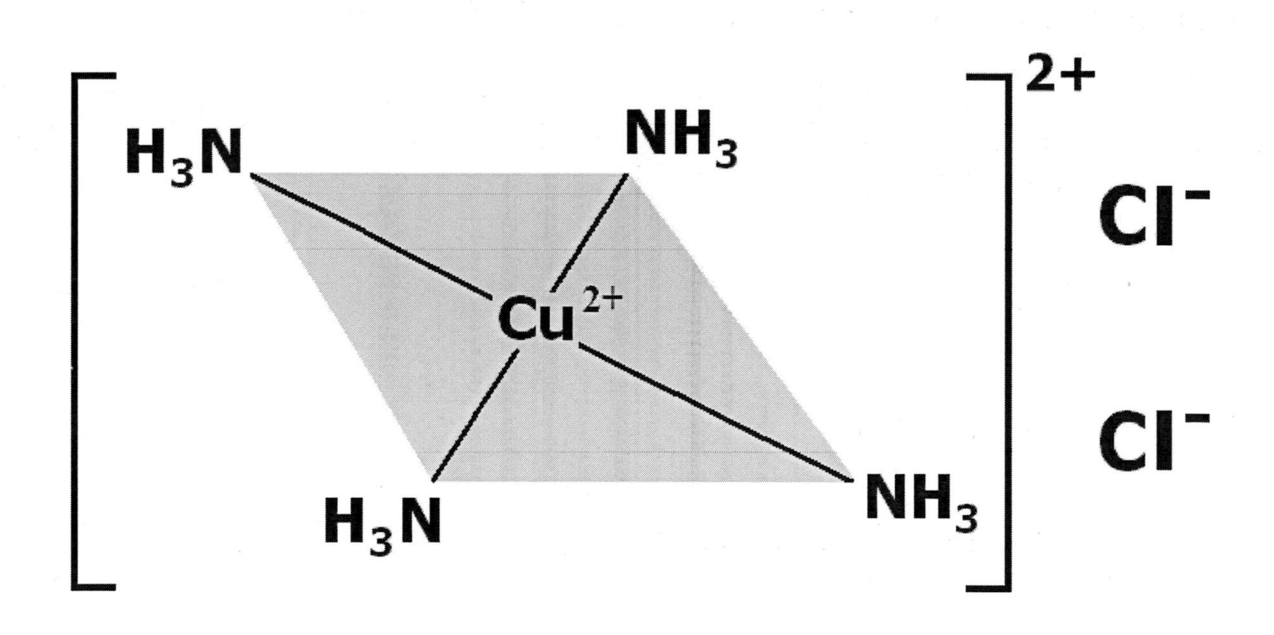

$$[Cu(NH_3)_4]Cl_2$$

Some ligands can bind to a metal ion at two places. These are called "bidentate" ligands.

```
        H       H
        |       |
    H - C ----- C - H
       /         \
  H   /           \   H
   \ N :         : N /
  H /               \ H
```

ethylenediamine (en)

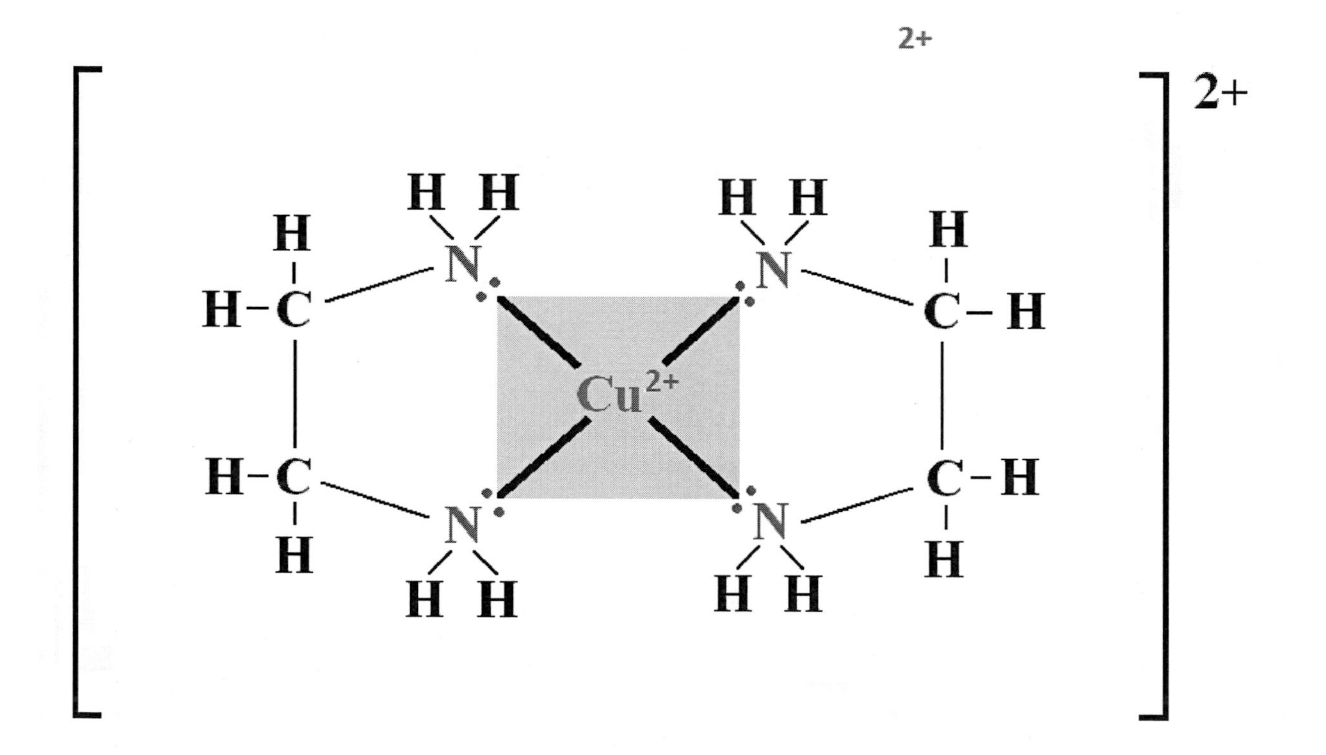

$Cu(en)_2^{2+}$

Chelate = Latin for "claw"

Dentate = Latin for "teeth"

Classes of Ligands

Monodentate	1 attachment point
Bidentate	2 attachment points
Tridentate	3 attachment points
Quadradentate	4 attachment points
Hexadentate	6 attachment points

Example of Another Bidentate Ligand

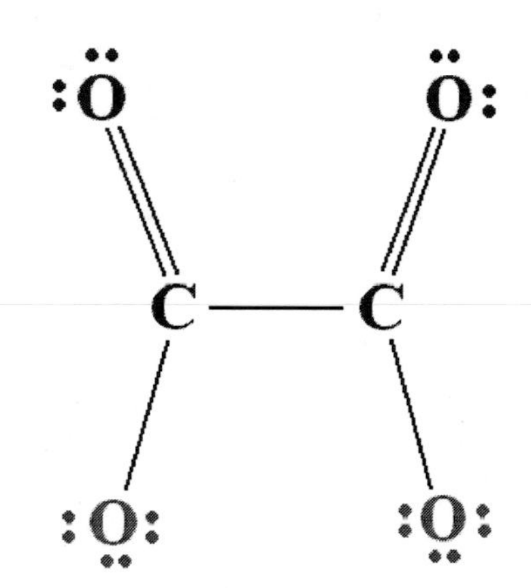

Oxalate Ion

$C_2O_4^{2-}$

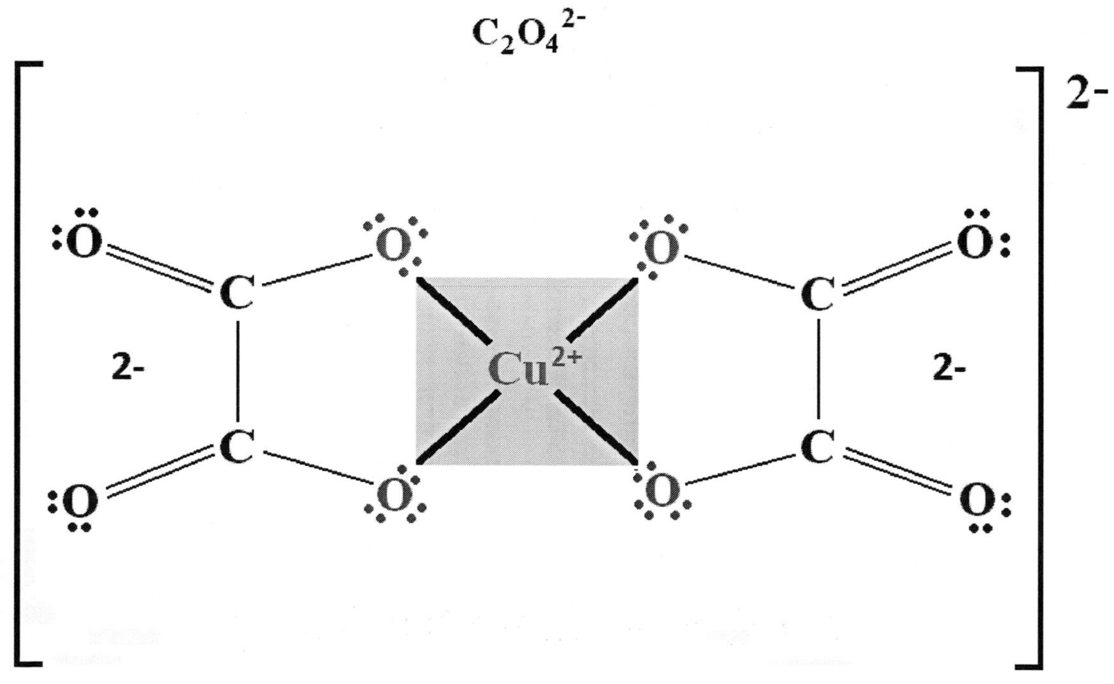

$Cu(C_2O_4)_2^{2-}$

Table 5 - Common Ligands in Complexes

(see p. 18)

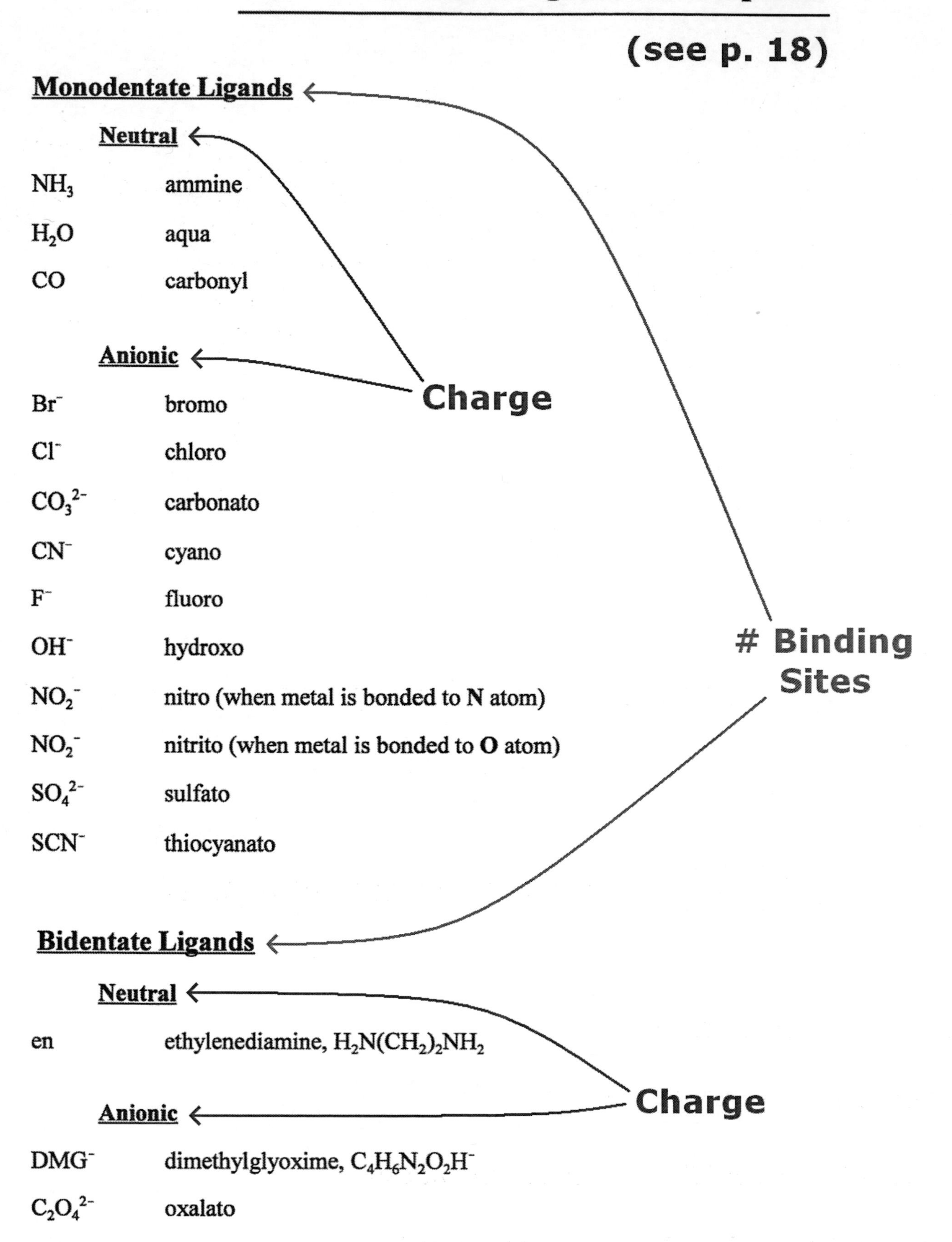

Monodentate Ligands

Neutral

NH_3	ammine
H_2O	aqua
CO	carbonyl

Anionic

Br^-	bromo
Cl^-	chloro
CO_3^{2-}	carbonato
CN^-	cyano
F^-	fluoro
OH^-	hydroxo
NO_2^-	nitro (when metal is bonded to **N** atom)
NO_2^-	nitrito (when metal is bonded to **O** atom)
SO_4^{2-}	sulfato
SCN^-	thiocyanato

Bidentate Ligands

Neutral

en	ethylenediamine, $H_2N(CH_2)_2NH_2$

Anionic

DMG^-	dimethylglyoxime, $C_4H_6N_2O_2H^-$
$C_2O_4^{2-}$	oxalato

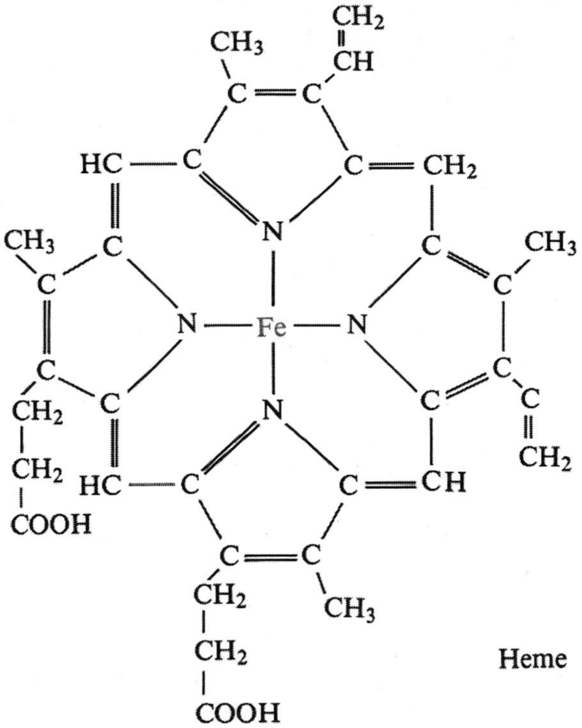

Heme

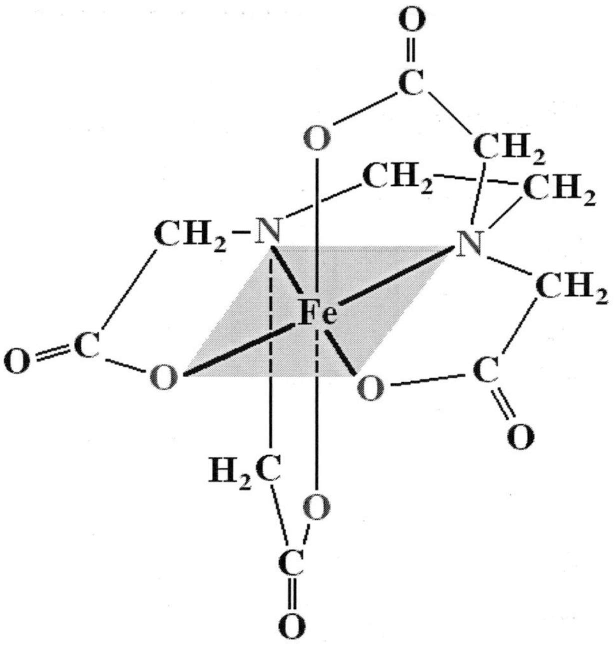

Complex of Fe^{2+} and EDTA

Coordination number = the number of attachment points to the metal ion

NOT the same as "number of ligands".

$SnCl_6^{2-}$ Coord #: 6

$Cu(NH_3)_4^{2+}$ Coord #: 4

$Cu(en)_2^{2+}$ Coord #: 4 (en is **bidentate**)

$Cu(C_2O_4)_2^{2-}$ Coord #: 4 ($C_2O_4^{2-}$ is **bidentate**)

Charges in Metal Ion Complexes

Calculating Charges in Complexes

Basic principle = the charge of the complex is the sum of charges of the metal ion and ligands.

Problem: What is the overall charge of the Cobalt(III) complex $Co(NO_2)_6$?

Co: 1 ion x (+3) = +3

NO_2^-: 6 ions x (−1) = −6

−3 **(Anion)**

Problem: What is the overall charge of the Platinum(II) complex $Pt(NH_3)_2Cl_2$?

Pt: 1 ion x (+2) = +2

NH_3: 0

Cl: 2 ions x (−1) = −2

0 **(Neutral Compound)**

Problem: What is the overall charge of the Chromium(III) complex $Cr(H_2O)_4Cl_2$?

Cr: 1 ion x (+3) = +3

H_2O: 0

Cl: 2 ions x (−1) = −2

+1 **(Cation)**

Note: Complexes can be **Anions**, **Cations**, or **Neutral Compounds**.

Formulas of Compounds Containing Complexes

Problem: Write the formula of the compound that forms between K^+ and $[Co(NO_2)_6]^{3-}$.

$$K^{+1} [Co(NO_2)_6]^{3-} \quad = \quad K_3[Co(NO_2)_6]$$

Problem: Write the formula of the compound that forms between $[Cr(H_2O)_4Cl_2]^+$ and SO_{42}^{-}.

$$[Cr(H_2O)_4Cl_2]^{+1} (SO_4)^{2-} \quad = \quad [Cr(H_2O)_4Cl_2]_2\, SO_4$$

If the complex is **neutral**, like $Pt(NH_3)_2Cl_2$ or $Ni(DMG)_2$, it doesn't combine with ions. It exists as a compound by itself.

Dissolving of Compounds Containing Complexes in Water

Compounds containing complexes split into ions in water, just like any ionic compound. The complex ion stays together just like a polyatomic ion does:

$$Na_2[SnCl_6] \xrightarrow{H_2O} 2\,Na^+(aq) + SnCl_{62}^{-}(aq)$$

$$[Cu(NH_3)_4](NO_3)_2 \xrightarrow{H_2O} Cu(NH_3)_4^{2+}(aq) + 2\,NO_3^-(aq)$$

Determining the Charge of the Metal Ion in a Complex

Problem: What is the charge of Co in the complex $[Co(NH_3)_2(C_2O_4)_2]^-$?
What is the coordination number?

Charge

$[Co(NH_3)_2(C_2O_4)_2]^-$

$x + 0 + 2 \cdot (-2) = -1$

$x - 4 = -1$

$x = +3$

Charge of Co: +3

Coordination Number

$[Co \ (NH_3)_2 \ (C_2O_4)_2]^-$

$2 \cdot (\text{mono}) + 2 \cdot (\text{bi}) =$

$2 \cdot (1) + 2 \cdot (2) = \mathbf{6}$

Coordination #: 6

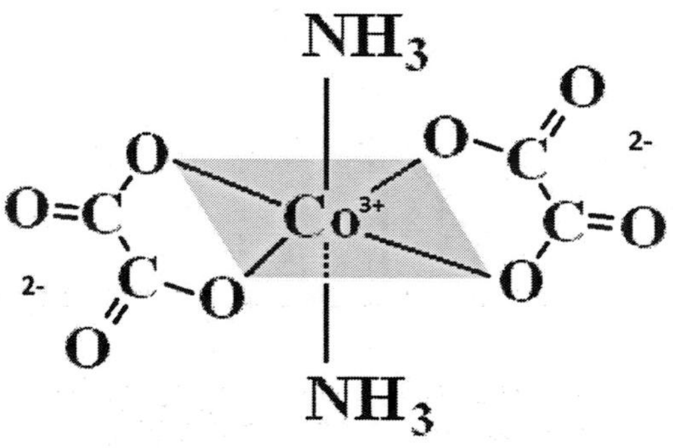

Problem: What is the charge on Cr in the complex $[Cr(NH_3)_2(H_2O)_2Br_2]^+$?
What is the coordination number?

Charge

$[Cr(NH_3)_2(H_2O)_2Br_2]^+$

$x + 0 + 0 + 2 \cdot (-1) = +1$

$x - 2 = +1$

$x = +3$

Charge of Cr: +3

Coordination Number

$[Cr \quad (NH_3)_2 \quad (H_2O)_2 \quad Br_2]^+$

$2 \cdot (\text{mono}) + 2 \cdot (\text{mono}) + 2 \cdot (\text{mono}) =$

$2 \cdot (1) + 2 \cdot (1) + 2 \cdot (1) = \mathbf{6}$

Coordination #: 6

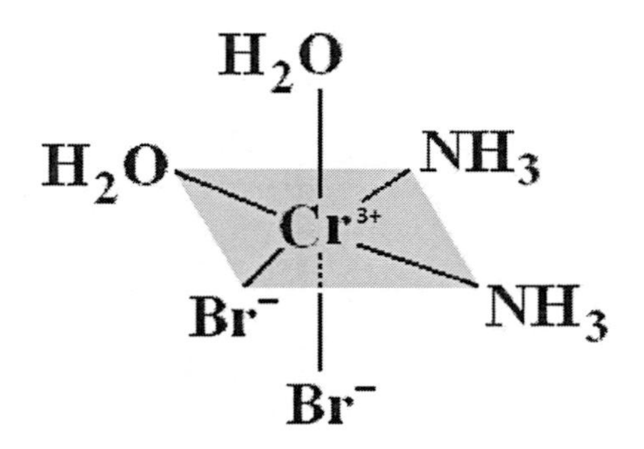

Problem: What are the charge and coordination number of Pt in $[Pt(en)_2]Cl_2$?

For **charge**, use the **"entire formula"** which adds up to 0.
For **coordination number**, use only the **part in brackets** (the complex itself).

Charge

$[Pt \ (en)_2] \ Cl_2$

$x + 0 + 2 \cdot (-1) = 0$

$x - 2 = 0$

$x = +2$

Charge of Pt: +2

Coordination Number

$[Pt \ (en)_2] \ Cl_2$

$2 \cdot (\text{bi}) = \mathbf{4}$

Coordination #: 4

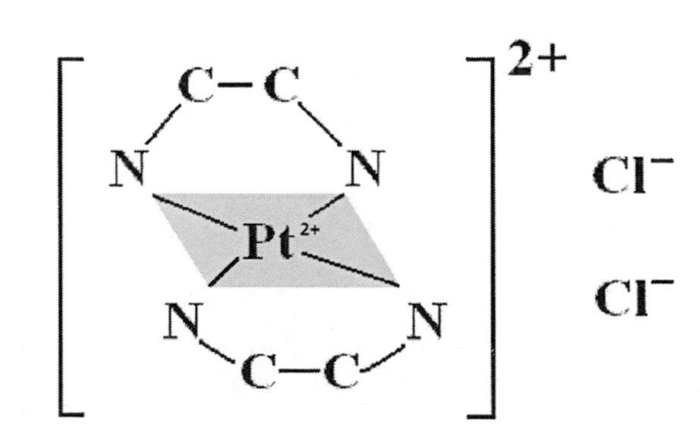

Problem: What are the charge and coordination number of Fe in $K_4[Fe(CN)_6]$?

Charge

$$K_4 \ [Fe \ (CN)_6]$$

$$4 \cdot (+1) + x + 6 \cdot (-1) = 0$$

$$4 + x + (-6) = 0$$

$$x - 2 = 0$$

$$x = +2$$

Charge of Fe: +2

Coordination Number

$$K_4 \ [Fe \ (CN)_6]$$

$$6 \cdot (\text{mono}) = 6$$

Coordination #: 6

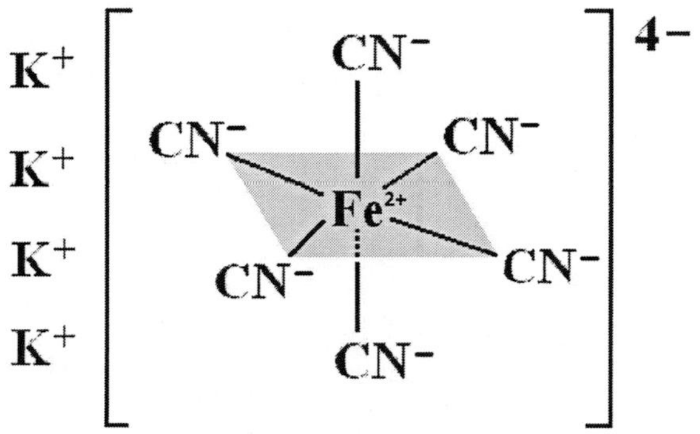

K^+ K^+ K^+ K^+ $[Fe^{2+}(CN^-)_6]^{4-}$

Strengths of Complexes

1. **Complexes are STRONG** = the metal ion and ligands are bonded VERY tightly.

2. **Equilibrium constant** = $\mathbf{K_f}$ = formation constant. "Formation" refers to the formation of the complex from the metal ion and ligands.

Example:

$$Co^{3+}(aq) + 6\ NH_3(aq) \rightleftharpoons Co(NH_3)_6^{3+}(aq)$$

$$K_f = \frac{[Co(NH_3)_6^{3+}]}{[Co^{3+}]\,[NH_3]^6} = 4.5 \times 10^{33}$$

(Square brackets mean "Molarity.")

a. **Very large** number (+ power of 10).

b. Shows that, when Co^{3+} and NH_3 are placed in solution, there is **almost 100% $Co(NH_3)_6^{3+}$ complex** and almost no "free" Co^{3+} and NH_3.

c. **The larger** the K_f, **the stronger** the complex.

d. True of complexes **in general**.

Molecular Geometries of Complexes

Complexes have molecular geometries similar to those of covalent compounds.

Coordination number	Molecular Geometry
2	Linear
4	Tetrahedral or Square Planar
6	Octahedral

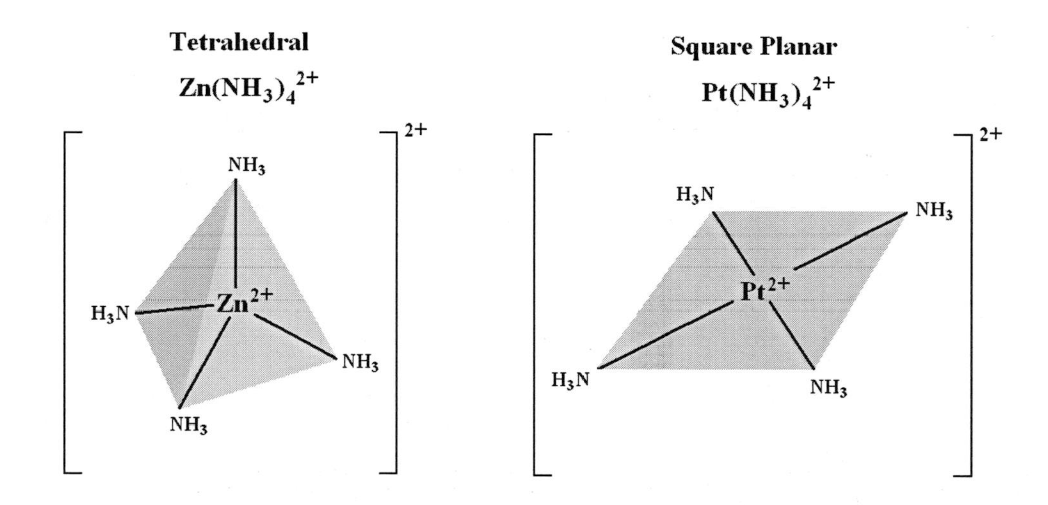

Octahedral complexes $[Co(NH_3)_4Cl_2]^+$

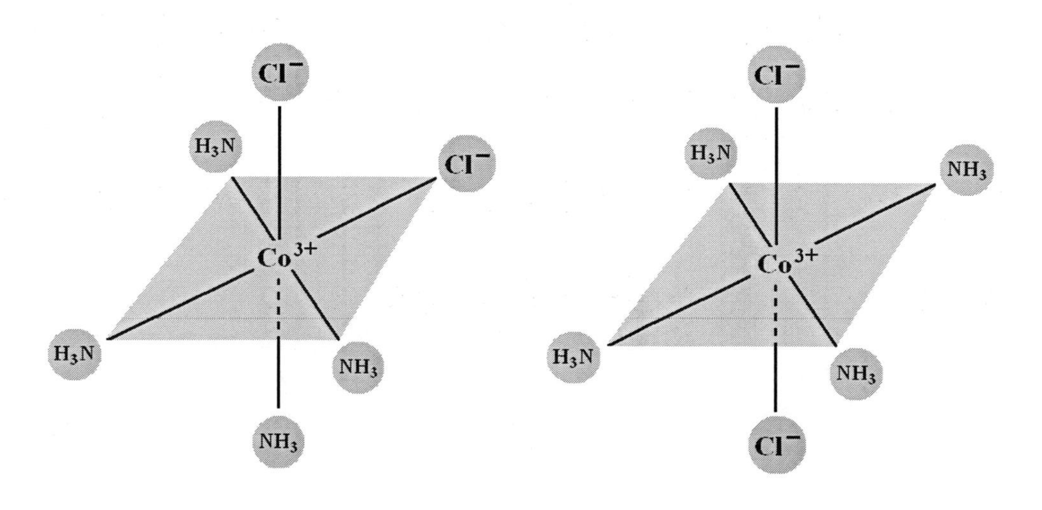

Color Of Complexes Is Determined By:

1. What metal ion is present.
2. What ligands are attached.
3. Where ligands are attached.

Isomers = compounds with the same formula but different structures.

Why Objects Appear Colored

1. White light is a combination of all colors.
2. If a color is "subtracted" from white light, the other colors are reflected.
3. These combine to form the complementary color to the one subtracted.
4. All molecules have electrons in distinct "energy levels."
5. Light is absorbed when electrons "jump up" into higher energy levels.
6. The color of light absorbed depends on the separation in energy between the levels.

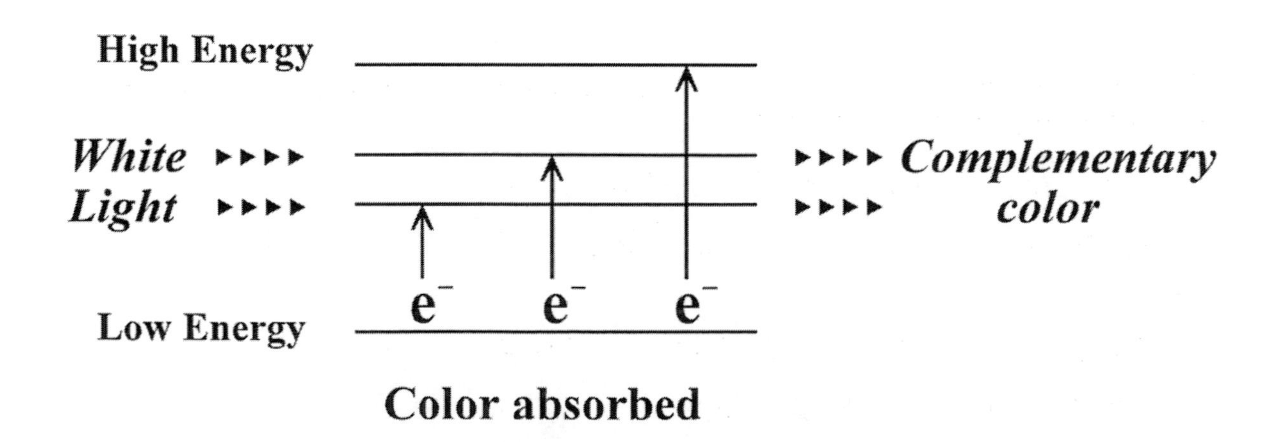

Colors of Complexes

1. Compounds that have e^-'s that are easy to excite are often colored.
2. Unpaired e^-'s are usually easier to excite than paired e^-'s.
3. Most transition metals that form complexes have unpaired d e^-'s.

   Fe (#26) $1s^2 2s^2 2p^6 3s^2 3p^6 4s^2 3d^6$

   ↑↓ ↑ ↑ ↑ ↑ 3d level

   Ni (#28) $1s^2 2s^2 2p^6 3s^2 3p^6 4s^2 3d^8$

   ↑↓ ↑↓ ↑↓ ↑ ↑ 3d level

4. The unpaired d e^-'s are responsible for the color. Different ligands produce different colors when combined with the same metal ion.
5. Colors of complexes are complementary to the color of light absorbed.

   Green complexes absorb **red** light. **Blue** complexes absorb **yellow** light.

6. Complexes of metals with d e^-'s that are all paired are usually colorless.

   Zn (#30) $1s^2 2s^2 2p^6 3s^2 3p^6 4s^2 3d^{10}$

   ↑↓ ↑↓ ↑↓ ↑↓ ↑↓ 3d level

Water as a ligand

Many cations exist in solution complexed to water:

$Co^{2+}(aq)$ is $Co(H_2O)_6^{2+}$ Pink

$Cu^{2+}(aq)$ is $Cu(H_2O)_4^{2+}$ Pale Blue

When other ligands are added, they often form stronger complexes than H_2O, so they displace water. Often, the color changes dramatically:

$$Cu(H_2O)_4^{2+} + 4\,NH_3 \longrightarrow Cu(NH_3)_4^{2+} + 4\,H_2O$$

Pale Blue **Deep Blue**

$$Co(H_2O)_6^{2+} + 4\,Cl^- \longrightarrow CoCl_4^{2-} + 6\,H_2O$$

Pink **Blue**

Some complexes have water only partially replaced:

$[Cr(NH_3)_2(H_2O)_2Br_2]^+$ $[Fe(H_2O)F_5]^{-2}$

Hydrates (like $CuSO_4 \cdot 5H_2O$ and $NiSO_4 \cdot 7H_2O$) often have water complexed to the metal ion.

Names of Complexes

There is a standardized naming system for complexes which I will not expect you to know.

$[Cr(H_2O)_4Cl_2]Cl$

Tetraaquadichlorochromium(III) chloride

Prefix for how many ligands | Ligands first in alphabetical order | Metal ion with charge ⟷ End with element name if **cation**

$K_3[Co(NO_2)_6]$

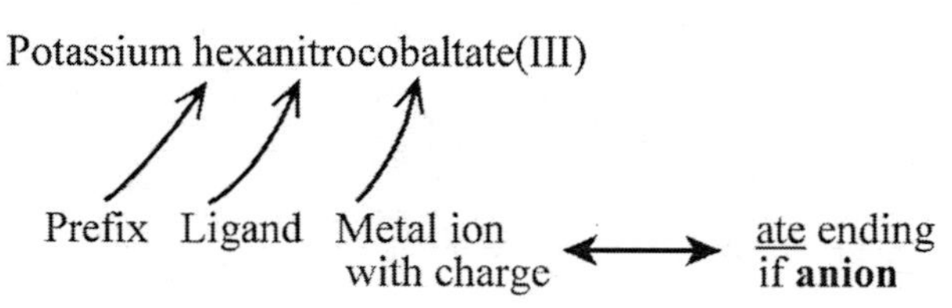

Three Ways of Altering the Solubility of a Sparingly Soluble Salt

1. **Solubility ↓ in a solution of a common ion.**
2. **Solubility ↑ in acid if the anion is from a weak acid.**
3. **Solubility ↑ if the metal ion can form a complex with a ligand in solution.**

(1 and 2) – **Discussed last lecture.**

Effect of Complex Formation on Solubility of Insoluble Salts

In Lecture 9, it was discussed that H^+ increases the solubility of an insoluble salt if the negative ion in the salt is a base (comes from a weak acid), but not if the negative ion comes from a strong acid (pp. 235, 236):

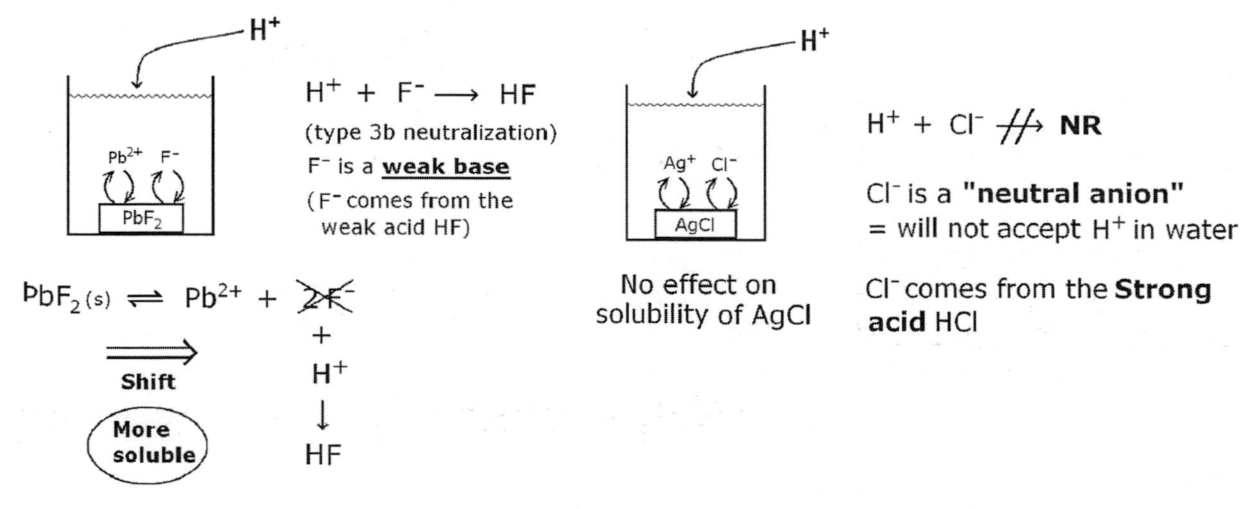

Salts can be dissolved not only when the negative ion reacts with H^+ but also when the metal ion reacts with a ligand of the metal ion. For example:

It is known that NH_3 forms a complex with Ag^+:

$$Ag^+ (aq) + 2\ NH_3 (aq) \rightleftharpoons Ag(NH_3)_2^+ (aq)$$

AgCl(s) is insoluble in pure water ($K_{sp} = 1.8 \times 10^{-10}$).

$$AgCl(s) \rightleftharpoons Ag^+ (aq) + Cl^- (aq)$$

However, it dissolves if NH_3 (aq) is added to the water because the NH_3 reacts with the Ag^+ ions and shifts the dissolving equilibrium toward dissolving of the solid.

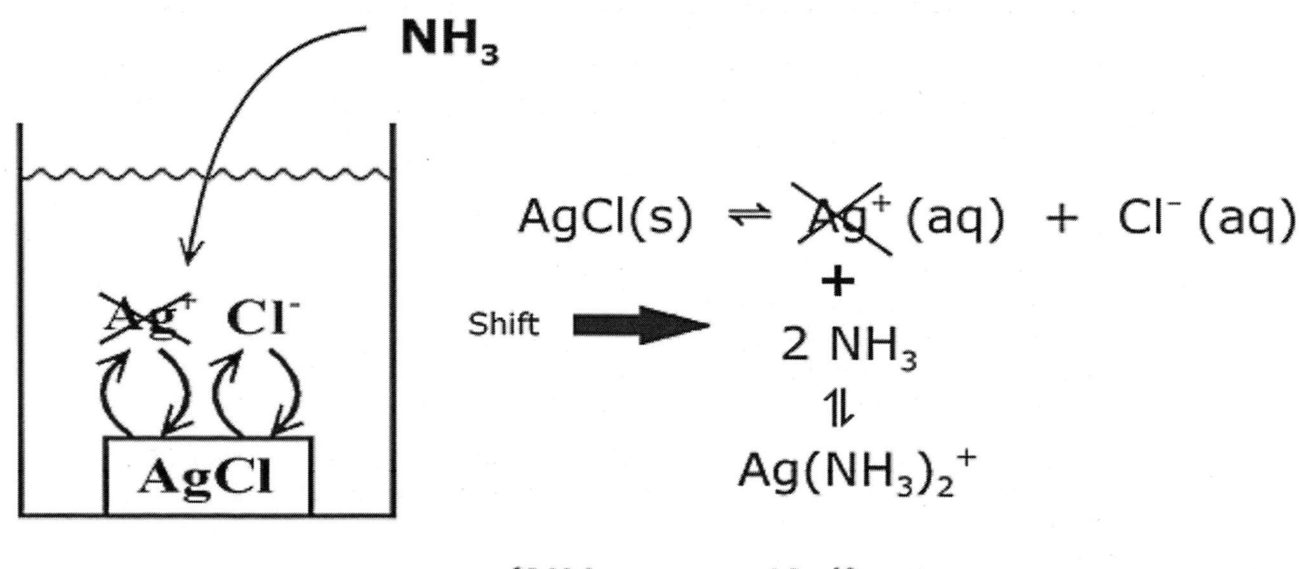

(NH_3 essentially "removes" Ag^+)

Kinetics and Thermodynamics

$$N_2\,(g) \quad + \quad 3\,H_2\,(g) \quad \rightleftharpoons \quad 2\,NH_3\,(g)$$

cheap   expensive

1. Want to know **how fast** NH_3 can be made.
   Rate of Reaction = **Kinetics**

2. Want to know how much NH_3 is present at $\rightleftharpoons$.
   Does the reaction "favor" products or reactants?

$$K_{eq} = \frac{\text{products}}{\text{reactants}}$$

If K_{eq} is large = favor products

If K_{eq} is small = favor reactants

There is a mathematical relationship between K_{eq} and the main function in **Thermodynamics**.

ΔG = Gibb's Free Energy

Basic Chemical Kinetics

Suppose the following data are collected for the reaction:

$$2\,N_2O_5(g) \longrightarrow 4\,NO_2(g) + O_2(g)$$

Time (min)	$[N_2O_5]$
0	0.160 M
1	0.113
2	0.079
3	0.056
4	0.039

A graph of these data looks like the following:

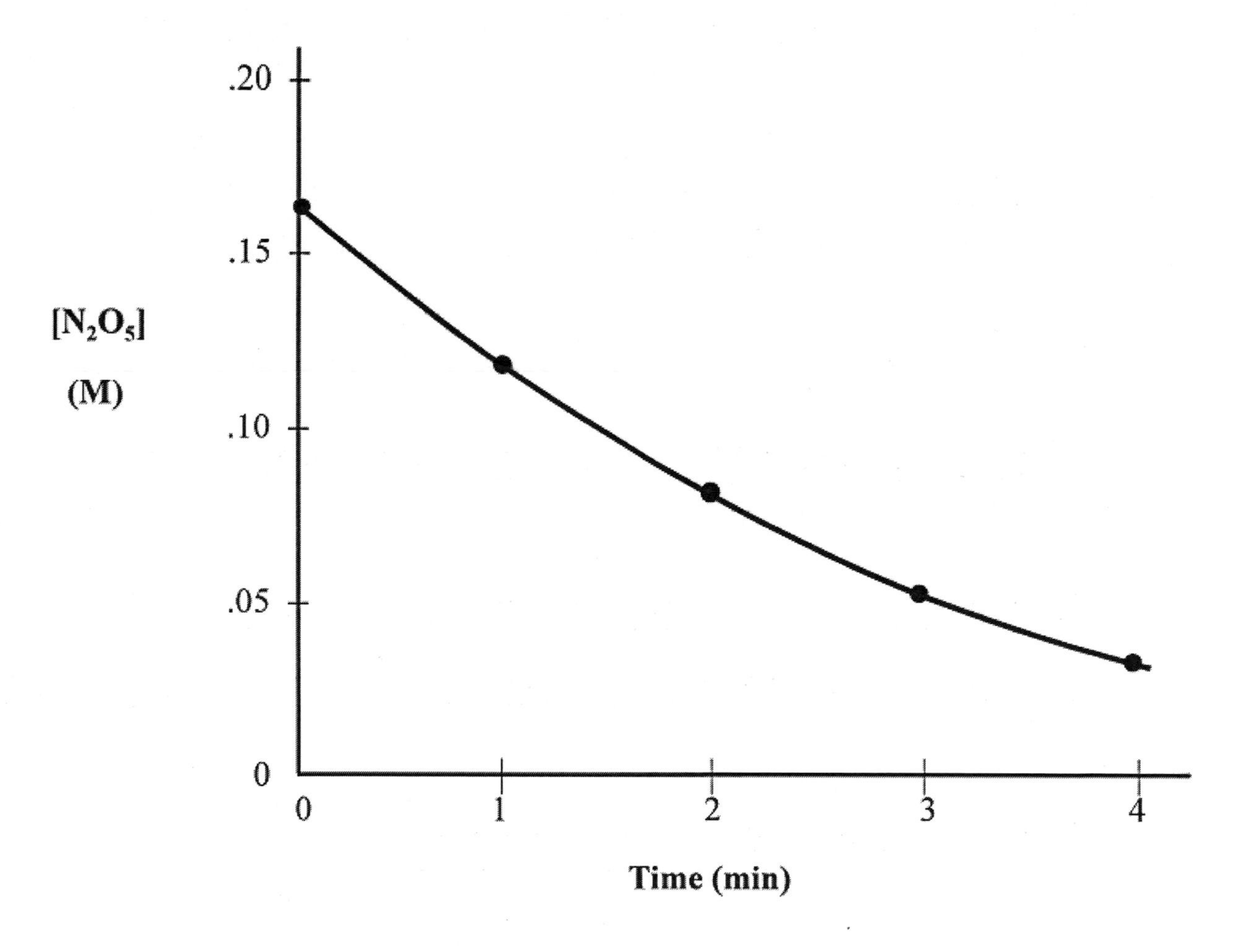

The **Initial Rate** is defined as the slope of the tangent line at Time = 0.

Kinetics

$$\text{Rate} = -\frac{\Delta [N_2O_5]}{\Delta \text{ time}}$$

Negative is used because N_2O_5 is disappearing, but rates must be +.

Problems:

What is the average rate for the first 2 min?

$$\text{Rate} = -\frac{(.079 - .160)}{(2 - 0)} = -\frac{-.081 \text{ M}}{2 \text{ min}} = .0405 \text{ M/min}$$

What is the average rate from 2 min to 4 min?

$$\text{Rate} = -\frac{(.039 - .079)}{(4 - 2)} = -\frac{-.040 \text{ M}}{2 \text{ min}} = .020 \text{ M/min}$$

Several time courses can be run, each starting with a different concentration of reactant:

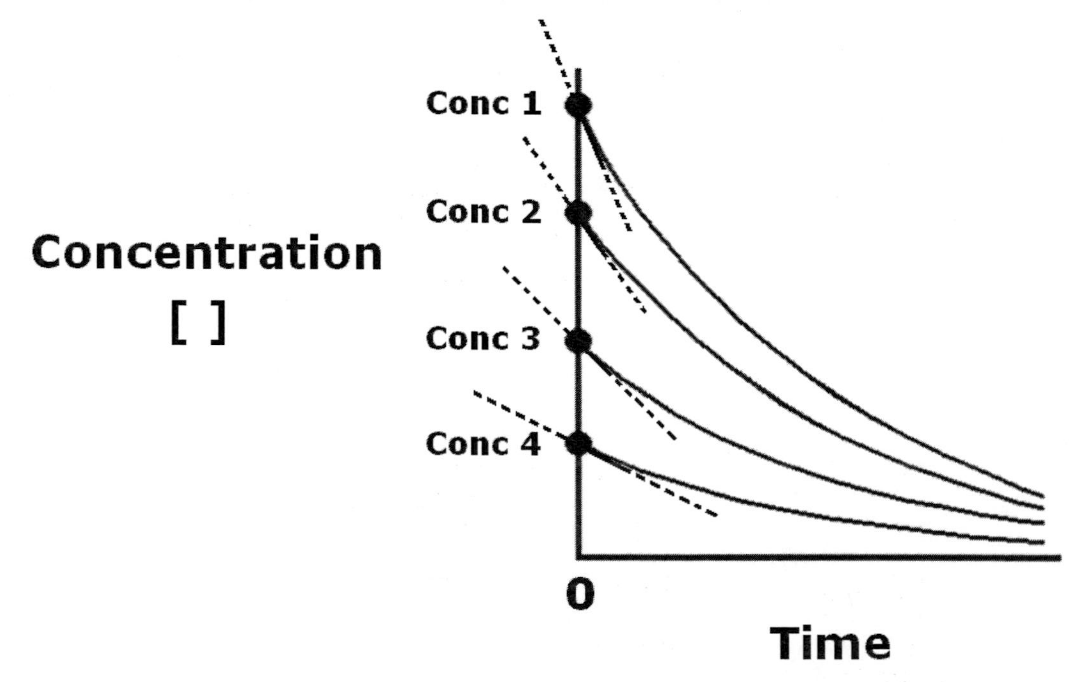

Each time course gives a different Initial Rate (slope of the tangent line at Time 0; dashed lines)

Rate Laws

If we start with a **higher** $[N_2O_5]$ initially, the **initial rate** is experimentally found to be **faster**. If we start with a **lower** $[N_2O_5]$, the **initial rate** is found to be slower.

Suppose the following data are collected for the **initial rate** at various initial concentrations of N_2O_5:

$[N_2O_5]$	Initial Rate
.040 M	.014 M/min
.057	.020
.080	.028
.114	.040
.160	.056

A graph of these data looks like the following:

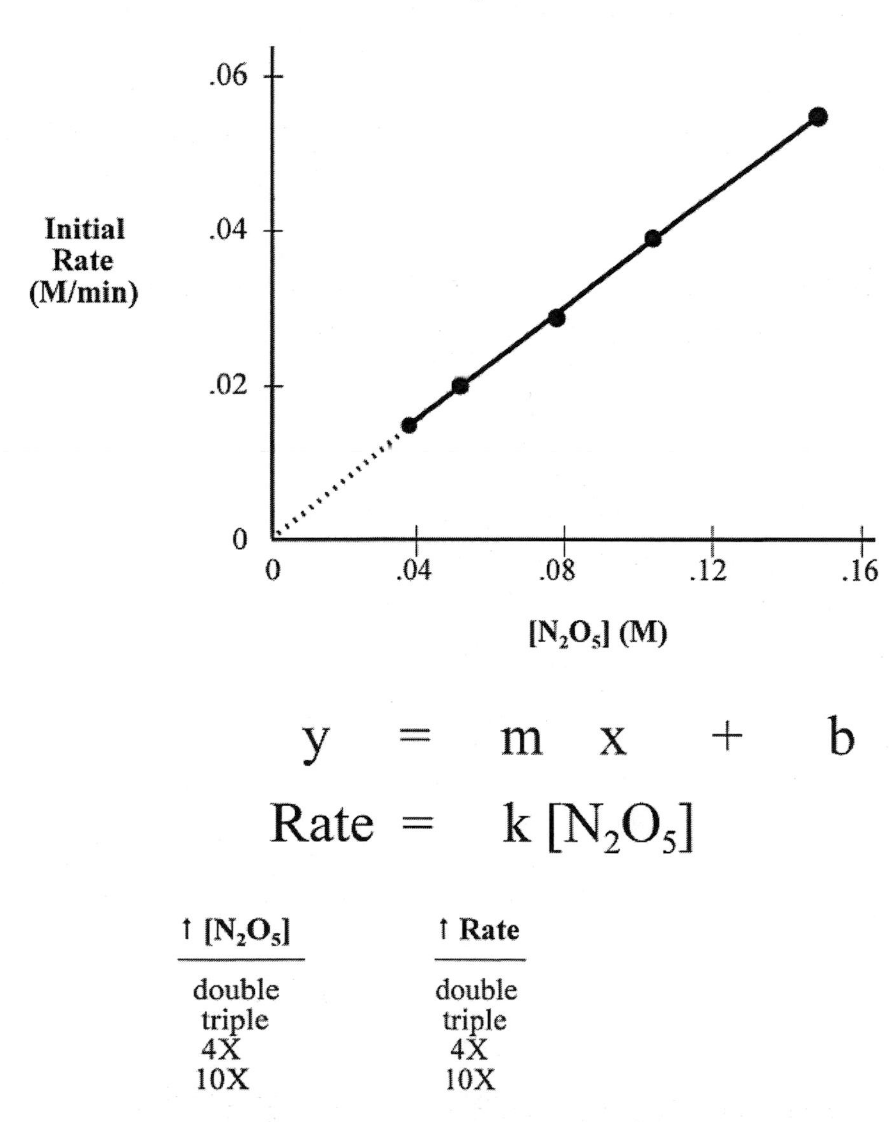

$$y = m\,x + b$$

$$\text{Rate} = k\,[N_2O_5]$$

↑ $[N_2O_5]$	↑ Rate
double	double
triple	triple
4X	4X
10X	10X

Sometimes the rate is not proportional in the same way. Suppose a chemist obtained the following data for the reaction:

$$A \longrightarrow \text{products}$$

[A]	Initial Rate
.01 M	.002 M/min
.02	.008
.03	.018
.04	.032
.05	.050

A graph of these data looks like the following:

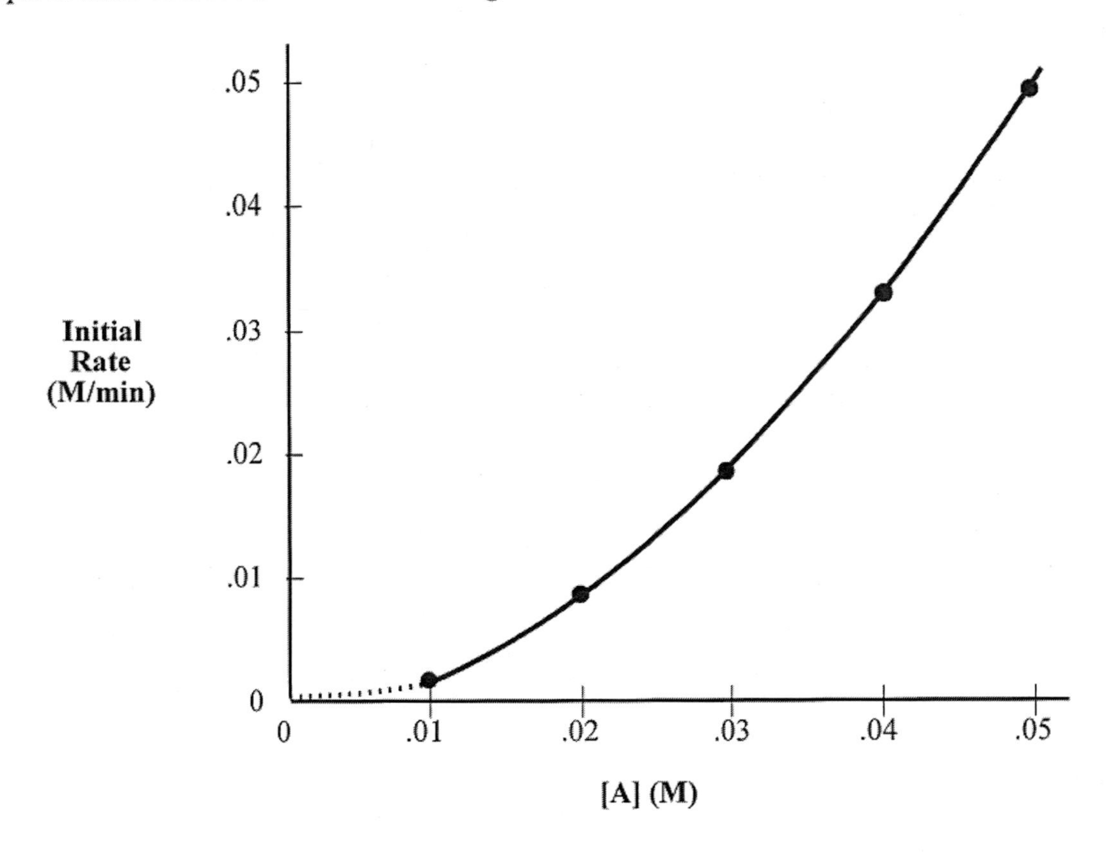

This curve is part of a <u>parabola</u>.

$$\text{Rate} = k[A]^2$$

↑[A]	↑ Rate
.01 - .02 **(2X)**	.008/.002 = **4X**
.01 - .03 **(3X)**	.018/.002 = **9X**
.01 - .04 **(4X)**	.032/.002 = **16X**
.01 - .05 **(5X)**	.050/.002 = **25X**

There is a third possibility. Sometimes the rate does not change <u>no matter what the concentration</u>.

Suppose the following are data for the reaction:

$$X \longrightarrow \text{products}$$

[X]	Initial Rate
.3 M	.149 M/min
.4	.150
.5	.148
.6	.149

A graph of these data looks like the following:

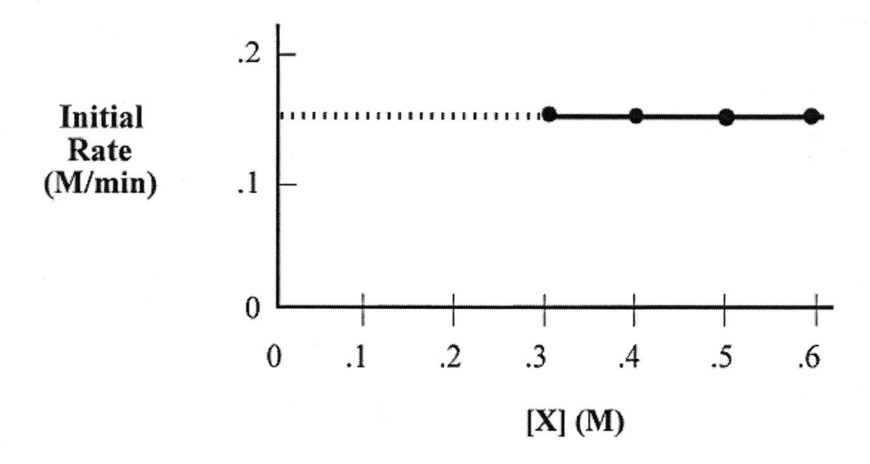

The rate does not depend on the concentration.

$$\text{Rate} = k \quad \text{OR} \quad \text{Rate} = k[X]^0$$

Order of Reaction

The **exponent** in the rate equation is referred to as the **order** of the reaction.

$$R \longrightarrow \text{products}$$

Zero Order **Rate = $k[R]^0$ (or just Rate = k)**

First Order **Rate = $k[R]^1$**

Second Order **Rate = $k[R]^2$**

The order of a reaction must be determined from **experimental data.**

Rate Laws

Rate Equations

→ ***Equivalent***

$$\textbf{Rate} = \textbf{k} [\ ]^{n}$$

rate constant (↗ k)

n = 0 Zero order

n = 1 First order

n = 2 Second order

Fill in the following chart for ?

[ ]	Rate
2	12
8	**?**

If zero order : **? = 12**

Rate stays the same no matter what the concentration.

If first order

Rate = k[ ]

If [ ] ↑ 4x, Rate ↑ 4x

? = 12 x 4 = **48**

If second order

Rate = k[ ]^2

If [ ] ↑ 4x, Rate ↑ 4^2 or 16x

? = 12 x 16 = **192**

Fill in for the ? in the following

	[ ]	Rate
3x	4.2	157
	12.6	**?**

First order: ↑ **3x**

Second order: ↑ **3^2 or 9x**

Zero order: **?** = **157**

First order: **?** = 157 x 3 = **471**

Second order: **?** = 157 x 9 = **1413**

Two Kinds of Graphs in Kinetics

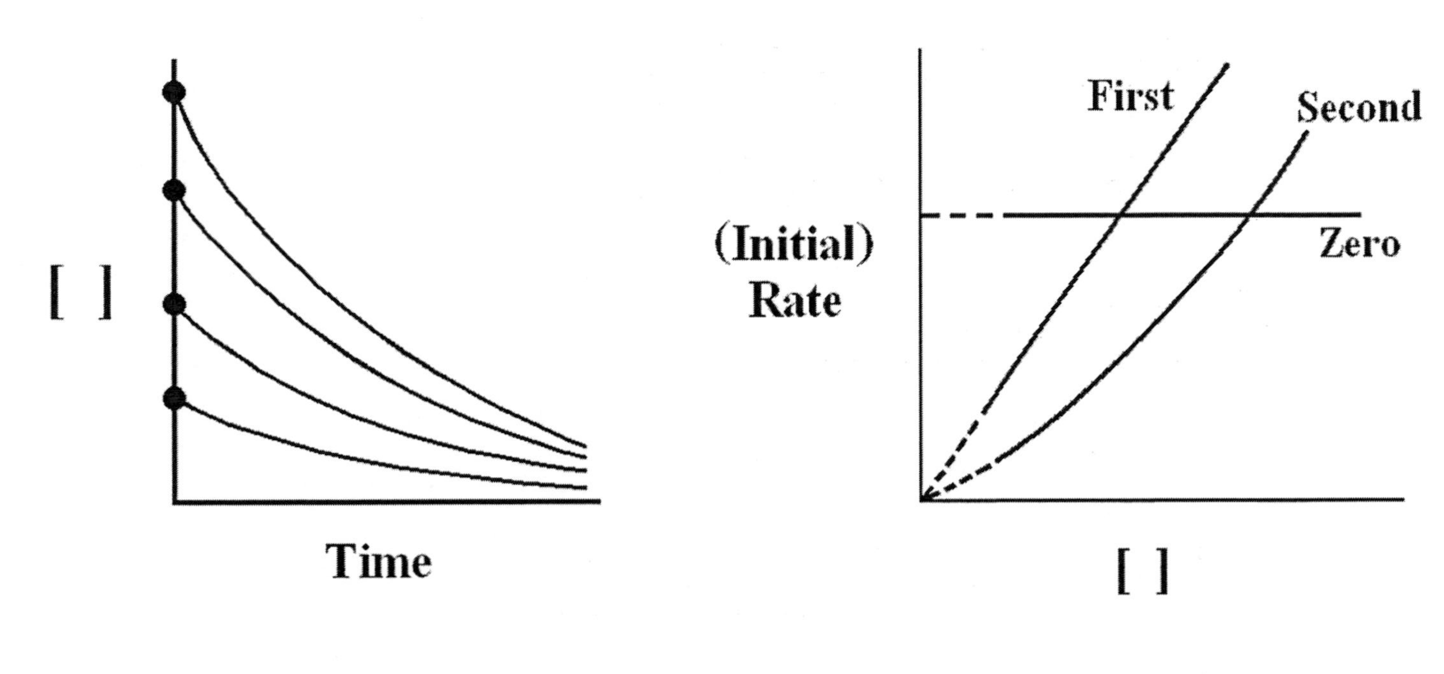

"Time course"

Time	[ ]		[ ]	Rate
.	.		.	.
.	.		.	.
.	.		.	.
.	.		.	.

Each time course gives <u>ONE</u> Initial Rate (slope of the tangent line at Time 0), so <u>several</u> <u>time</u> <u>courses</u> are needed to get the other graph.

Mathematics of Chemical Kinetics

(Homework #11)

Units of the Rate Constant k

***Concentration* [ ]**

expressed as: M mol / L $\text{mol} \cdot \text{L}^{-1}$

Rate

expressed as: M / min $\text{M} \cdot \text{min}^{-1}$ $\text{mol} \cdot \text{L}^{-1} \cdot \text{min}^{-1}$

Zero Order

Rate = k

Units: $\mathbf{M \cdot min^{-1}}$ OR

$\mathbf{mol \cdot L^{-1} \cdot min^{-1}}$

First Order

Rate = k [ ]

$\text{M} \cdot \text{min}^{-1} = \text{k} \cdot \text{M}$

$$\frac{\cancel{\text{M}} \cdot \text{min}^{-1}}{\cancel{\text{M}}} = \frac{\text{k} \cdot \cancel{\text{M}}}{\cancel{\text{M}}}$$

$\text{min}^{-1} = \text{k}$

Units: $\mathbf{min^{-1}}$

Second Order

Rate = $\text{k} [\,]^2$

$\text{M} \cdot \text{min}^{-1} = \text{k} \cdot \text{M}^2$

$$\frac{\cancel{\text{M}} \cdot \text{min}^{-1}}{\text{M}^{\cancel{2}}} = \frac{\text{k} \cdot \cancel{\text{M}^2}}{\cancel{\text{M}^2}}$$

$$\frac{\text{min}^{-1}}{\text{M}} = \text{k}$$

$\text{M}^{-1} \cdot \text{min}^{-1} = \text{k}$

Units: $\mathbf{M^{-1} \cdot min^{-1}}$ OR

$\mathbf{L \cdot mol^{-1} \cdot min^{-1}}$

Mathematics of Chemical Kinetics

Determining the Order of a Reaction from Experimental Data

Problem: For the following reaction: $A \longrightarrow \text{products}$

a. Determine the order.
b. Write the rate equation.
c. Determine the value of **k.**

[A]	Initial Rate
.1 M	$4.1 \times 10^{-7}\ M \cdot s^{-1}$
.3	4.1×10^{-7}
.4	4.0×10^{-7}
.7	4.2×10^{-7}

a. The rate does not change with concentration, so **Zero Order.**

b. $\text{Rate} = k[A]^0$ or $\text{Rate} = k$

c. Rate and k are the same, so $k = 4.1 \times 10^{-7}\ M \cdot s^{-1}$

Problem: For the following reaction: $2H_2O_2 \longrightarrow 2H_2O + O_2$

a. Determine the order.
b. Write the rate equation.
c. Determine the value of **k.**

$[H_2O_2]$	Initial Rate
.2 M	$6.42 \times 10^{-6}\ M \cdot s^{-1}$
.3	9.63×10^{-6}
.7	2.25×10^{-5}
1.0	3.21×10^{-5}

Note! The **exponent** in the rate equation is **NOT NECESSARILY** the same as the **coefficient** in the balanced equation. This is different from the equilibrium constant $\mathbf{K_{eq}}$.

The "Ratio Technique"

One way to determine the order is to graph [ ] vs. initial rate.
If linear, first order; if parabola, second order.

Without having to graph, use ratios.
We choose the first and third points: Choose <u>any</u> two points.

a. $\frac{Conc_2}{Conc_1} = \frac{0.7}{0.2} = \textbf{3.5 x}$

$\frac{Rate_2}{Rate_1} = \frac{2.25 \times 10^{-5}}{6.42 \times 10^{-6}} = \textbf{3.5 x}$

Rate changes by the same factor as concentration.

First Order

b. **Rate = k[H_2O_2]**

c. Plug in any point and solve for k.

Rate = k[H_2O_2]

$$\frac{9.63 \times 10^{-6}\ \cancel{M} \cdot s^{-1}}{0.3\ \cancel{M}} = \frac{k \cdot \cancel{0.3\ M}}{\cancel{0.3\ M}}$$

$$k = \mathbf{3.21 \times 10^{-5}\ s^{-1}}$$

Notice: Even though H_2O_2 has a coefficient of 2 in the balanced equation the reaction is **First Order**.

Problem: For the following reaction: $CH_3CHO \longrightarrow CH_4 + CO$

a. Determine the order
b. Write the rate equation
c. Determine the value of **k**.

One way to express data is as follows:

$[CH_3CHO]$ (M)	0.10	0.20	0.30	0.40
Rate ($M \cdot s^{-1}$)	0.085	0.34	0.76	1.4

Previous examples in this handout have recorded the data as:

$[CH_3CHO]$	Initial Rate
0.10 M	0.085 $M \cdot s^{-1}$
0.20	0.34
0.30	0.76
0.40	1.4

a. $\dfrac{\text{Conc}_2}{\text{Conc}_1} = \dfrac{0.3}{0.2} = \boxed{1.5\ \text{x}}$

$\dfrac{\text{Rate}_2}{\text{Rate}_1} = \dfrac{0.76}{0.34} = \boxed{2.24\ \text{x}}$

Since $1.5^2 = 2.25$, rate changes by the **square** of the concentration.

b. **Rate = k$[CH_3CHO]^2$**

Notice: Even though CH_3CHO has a coefficient of 1 in the balanced equation, the reaction is **Second Order**.

c. Plug in any point and solve for k.

$$\text{Rate} = k[CH_3CHO]^2$$

$$0.34\ \text{M} \cdot \text{s}^{-1} = k \cdot (0.2\ \text{M})^2$$

$$\frac{0.34\ \text{M} \cdot \text{s}^{-1}}{(0.2\ \text{M})^2} = \frac{k \cdot \cancel{(0.2\ \text{M})^2}}{\cancel{(0.2\ \text{M})^2}}$$

$$k = \frac{0.34\ \cancel{\text{M}} \cdot \text{s}^{-1}}{0.04\ \text{M}^{\cancel{2}}}$$

$$\mathbf{k = \boxed{8.5\ M^{-1} \cdot s^{-1}}\ \text{or}\ 8.5\ L \cdot mol^{-1} \cdot s^{-1}}$$

(Second order units for k.)

Reactions with More Than One Reactant

Problem: For the following reaction and data:

$$X + Y \longrightarrow \text{products}$$

[X]	[Y]	Initial Rate
0.50 M	0.05 M	$0.0050\ M \cdot s^{-1}$
1.0	0.05	0.010
1.5	0.05	0.015
1.0	0.10	0.010
1.0	0.20	0.010

a. Determine the order in **X** and in **Y**, as well as the overall order.

b. Write the rate equation.

c. Determine **k**.

In doing this sort of problem, figure out the order of each reactant **individually**, then **put them together** into a rate equation.

Rate law will be $\text{Rate} = k[X]^m[Y]^n$. We need to find **m** and **n**.

a. We will do **X** first. Strategy is to choose points at which the other reactant **[Y]** is constant. Then, only the **X** affects the rate.

[X]	[Y]	Initial Rate
0.50 M	0.05 M	$0.0050\ M \cdot s^{-1}$
1.0	0.05	0.010
1.5	0.05	0.015

$$\frac{[X]_2}{[X]_1} = \frac{1.5}{1.0} = 1.5 \qquad \frac{\text{Rate}_2}{\text{Rate}_1} = \frac{.015}{.010} = 1.5$$

Reaction is **First Order in X**.

To do Y, choose [X] constant.

[X]	[Y]	Initial Rate
1.0 M	0.05 M	0.010 $M \cdot s^{-1}$
1.0	0.10	0.010
1.0	0.20	0.010

Reaction is **Zero Order in Y**.

Reaction is **First Order overall**.

b. **Rate = k[X][Y]^0** or **Rate = k[X]**

c. Plug in <u>any</u> point.

Rate = k[X]

$$0.010\ M \cdot s^{-1} = k \cdot 1.0\ M$$

$$\frac{0.010\ \cancel{M} \cdot s^{-1}}{1.0\ \cancel{M}} = \frac{k \cdot 1.0\ \cancel{M}}{1.0\ \cancel{M}}$$

k = 0.010 s^{-1}

<u>Overall Order</u>

Suppose Rate = k[A]^2[B]^3

"Overall Order" 2 + 3 = **5th Order**

(k will have 5th order units.)

Change of Reactant Concentration with Time

Recall the equation and data for the first order reaction from the section earlier in this book called **Basic Chemical Kinetics:**

Suppose the following data are collected for the reaction:

$$2N_2O_5(g) \longrightarrow 4NO_2(g) + O_2(g)$$

Time (min)	$[N_2O_5]$
0	0.160 M
1	0.113
2	0.079
3	0.056
4	0.039

A graph of the data looks like the following:

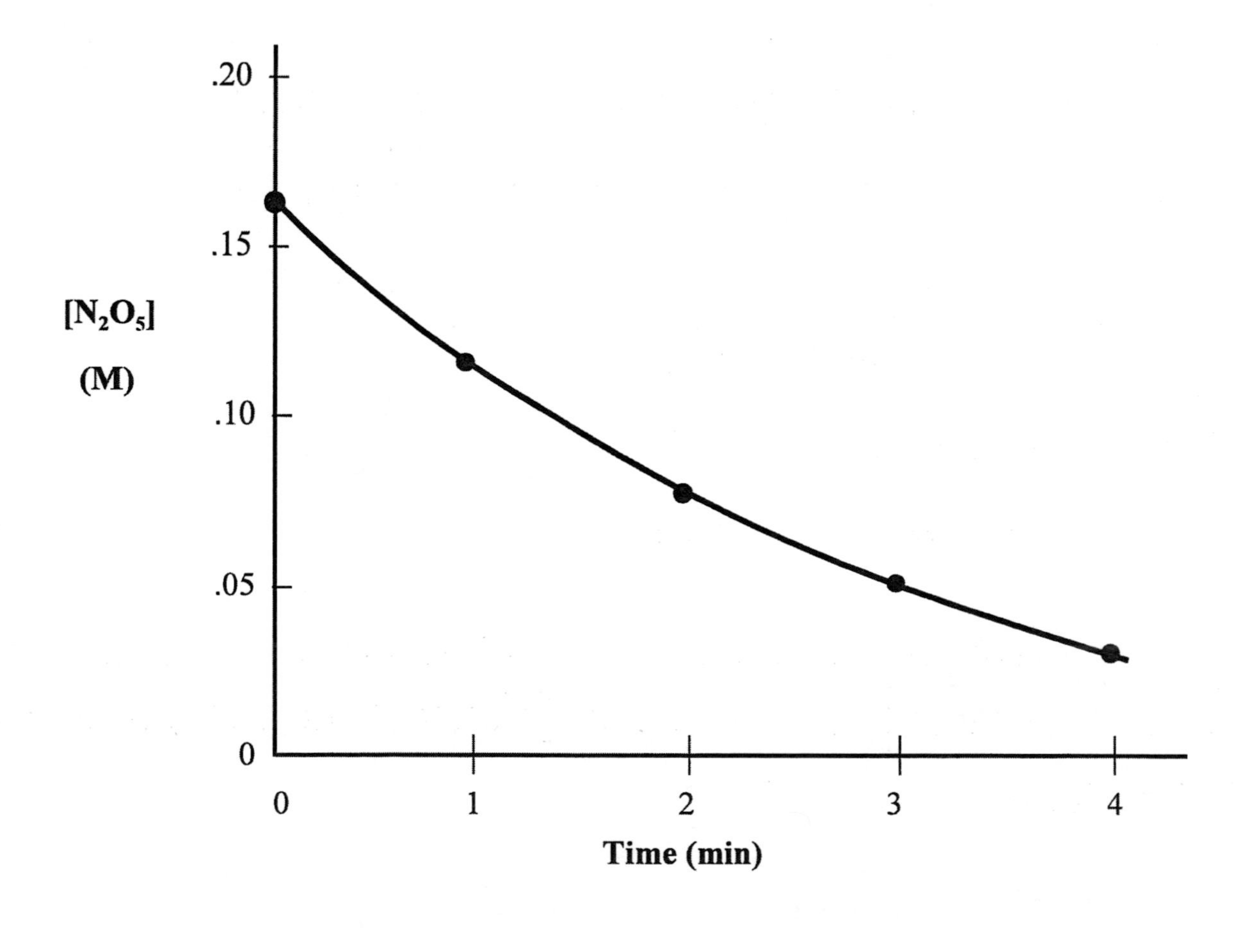

It can be shown using calculus that, for a first order reaction:

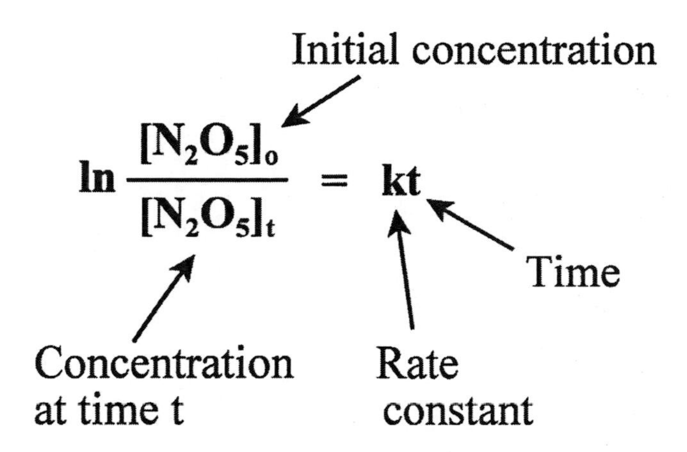

Relationship between $\log_{10}$ and ln

$\log 10 = 1$ $\quad\quad$ $\ln 10 = 2.30...$

↳ ln is always 2.30... times larger than log.

↳ The base of ln is the irrational number "e".

ln → e^x = number ← 2nd or INV ln

Do on calculator:

$2^{nd}\ \ln 1 \Longrightarrow e^1 = 2.71...$

The major difference for you is that if a formula has log, use the log key. IF formula has ln, use the ln key. Otherwise, they work the same way.

$$\ln \frac{[N_2O_5]_o}{[N_2O_5]_t} = kt$$

The equation can be rearranged into linear form by some algebraic manipulations:

$$\ln[N_2O_5]_o - \ln[N_2O_5]_t = kt$$

$$-\ln[N_2O_5]_t = kt - \ln[N_2O_5]_o$$

$$\ln[N_2O_5]_t = -kt + \ln[N_2O_5]_o$$

$$y = mx + b$$

If you plot **time t** on the **x-axis** and $\ln[N_2O_5]_t$ on the **y-axis,** you get a line with:

Slope = **-k** and **y-intercept** = $\mathbf{\ln[N_2O_5]_o}$

First Order

If you plot Time (x-axis) vs. [ ] (y-axis) -- Curve

If you plot Time (x-axis) vs. ln[ ] (y-axis) -- Line

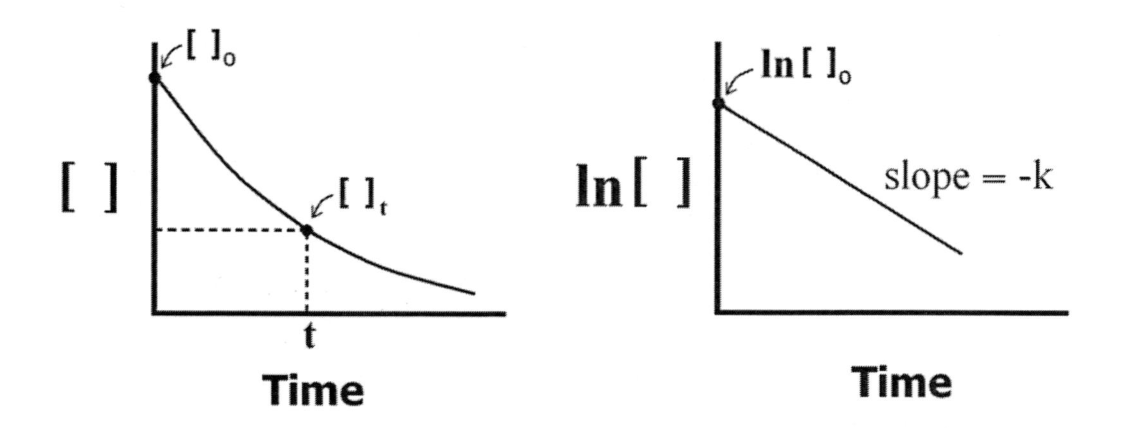

If given Times and [ ]'s, make a third column

x Time	[ ]	y ln[ ]
0	:	:
:	:	:

← *you calculate these numbers*

Problem: Use the data on page 278 (shown again below) to show that a graph of time (**x–axis**) vs. ln $[N_2O_5]$ (**y–axis**) is linear. Then do the following problems:

a. Determine the value of **k** (first order).
b. What is $[N_2O_5]$ at 2.75 min?
c. How long does it take to reach $[N_2O_5] = 0.100$ M?

Solution

a. Make a third column of ln$[N_2O_5]$:

Time (min)	$[N_2O_5]$	ln $[N_2O_5]$
0	0.160 M	-1.83
1	0.113	-2.18
2	0.079	-2.54
3	0.056	-2.88
4	0.039	-3.24

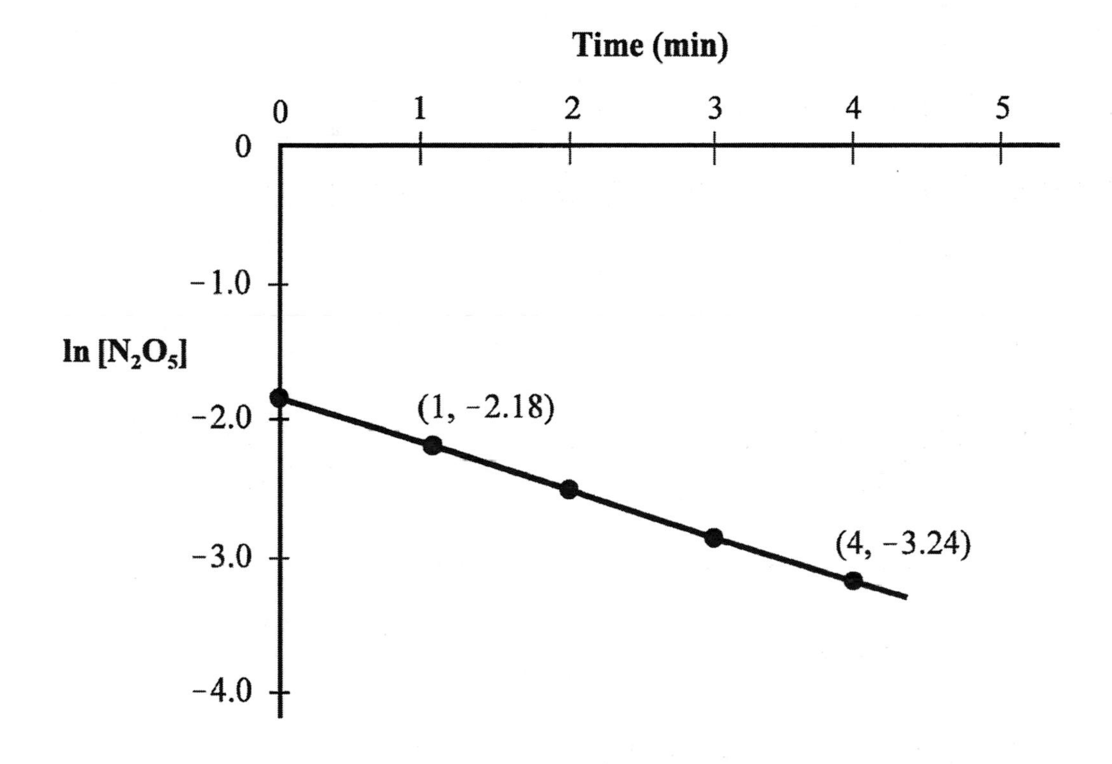

When you are given data with time vs. [ ] (type 2 problem), calculate **k** as follows: (**First Order**)

1) Make a **third column** of **ln[ ]** values.

2) Choose any two points and calculate the **slope** using the **ln[ ]** values for *y* and **Time** values for *x*.

3) Since slope = -**k** for the First Order graph, remove the – sign.

I will use the second and fifth points.

$$\text{Slope} = \frac{y_2 - y_1}{x_2 - x_1} = \frac{-3.24 - (-2.18)}{(4 - 1)\ \text{min}}$$

$$= \frac{(-3.24 + 2.18)}{(4 - 1)} = -0.35\ \text{min}^{-1}$$

$$\text{Slope} = -\mathbf{k} = -0.35\ \text{min}^{-1}$$

$$\mathbf{k} = \mathbf{0.35\ min^{-1}}$$

When asked "what is $[\ ]_t$ at time t" or "how long will it take to get a certain concentration" (as in part c) use the First Order time equation.

b) $$\ln \frac{[N_2O_5]_o}{[N_2O_5]_t} = kt$$

$$\ln \frac{.160}{[N_2O_5]_{2.75}} = (0.35\ \cancel{\text{min}^{-1}})(2.75\ \cancel{\text{min}})$$

$$\ln \frac{.160}{[N_2O_5]_{2.75}} = 0.9625$$

$$\cancel{2^{nd}\ \ln}\left[\cancel{\ln}\ \frac{.160}{[N_2O_5]_{2.75}}\right] = 2^{nd}\ \ln(0.9625)$$

$$\frac{.160}{[N_2O_5]_{2.75}} = 2.62$$

Cross Multiply

$$.160 = 2.62 \cdot [N_2O_5]_{2.75}$$

$$\frac{.160}{2.62} = \frac{\cancel{2.62} \cdot [N_2O_5]_{2.75}}{\cancel{2.62}}$$

$$[N_2O_5]_{2.75} = \boxed{0.061\ M}$$

c) $\ln \frac{[N_2O_5]_o}{[N_2O_5]_t} = kt$

$$\ln \frac{.160}{.100} = (0.35\ \text{min}^{-1})t$$

$$0.47 = (0.35\ \text{min}^{-1})t$$

$$\frac{0.47}{(0.35\ \text{min}^{-1})} = \frac{\cancel{(0.35\ \text{min}^{-1})}t}{\cancel{(0.35\ \text{min}^{-1})}}$$

$$t = \boxed{\mathbf{1.34\ min}}$$

Half-Life of a Reaction

The **half-life ($t_{1/2}$)** of a reaction = the amount of time required for half the reactant to be consumed

For the reaction we have been talking about:

$$2\,N_2O_5(g) \longrightarrow 4\,NO_2(g) + O_2(g)$$

The reaction was followed for 8 minutes. The data are:

Time (min)	$[N_2O_5]$
0	.160 M
2	.080
4	.040
6	.020
8	.010

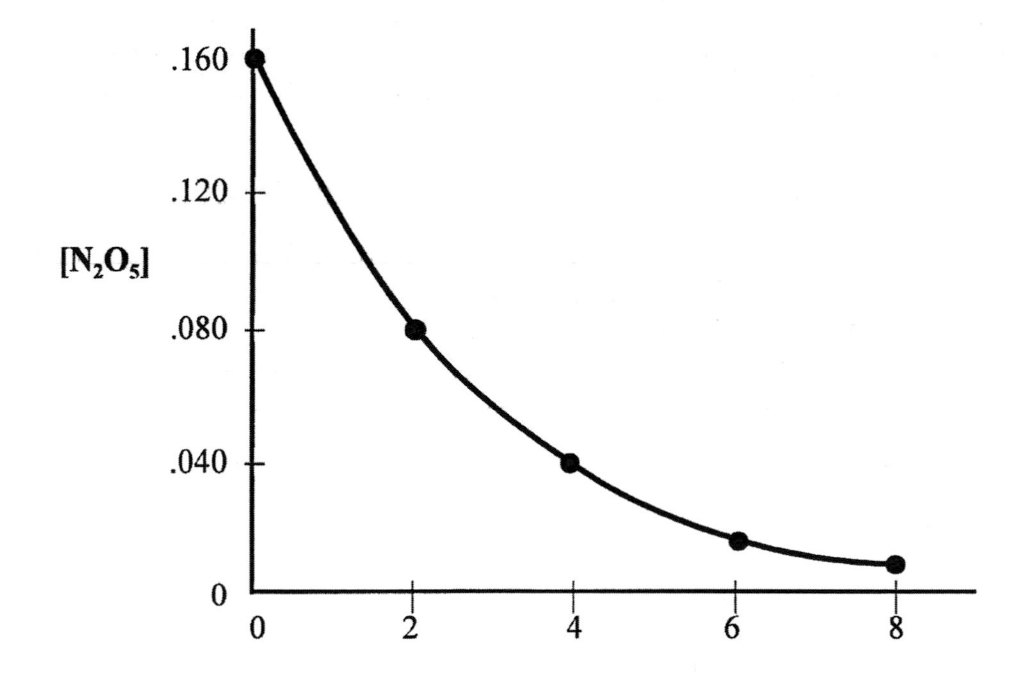

This reaction is known to be first order, so:

$$\ln \frac{[N_2O_5]_o}{[N_2O_5]_t} = kt$$

At the half-life ($t_{½}$), $[A] = ½[A]_o$, so:

$$\ln \frac{\cancel{[N_2O_5]_o}}{½\cancel{[N_2O_5]_o}} = kt_{½}$$

$$\ln 2 = kt_{½}$$

$$t_{½} = \frac{\ln 2}{k}$$

$$t_{½} = \frac{0.693}{k} \quad \textbf{and} \quad k = \frac{0.693}{t_{½}}$$

For the reaction we have been talking about:

$$t_{½} = \frac{0.693}{k} = \frac{0.693}{0.35\ \text{min}^{-1}} = \mathbf{2.0\ min}$$

Two Kinds of Problems in Kinetics

For the reaction: A ⟶ products, two basic kinds of kinetics problems can be done:

1. The kind we have done so far are:

   Given: data of the type:

[A]	Initial Rate
.	.
.	.
.	.
.	.

   "Ratio Technique"

   See the graph on the right on p. 288

   Determine: a. the order
   b. the rate equation
   c. the value of **k**

   } ***Plug in a point***

   Several experiments are needed for this kind of problem, because an initial rate is needed for each [A].

2. The kind of problems you do with the time equation are:

   Given: the order (first or second) and data of the type:

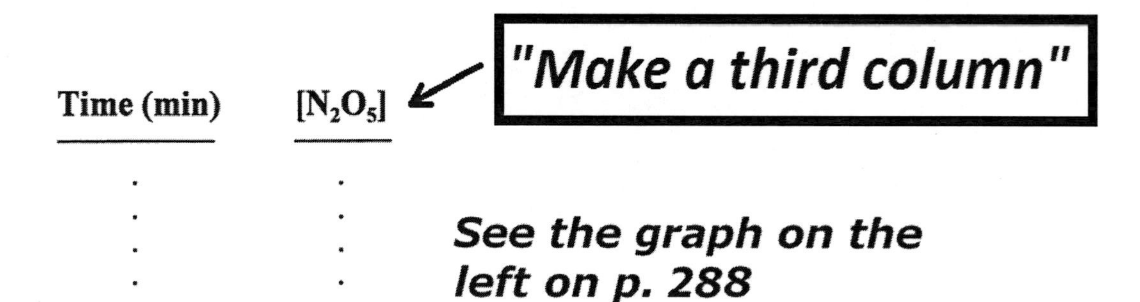

   Determine: a. the value of **k**
   b. the amount of A left at time **t**
   c. How long it takes to get to some [A]

   } ***Plug in time equations***

   Only one experiment is required for this type of problem – starting with an initial concentration of A, follow the decrease in [A] with time.

Two Kinds of Graphs in Kinetics

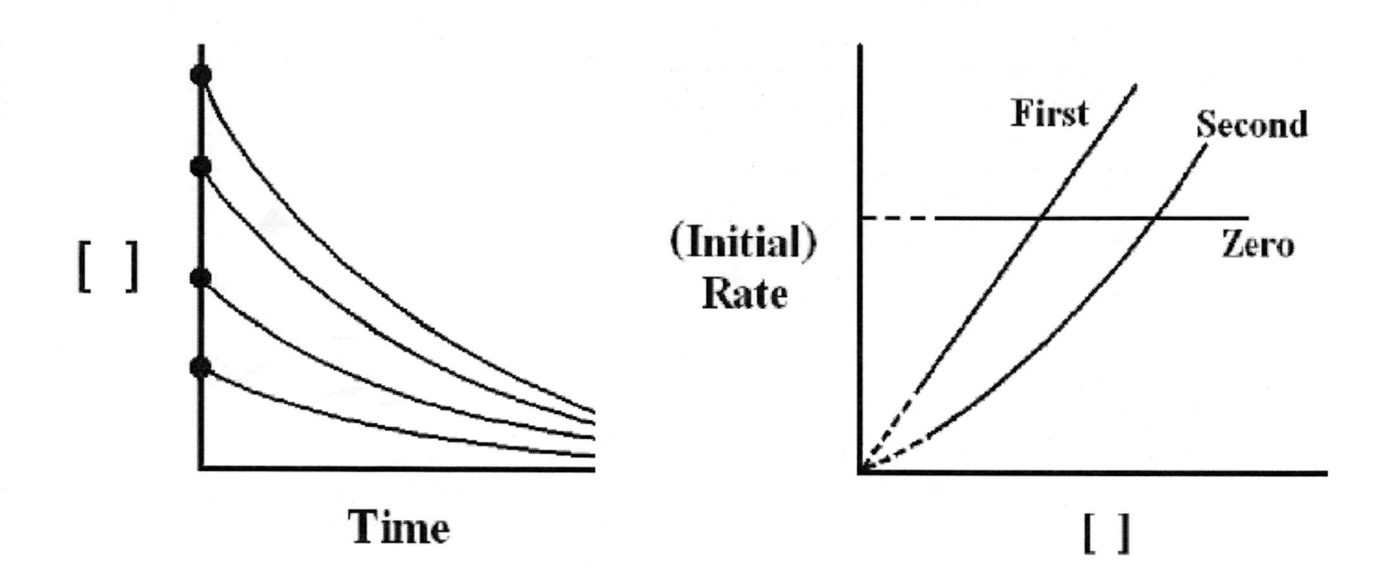

"Time course"

Time	[ ]		[ ]	Rate
.	.		.	.
.	.		.	.
.	.		.	.
.	.		.	.

First Order Kinetics – Complete Example Problem

Problem: For the reaction A $\longrightarrow$ products, the following initial rate data were obtained:

[A]	Initial Rate
1.32×10^{-4} M	9.51×10^{-6} M/min
6.21×10^{-3}	4.48×10^{-4}
3.47×10^{-1}	2.50×10^{-2}
1.72	1.24×10^{-1}

a. Determine the order.
b. Write the rate equation.
c. Determine the value of **k** using data from the above table.

Solution:

a. You can use any two points from the top table. We will use the second and fourth points:

$$\frac{[A]_2}{[A]_1} = \frac{1.72}{6.21 \times 10^{-3}} = 277$$

First Order

$$\frac{\text{Rate}_2}{\text{Rate}_1} = \frac{1.24 \times 10^{-1}}{4.48 \times 10^{-4}} = 277$$

b. **Rate = k[A]**

c. You can substitute any point from the top table. We will use the second point:

$$\text{Rate} = k[A]$$

$$1.24 \times 10^{-1}\ \text{M/min} = k \times 1.72\ \text{M}$$

$$k = \frac{1.24 \times 10^{-1}\ \cancel{\text{M}}/\text{min}}{1.72\ \cancel{\text{M}}} = \mathbf{7.2 \times 10^{-2}\ min^{-1}}$$

Problem: The time course for one of the concentrations in the problem above (a first order reaction) was followed, and the following data were obtained:

time	[A]
0 min	1.72 M
20	0.378
40	9.61×10^{-2}
60	2.27×10^{-2}
80	5.38×10^{-3}

a. Determine the value of **k** from the time course data.
b. What is [A] at 65 min?
c. How long would it take for [A] to get to 6.17×10^{-7} M?
d. What is the half-life, $t_{1/2}$?

Solution:

a. To calculate **k** from the time course, you must first calculate the **ln** values for each point:

time	[A]	ln [A]
0 min	1.72 M	0.542
20	0.378 M	-0.973
40	9.61×10^{-2} M	-2.34
60	2.27×10^{-2} M	-3.79
80	5.38×10^{-3} M	-5.23

You can do this problem without graphing it, but the graph is shown below to help you visualize calculation of the slope:

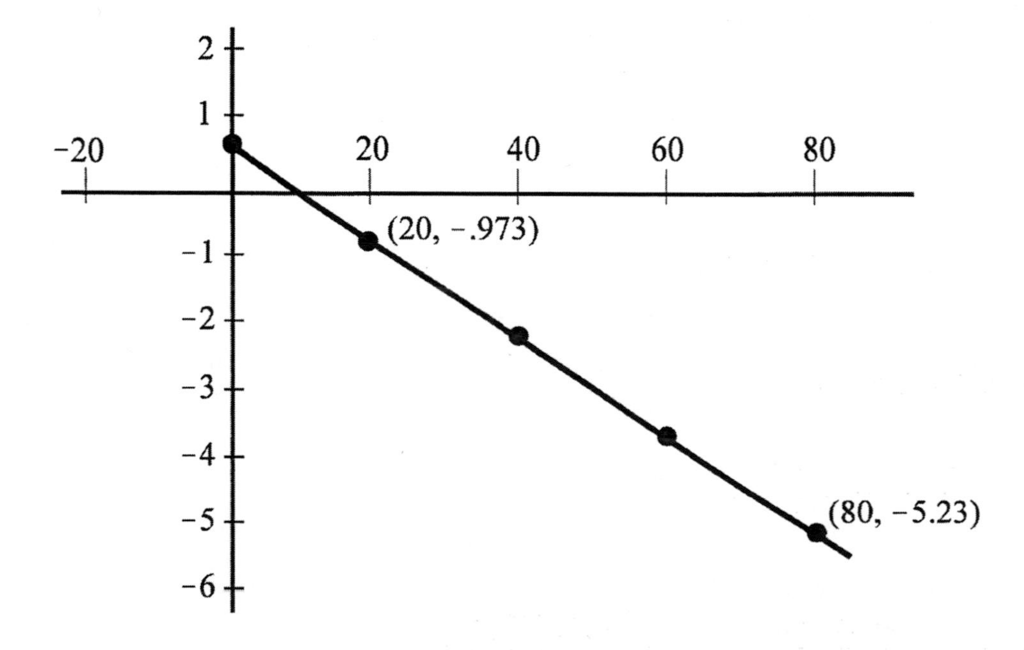

Using the two points shown above to calculate the slope gives:

$$\text{slope} = \frac{y_2 - y_1}{x_2 - x_1} = \frac{[-5.23 - (-0.973)]}{(80 - 20)\text{ min}} = \frac{-4.257}{60\text{ min}} = -7.1 \times 10^{-2}\text{ min}^{-1}$$

$$k = -\text{slope} = \boxed{7.1 \times 10^{-2}\text{ min}^{-1}}$$

b.

$$\ln\frac{[A]_0}{[A]_t} = kt$$

$$\ln\frac{1.72\text{ M}}{[A]_{65}} = (7.1 \times 10^{-2}\text{ min}^{-1}) \times 65\text{ min}$$

$$\ln\frac{1.72}{[A]_{65}} = 4.615 \Rightarrow \cancel{2\text{nd}\ln}\left(\cancel{\ln}\frac{1.72}{[A]_{65}}\right) = 2\text{nd}\ln(4.615)$$

$$\Rightarrow \frac{1.72}{[A]_{65}} = 2\text{nd}\ln(4.615) \Rightarrow \frac{1.72}{[A]_{65}} = 101$$

$$\Rightarrow \cancel{[A]_{65}} \cdot \frac{1.72}{\cancel{[A]_{65}}} = 101 \cdot [A]_{65} \Rightarrow 1.72 = 101 \cdot [A]_{65}$$

$$\Rightarrow \frac{1.72}{101} = \frac{\cancel{101} \cdot [A]_{65}}{\cancel{101}}$$

$$\Rightarrow [A]_{65} = \frac{1.72\text{ M}}{101} = \boxed{1.7 \times 10^{-2}\text{ M}}$$

c.

$$\ln\frac{[A]_0}{[A]_t} = kt$$

$$\ln\frac{1.72}{6.17 \times 10^{-7}} = 7.1 \times 10^{-2}\text{ min}^{-1} \times t$$

$$14.8 = 7.1 \times 10^{-2}\text{ min}^{-1} \times t$$

$$t = \frac{14.8}{7.1 \times 10^{-2}\text{ min}^{-1}} = \boxed{209\text{ min}}$$

d.

$$t_{1/2} = \frac{0.693}{k} = \frac{0.693}{7.1 \times 10^{-2}\text{ min}^{-1}} = \boxed{9.76\text{ min}}$$

Second Order Equations

Consider the **second order** equation: $2\,HI \longrightarrow H_2(g) + I_2(g)$

Suppose that the following data are collected:

Time (hr)	[HI]
0	1.500 M
0.65	1.008
0.95	0.876
1.72	0.655
2.47	0.526

A graph of the data looks like the following:

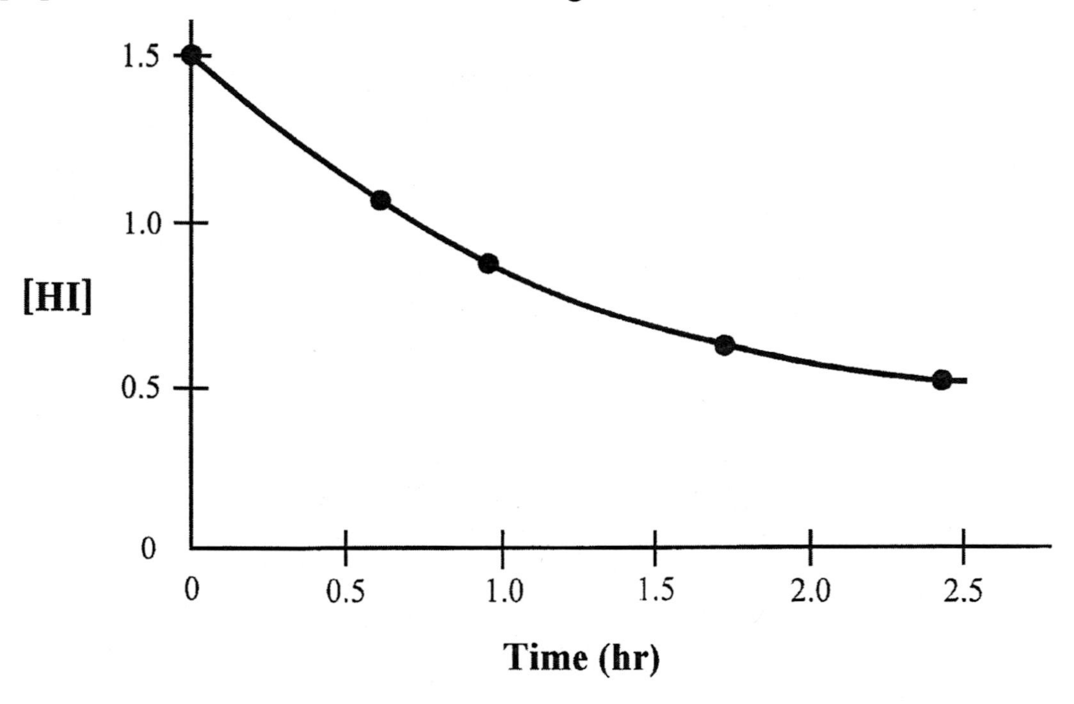

It can be shown using calculus that, for a second order reaction (A $\longrightarrow$ products):

$$\frac{1}{[A]_t} = kt + \frac{1}{[A]_o}$$

$[A]_t$: Concentration at time t

k: Rate constant

t: Time

$[A]_o$: Initial concentration

This equation is in the form:

$$y = mx + b$$

If you plot **time t** on the **x–axis** and **1/[A]** on the **y–axis**, you get a line with:

Slope = **k** and **y–intercept** = **$1/[A]_o$**

Second Order

If you plot time (x-axis) vs. [ ] (y-axis) -- CURVE

If you plot time (x-axis) vs. $\frac{1}{[\ ]}$ (y-axis) -- LINE

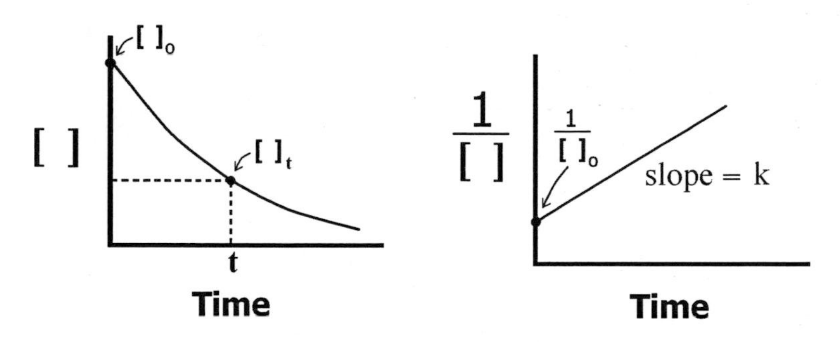

If given Times and [ ]'s, make a third column

(x) Time	[ ]	(y) $\frac{1}{[\ ]}$
0	⋮	⋮
⋮		

← *you calculate these numbers*

The **half-life ($t_{1/2}$)** occurs when $[HI] = \frac{1}{2}[HI]_o$
Substituting and solving for $t_{1/2}$ gives:

$$\frac{1}{\frac{1}{2}[A]_o} = kt_{1/2} + \frac{1}{[A]_o} \quad >>> \quad \frac{2}{[A]_o} = kt_{1/2} + \frac{1}{[A]_o}$$

$$>>> \quad \frac{2}{[A]_o} - \frac{1}{[A]_o} = kt_{1/2} \quad >>> \quad \frac{1}{[A]_o}(2-1) = kt_{1/2}$$

$$>>> \quad \frac{1}{[A]_o} = kt_{1/2} \quad >>> \quad t_{1/2} = \frac{1}{k[A]_o}$$

First Order	**Second Order**
$t_{1/2} = \frac{0.693}{k}$	$t_{1/2} = \frac{1}{k[A]}$
Does not depend on concentration	*Depends on concentration*
$t_{1/2}$ *constant*	$t_{1/2}$ *keeps changing*

Second Order Example – Complete Time Course Problem

Problem: Use the data on page 292 (shown again below) to show that a graph of time (**x–axis**) vs. 1/[HI] (**y–axis**) is linear. Then do the following problems:

a. Determine the value of **k** (the **second order** rate constant).
b. What is [HI] at 4.71 hr?
c. How long does it take for [HI] to reach 0.70 M?
d. Determine the half–life $t_{½}$ when [HI] = 0.80 M.

Solution

a. Make a third column of 1/[A]:

Time (hr)	[HI]	$\frac{1}{[HI]}$
0	1.500 M	0.667 M^{-1}
0.65	1.008	0.992
0.95	0.876	1.142
1.72	0.655	1.527
2.47	0.526	1.901

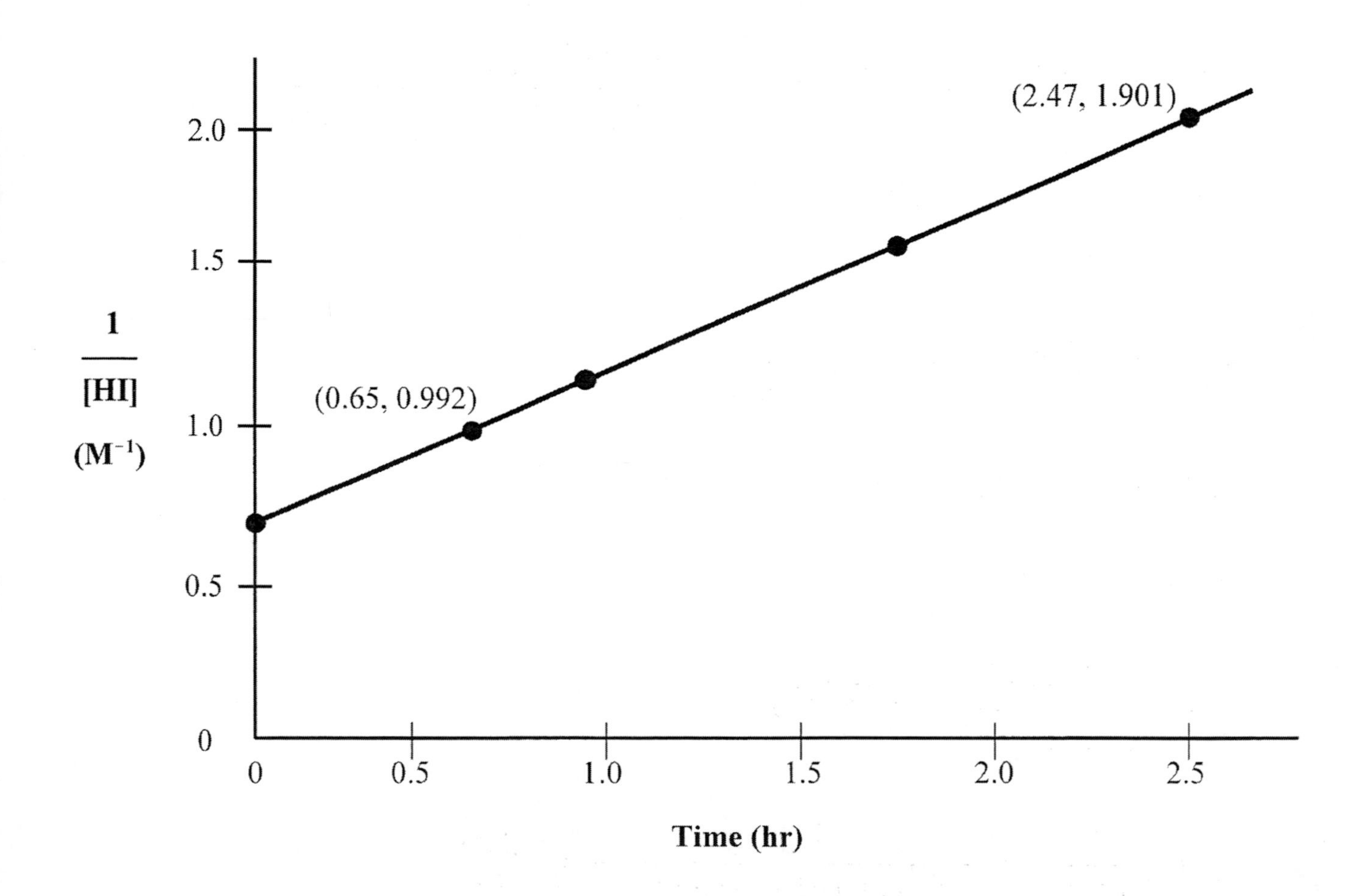

a. Since slope = k, find the slope.

$$\text{slope} = \frac{(1.901 - 0.992)\ M^{-1}}{(2.47 - 0.65)\ hr} = \frac{0.909}{1.82} M^{-1}\cdot hr^{-1} = 0.50\ M^{-1}\cdot hr^{-1}$$

$$k = \boxed{\mathbf{0.50\ M^{-1}\cdot hr^{-1}}} \quad \text{or} \quad \boxed{\mathbf{0.50\ L\cdot mol^{-1}\cdot hr^{-1}}}$$

<u>**Note:**</u> You **DO NOT** need to make the graph to get the value of **k**; just make the third column of 1/[A] values and calculate the slope.

b.

$$\frac{1}{[A]} = kt + \frac{1}{[A]_o}$$

$$\frac{1}{[A]} = (0.50\ M^{-1}\cdot \cancel{hr^{-1}})(4.71\ \cancel{hr}) + \frac{1}{1.500\ M}$$

$$\frac{1}{[A]} = 3.022\ M^{-1} \quad \Rightarrow \quad \cancel{[A]}\cdot\frac{1}{\cancel{[A]}} = 3.022\ M^{-1}\cdot [A]$$

$$\Rightarrow 3.022\ M^{-1}\cdot [A] = 1 \quad \Rightarrow \quad \frac{\cancel{3.022\ M^{-1}}\cdot [A]}{\cancel{3.022\ M^{-1}}} = \frac{1}{3.022\ M^{-1}}$$

$$\Rightarrow [A] = \frac{1}{3.022\ M^{-1}} = \boxed{\mathbf{0.331\ M}}$$

c.

$$\frac{1}{0.7\ M} = (0.50\ M^{-1}\cdot hr^{-1})t + \frac{1}{1.500\ M}$$

$$1.429\ M^{-1} = (0.50\ M^{-1}\cdot hr^{-1})t + 0.667\ M^{-1}$$

$$0.762\ M^{-1} = (0.50\ M^{-1}\cdot hr^{-1})t$$

$$t = \frac{0.762\ M^{-1}}{0.50\ M^{-1}\cdot hr^{-1}} = \boxed{\mathbf{1.52\ hr}}$$

d.

$$t_{1/2} = \frac{1}{k[A]} = \frac{1}{0.50\ M^{-1}\cdot hr^{-1} \times 0.80\ M} = \boxed{\mathbf{2.5\ hr}}$$

Summary of Kinetics Graphs and Equations

Zero Order	First Order	Second Order

Zero Order

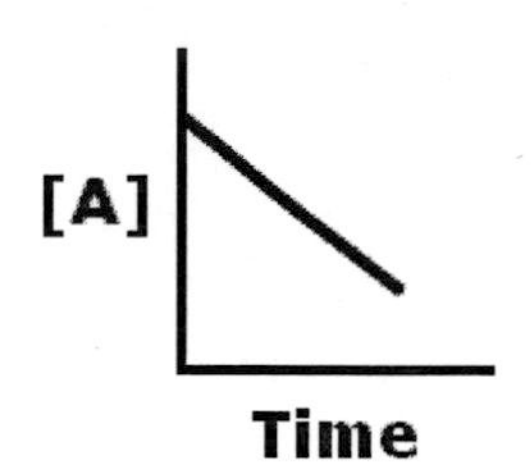

Initial Rate

[A]

Rate = k

$[A]_t = -kt + [A]_0$

$t_{1/2} = \frac{[A]}{2k}$

First Order

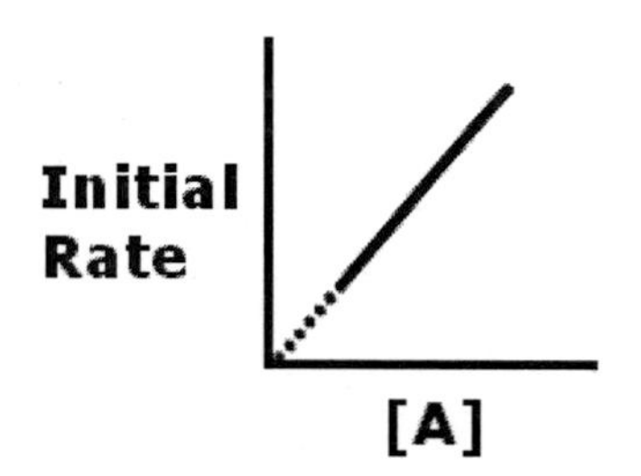

Rate = k[A]

Time Graph Above Is Linear

ln[A] — slope = −k

Time

$$\ln\frac{[A]_0}{[A]_t} = kt$$

$$\ln[A]_0 = -kt + \ln[A]_t$$

$$t_{1/2} = \frac{0.693}{k}$$

Second Order

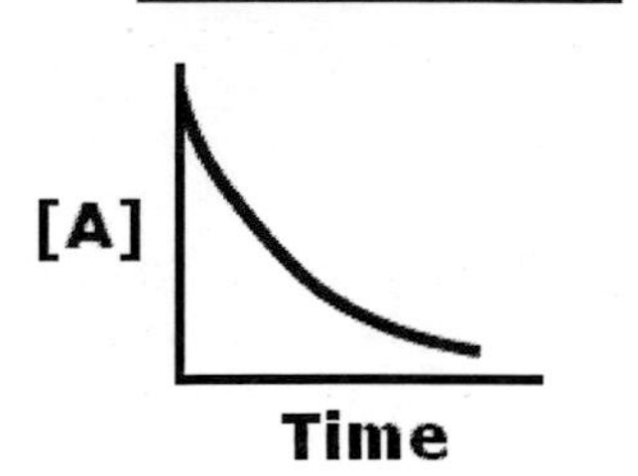

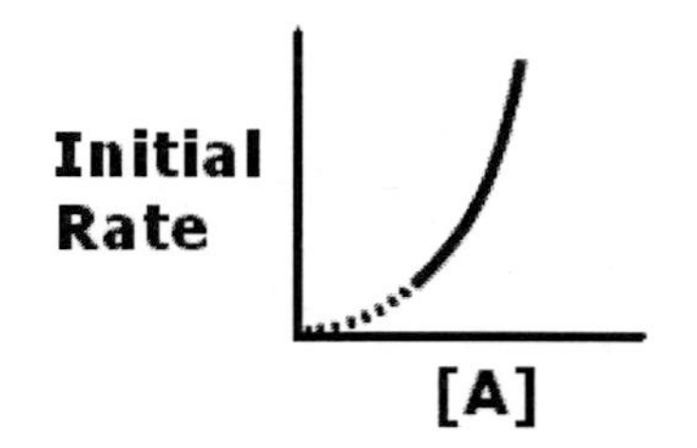

Rate = $k[A]^2$

$\frac{1}{[A]}$ — slope = k

Time

$$\frac{1}{[A]_t} = kt + \frac{1}{[A]_0}$$

$$t_{1/2} = \frac{1}{k[A]}$$

Determining the order of a reaction from just one time course

Suppose a chemist collects time vs. [ ] data for only one time course, and then graphs the data.

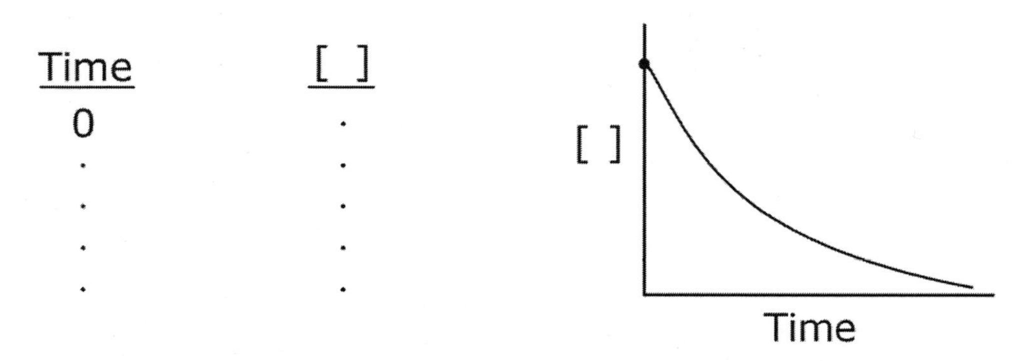

Because both First and Second order time courses are curved, the order cannot be determined visually.

The order can be determined by graphing <u>both</u> Time vs. ln[ ] and Time vs 1/[ ]. The ln[ ] and 1/[ ] columns are calculated from the original data.

Time	[ ]	ln[ ]	1/[ ]
0	.	.	.
.	.	.	.
.	.	.	.
.	.	.	.
.	.	.	.

Calculate the ln[ ] and the 1/[ ] columns using the original [ ] data column.

First Order

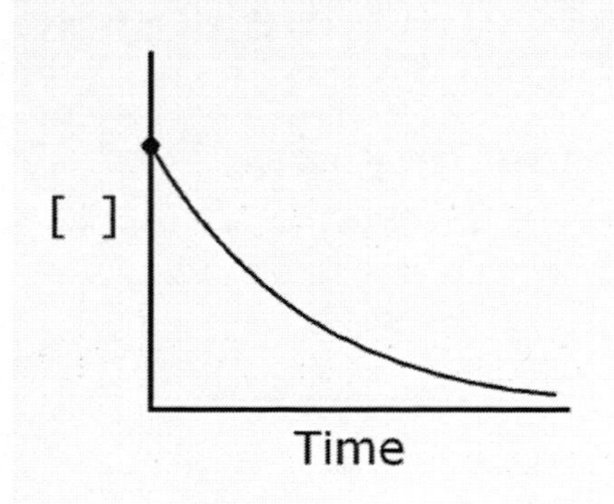

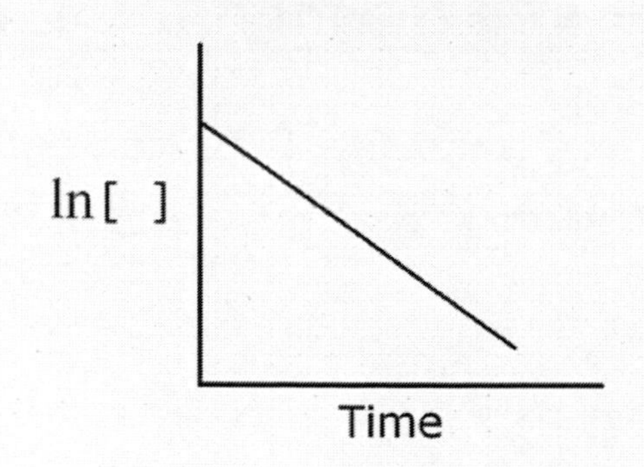

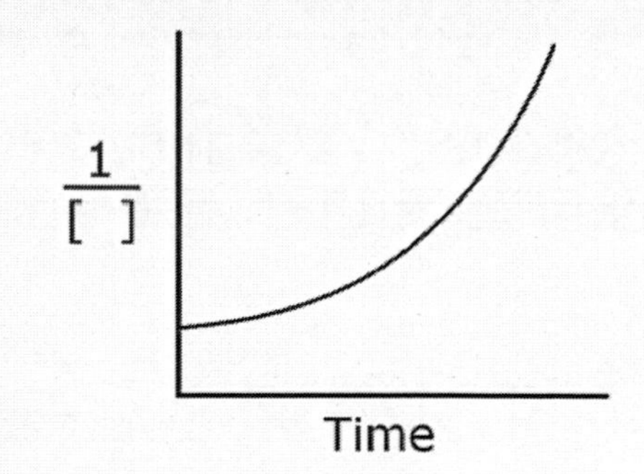

Second Order

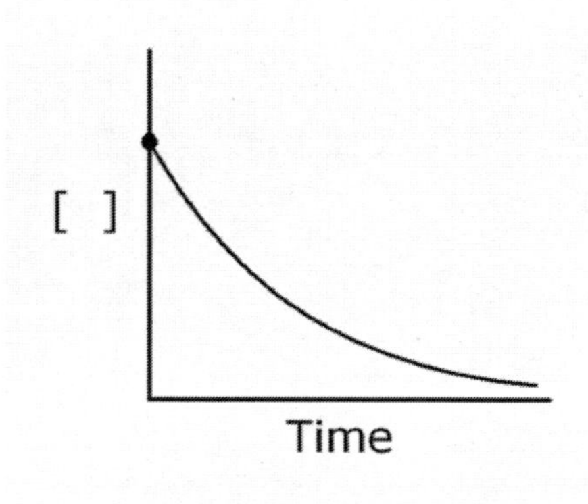

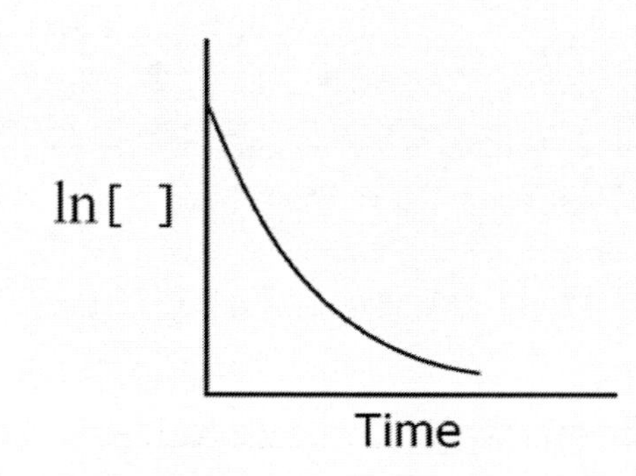

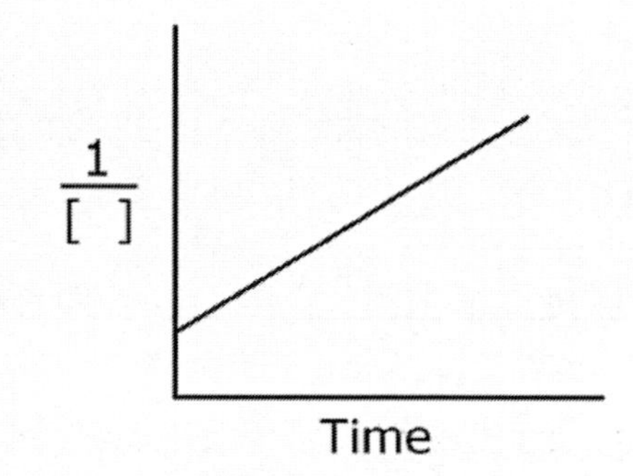

Relationship Between Kinetic and Thermodynamics

$$A + B \underset{k_r}{\overset{k_f}{\rightleftharpoons}} C + D$$

$$K_{eq} = \frac{[C][D]}{[A][B]}$$

If forward reaction is faster ⇒ More C and D at equilibrium ⇒ Large K_{eq} (lots of product)

If reverse reaction is faster ⇒ More A and B at equilibrium ⇒ Small K_{eq} (mostly reactants)

Collision Theory of Reaction Rates:

$$A + B \rightleftharpoons C + D$$

Principle: Molecules A and B cannot react unless they collide.

"Diffusion-Controlled" Reaction: Every collision between A and B is successful (produces the desired products). So, the rate is limited only by how fast A and B can **"diffuse"** together.

Example: $H^+(aq) + OH^-(aq) \rightarrow H_2O(\ell)$

Second Order Rate constants (**k**) are 10^{10}-10^{12} $L \cdot mol^{-1} \cdot s^{-1}$

Two Requirements for a collision to be successful

1. Reactant molecules must have enough **Energy.**
2. Reactant molecules must have the correct **"orientation"** = must be facing the right way.

Lewis Structures

NO_2 $\quad$ CO $\quad$ NO $\quad$ CO_2

$O{=}\dot{N}{-}\ddot{O}{:}$ $\quad$ $:C{\equiv}O:$ $\quad$ $\cdot\ddot{N}{=}\ddot{O}{:}$ $\quad$ $:\ddot{O}{=}C{=}\ddot{O}:$

$$NO_2 + CO \rightarrow NO + CO_2$$

Correct

O=N–O ←←← C≡O → O=N + O=C=O

Incorrect

O=N–O ←←← O≡C

C≡O → O=N–O

O≡C → O=N–O

If the collision has correct orientation

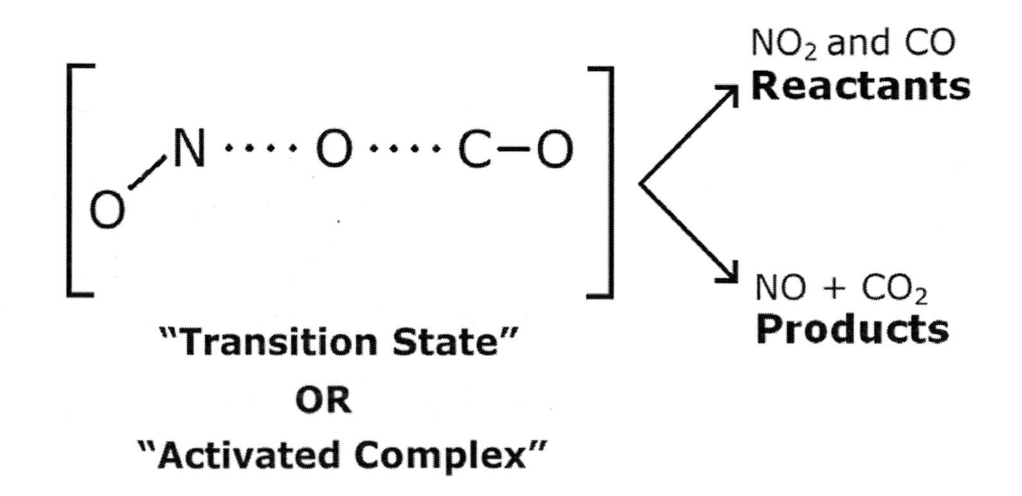

"Transition State"

OR

"Activated Complex"

Even when Transition State is reached two possibilities exist:

1. O returns to N ⟹ back to reactants
2. O goes to C ⟹ products (successful)

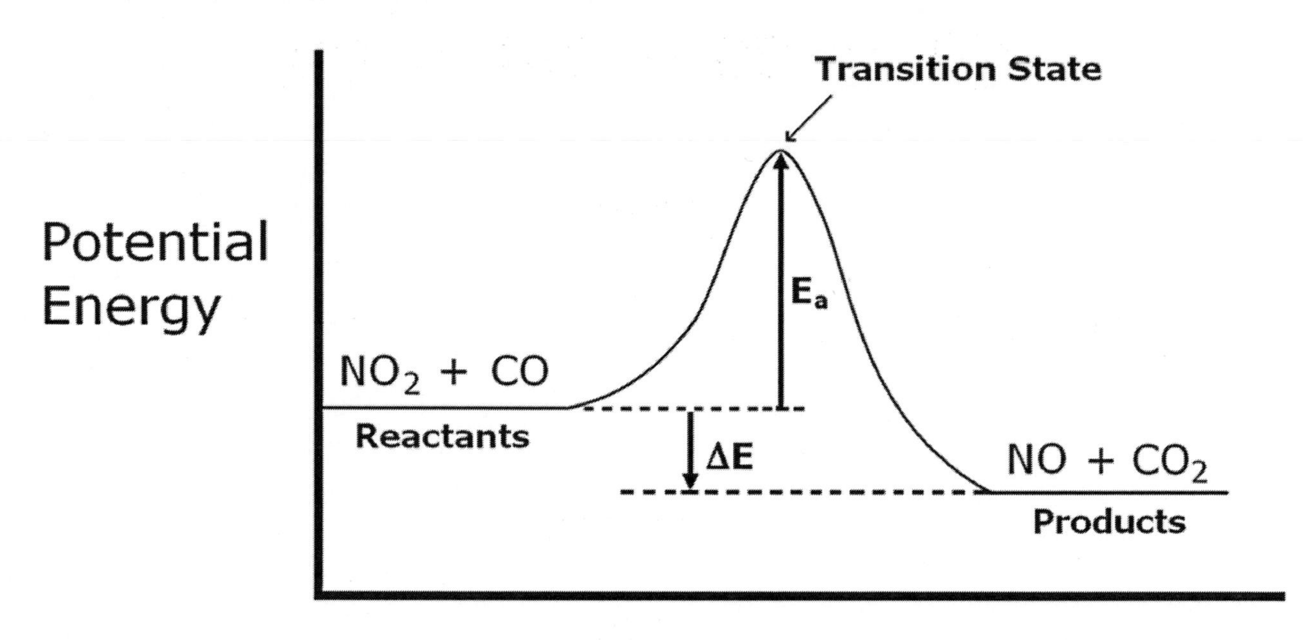

Kinetics = controlled largely by the size of
$\mathbf{E_a}$ = energy of activation

↑$\mathbf{E_a}$ slower rate ↓$\mathbf{E_a}$ faster rate

Thermodynamics = controlled largely by the size of $\mathbf{\Delta E}$ = the difference in energy between reactants and products.

Basic Idea = all systems tend to try to reach a minimum energy. Referred to as "more stable."

$$A + B \rightleftharpoons C + D$$

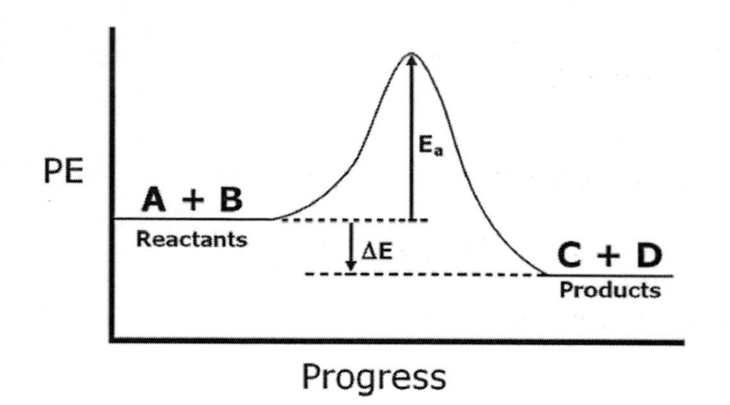

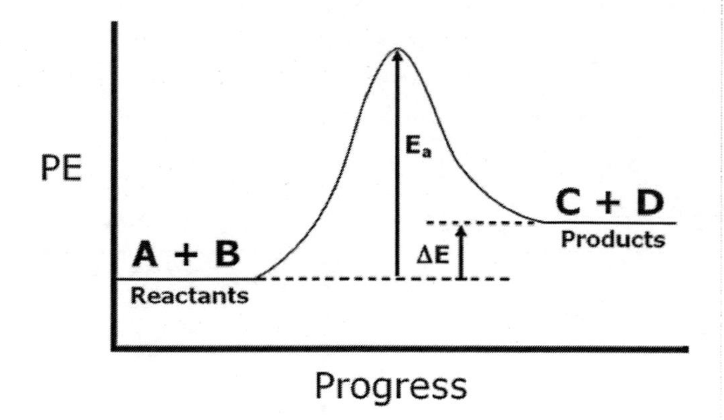

Energy decreases

Energy given off

Exothermic

Favors Products

$$K_{eq} = \frac{\text{products}}{\text{reactants}}$$

= **Large**

Energy increases

Energy absorbed

Endothermic

Favors Reactants

$$K_{eq} = \frac{\text{products}}{\text{reactants}}$$

= **Small**

Factors Affecting Reaction Rate

1. **State of subdivision of reactants**. Smaller particles have more surface area, so faster reaction.

   Examples: Sawdust burns faster than wood.
   Powdered salt dissolves faster than rock salt.

2. **Concentration of reactants**. **Higher** concentrations usually give **higher** rates.

   Example: Rate = $k[N_2O_5]$ (concentration involved in rate equation.)

   Higher concentrations give **more collisions**, so greater chance for **successful** ones.

3. **Temperature**. **ALL** reaction rates **increase** with ↑ temperature. A rough rule of thumb is:

   Rate doubles when ↑ temperature **10°C**. (Approximate rule.)

   Why? For any sample of molecules, energies are distributed according to **Boltzmann's Distribution**:

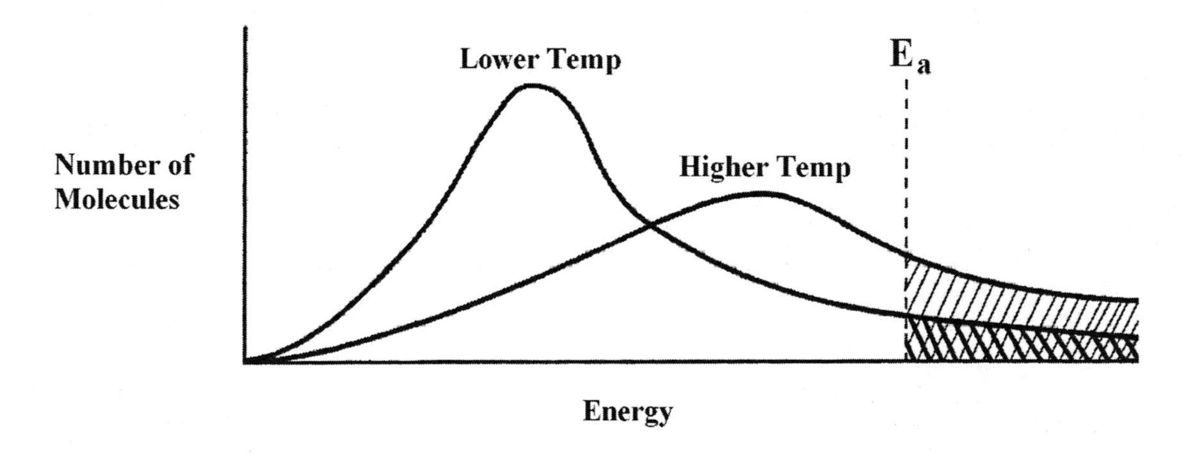

   In order to react, molecules must have an energy **greater than or equal to** E_a. At **low temperature**, only a **few molecules** have enough energy to react (see thick slashes above). At **higher temperature**, the average energy of the molecules increases, so **more molecules have enough energy** to react (see thin slashes above). **Temperature does not change E_a.**

   This energy factor is the main reason that **rate is faster as ↑ temperature.**

4. **Energy of Activation** **(E_a).**

   E_a can be changed by adding a **catalyst** = substance that speeds up a reaction without being consumed.

   Catalysts act by making E_a for a reaction **lower**.

   Catalysts do not change the position of equilibrium (K_{eq}).

<u>Catalysts</u> = speed up chemical reactions by lowering the Energy of Activation (E_a).

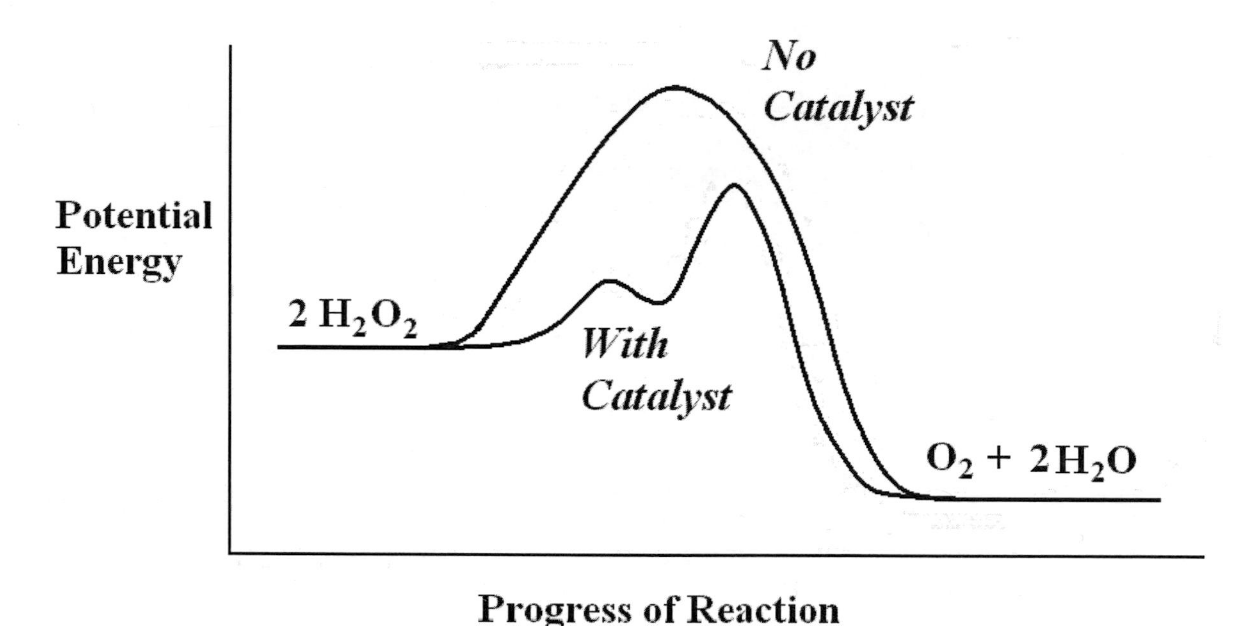

Which Changes Have the Greatest Effect?

According to the following theoretical equation used by physical chemists:

$$\text{Rate} = Ze^{-E_a/RT}$$

1) Subdivision and concentration have effects that change the rate mainly by <u>multiplication.</u> They affect the value of Z.

2) E_a and T are both in the <u>exponent</u>, so they affect the rate <u>much more</u>.

Thermodynamics Part 1

(Homework #12)

Reaction Mechanisms

1. Most reactions do not occur exactly as written, but instead, occur in a series of steps called a **reaction mechanism.**

2. An **overall reaction** just gives a list of what reacts and what is produced, whereas the **reaction mechanism** shows the actual series of steps by which the reaction is believed to occur.

   For example, the overall reaction:

   $$2\ O_3(g) \longrightarrow 3\ O_2(g)$$

   probably does not occur as written, that is, with two **O_3 (ozone)** molecules colliding and immediately producing three **O_2 (normal oxygen)** molecules. It is believed that the reaction occurs by the following two-step mechanism:

   $$O_3 \longrightarrow O_2 + O \quad \textbf{(slow)}$$

   $$O + O_3 \longrightarrow O_2 + O_2 \quad \textbf{(fast)}$$

3. Each step in a mechanism is called an **elementary step** because these steps are believed to occur exactly as written.

4. In other words, in the first step, one O_3 molecule actually breaks apart into an O_2 molecule and an oxygen atom.

5. In the second step, an oxygen atom formed in the first step collides with another O_3 to form two O_2 molecules.

6. To determine whether such a proposed mechanism is correct, the **kinetics of the overall reaction** are determined.

7. Techniques discussed in the previous class (such as **TIME vs. [A]** graphs and **[A] vs. INITIAL RATE** graphs) are used to determine the order in each reactant and the value of the rate constant **k.**

8. The rate law obtained in the lab by doing such experiments is considered **an experimental "fact"** if the data are collected correctly.

9. In order for a mechanism to be the correct one for the overall reaction, the mechanism **must predict the same rate law** as the experimental rate law determined in lab.

   A. For each mechanism, there is a rate law that the mechanism predicts **must be true** if that mechanism occurs.

   B. This **predicted rate law** is derived mathematically from the steps in the mechanism.

   C. The predicted rate law is obtained by **correctly combining the individual rate laws** for each elementary step.

   D. The rate law for an elementary step depends on which of the following three types the step it is.

Types of Elementary Steps and Their Rate Laws

Because an elementary step occurs exactly as written, **coefficients in the equation can be used as exponents** in the rate law. **Only reactants** appear in the rate law, **not products.**

1. **Unimolecular step** = reaction occurs when one molecule decomposes.

   An example is the first step in the ozone mechanism.

   $$O_3 \longrightarrow O_2 + O$$

   The rate law can be written as: **Rate = $k[O_3]$**

2. **Bimolecular step** = reaction occurs when two molecules collide.

   An example is the second step in the ozone mechanism.

   $$O + O_3 \longrightarrow O_2 + O_2$$

   The rate law can be written as: **Rate = $k[O][O_3]$**

   In some bimolecular steps, the two molecules that collide are identical.

   $$NO_2 + NO_2 \longrightarrow NO + NO_3$$

   or

   $$2\,NO_2 \longrightarrow NO + NO_3$$

   The rate law can be written as: **Rate = $k[NO_2]^2$**

3. **Termolecular step** = reaction occurs when three molecules collide.

   These are **very rare** because they require that three molecules collide with one another at the same place at the same time. The mathematical probability of such a collision is extremely small.

How is a mechanism verified experimentally?

A mechanism must fulfill two basic requirements in order to have a possibility of being correct.

1. The elementary steps in the mechanism **must add up to the overall reaction.**
2. The mechanism **must predict the correct rate law.** Determining the predicted rate law for a mechanism depends on the following **Basic Principle for Reaction Mechanisms.**

Basic Principle for Reaction Mechanisms

An overall reaction **cannot be faster** than the slowest step in the mechanism. The **slowest step** determines the rate law and is also called the **rate-limiting** or **rate-determining step**.

1. If the first step in the mechanism is the slowest step, the rate law that the mechanism predicts for the overall reaction is the **same as the rate law for the first step**. Reaction steps after the first step are fast and do not affect the overall rate law.

2. If the slowest step is not the first step, substances in the preceding steps can also appear in the overall rate law because the reaction tends to "back up" behind the slow step. Reaction steps following the slow step still do not affect the rate law. This case can be somewhat complicated mathematically, and we will not discuss how to derive a predicted rate law in this case.

Test of the Proposed Mechanism for the Ozone Reaction

1. **The elementary steps must add up to the overall reaction, which they do.**

$$O_3 \longrightarrow O_2 + \cancel{O}$$
$$\cancel{O} + O_3 \longrightarrow O_2 + O_2$$
$$\overline{\qquad 2\,O_3 \longrightarrow 3\,O_2 \qquad}$$

   The O atom is called a **reactive intermediate.** It is **reactive** because it is unstable and cannot be isolated as a pure substance. It is an **intermediate** because it forms in one step, but is consumed in the next step, so it does not appear in the products.

2. **The mechanism must predict the correct rate law.**

   According to the **Basic Principle for Reaction Mechanisms,** the proposed mechanism for the ozone reaction:

$$O_3 \longrightarrow O_2 + O \qquad \textbf{(slow)}$$
$$O + O_3 \longrightarrow O_2 + O_2 \qquad \textbf{(fast)}$$

   predicts that the overall rate law for the reaction would be **Rate = k[O_3]** because, since the **first step is the slowest step,** the overall reaction has the **same rate law as the slowest step.**

   Suppose the rate law for the overall ozone reaction was determined (by kinetic experiments in the lab) to be **Rate = k[O_3].** This rate law would then be considered an **experimental "fact."** The proposed mechanism would therefore be **possible,** that is, **consistent with the experimental data,** because it **predicts the same rate law** as the experimental "fact."

   On the other hand, if the experimental rate law were determined to be **Rate = k[O_3]^2**, the proposed mechanism could be **eliminated as a possibility** because it predicts the wrong rate law.

Proving Mechanisms

Even if a mechanism adds up to the overall rate law and predicts the same rate law as the experimentally determined rate law, the mechanism is **not proved.** Other mechanisms could be proposed that would add up correctly and predict the same rate law. Experiments of other types are required to provide further evidence for a proposed mechanism. Even after many experiments provide support for a given mechanism, the mechanism is **never considered to be proved.** Chemists refer to mechanisms with a great deal of support as **"well established."**

Questions that can be asked about reaction mechanisms

1. Does the mechanism add up to the overall reaction? (Know how to add mechanism steps.)
2. What substance(s) in the reaction is (are) reactive intermediates?
3. What is the rate law for an elementary step in a mechanism?
4. What rate law would a given mechanism predict and is the predicted rate law consistent with the known experimental rate law? (Only a mechanism in which the first step is the slow step would be asked about in such a question, so the rate law for the slow step is the same as for the overall reaction.)

Another Example

The following reaction:

$$CO + NO_2 \longrightarrow CO_2 + NO$$

has been found experimentally to have two different rate laws depending on temperature:

High temp (above 225°C): **Rate = k[CO][NO_2]**

Low temp (below 225°C): **Rate = k[NO_2]^2**

It has been proposed that the difference in rate law is observed because the reaction occurs by a **different mechanism** at high temperatures than at low temperatures. The following two mechanisms have been proposed as possibilities:

Mechanism 1 (a single-step mechanism in which the reaction occurs exactly as in the overall reaction)

$$CO + NO_2 \longrightarrow CO_2 + NO$$

Mechanism 2 (two-step mechanism)

$$NO_2 + NO_2 \longrightarrow NO + NO_3 \quad \textbf{(slow)}$$

$$NO_3 + CO \longrightarrow NO_2 + CO_2 \quad \textbf{(fast)}$$

To test each mechanism, apply the tests described previously:

A. Do the steps add up to the overall reaction?

B. Does the mechanism predict the correct rate law?

Test of Mechanism 1

1. Since the mechanism only has one step, which is the same as the overall reaction, there is **nothing to add.**
2. The **rate law predicted** by Mechanism 1 is: **Rate = k[NO_2][CO]**

Test of Mechanism 2

1. Mechanism 2 does **add up to the overall reaction.**

$$\cancel{NO_2} + NO_2 \longrightarrow NO + \cancel{NO_3}$$

$$\cancel{NO_3} + CO \longrightarrow \cancel{NO_2} + CO_2$$

$$NO_2 + CO \longrightarrow NO + CO_2$$

Note: NO_3 is a **reactive intermediate** (produced in one step, used up in a later step, and does not appear in the final reaction).

NO_2 is **not** considered an intermediate because it is present when the reaction starts and because it appears in the final product, even though one molecule does cancel.

2. The **predicted rate law** for Mechanism 2 can be determined as follows.

First, the rate law for each of the elementary steps is written:

$NO_2 + NO_2 \longrightarrow NO + NO_3$ **Step 1 rate law:** **Rate** = $k[NO_2]^2$

$NO_3 + CO \longrightarrow NO_2 + CO_2$ **Step 2 rate law:** **Rate** = $k[NO_3][CO]$

Since the first step in the mechanism is the slow step:

$NO_2 + NO_2 \longrightarrow NO + NO_3$ **(slow)**

$NO_3 + CO \longrightarrow NO_2 + CO_2$ **(fast)**

The predicted rate law for the mechanism would be **Rate = $k[NO_2]^2$.**

For each temperature, which mechanism is consistent with the observed rate law?

Mechanism 1 (single step)

$CO + NO_2 \longrightarrow CO_2 + NO$

Predicted rate law: **Rate** = $k\,[CO]\,[NO_2]$

Consistent with the observed **high temperature** rate law.

Not consistent with the observed low temperature rate law.

Mechanism 2 (two steps)

$NO_2 + NO_2 \longrightarrow NO + NO_3$ **(slow)**

$NO_3 + CO \longrightarrow NO_2 + CO_2$ **(fast)**

Predicted rate law: **Rate** = $k\,[NO_2]^2$

Not consistent with the observed high temperature rate law.

Consistent with the observed **low temperature** rate law.

Based on the data, it is believed that the overall reaction occurs by **Mechanism 1 at high temp** and by **Mechanism 2 at low temp**. In other words, there is a **change of mechanism** when the temperature falls below 225°C.

However, the data do not **prove** that Mechanism 1 occurs at high temperatures and Mechanism 2 at low temperatures. **Other mechanisms could be found** that are consistent with the rate laws. **Further experiments** would be needed before these mechanisms could be referred to as "well established."

Catalysts = speed up chemical reactions by increasing the number of steps in the mechanism.

The slow step is divided into two or more steps, each of which has a lower Energy of Activation (E_a).

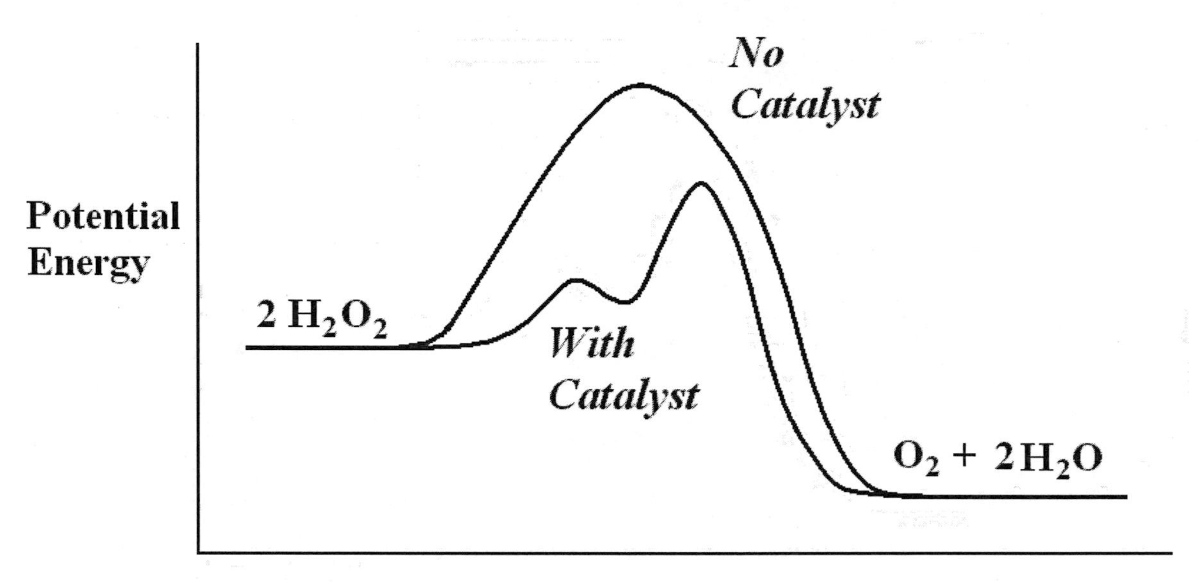

Overall Reaction:

$$2H_2O_2 \longrightarrow O_2(g) + 2\,H_2O(\ell)$$

Catalyst: Br^- (aq)

Mechanism With the Catalyst:

$$2\,Br^-(aq) + H_2O_2 + 2\,H^+ \longrightarrow Br_2(aq) + 2\,H_2O(\ell)$$

$$Br_2(aq) + H_2O_2(aq) \longrightarrow 2\,Br^-(aq) + 2\,H^+ + O_2$$

Check that reactions add up correctly:

$$\cancel{2\,Br^-}(aq) + H_2O_2(aq) + \cancel{2\,H^+}(aq) \longrightarrow \cancel{Br_2}(aq) + 2\,H_2O(\ell)$$

$$\cancel{Br_2}(aq) + H_2O_2(aq) \longrightarrow \cancel{2\,Br^-}(aq) + \cancel{2\,H^+}(aq) + O_2(g)$$

$$2\,H_2O_2(aq) \longrightarrow O_2(g) + 2\,H_2O(\ell)$$

Thermodynamics

In chemistry, Thermodynamics is related to the **"position of equilibrium"** = $\mathbf{K_{eq}}$

Kinetics and **Thermodynamics** are two separate ways of looking at a reaction.

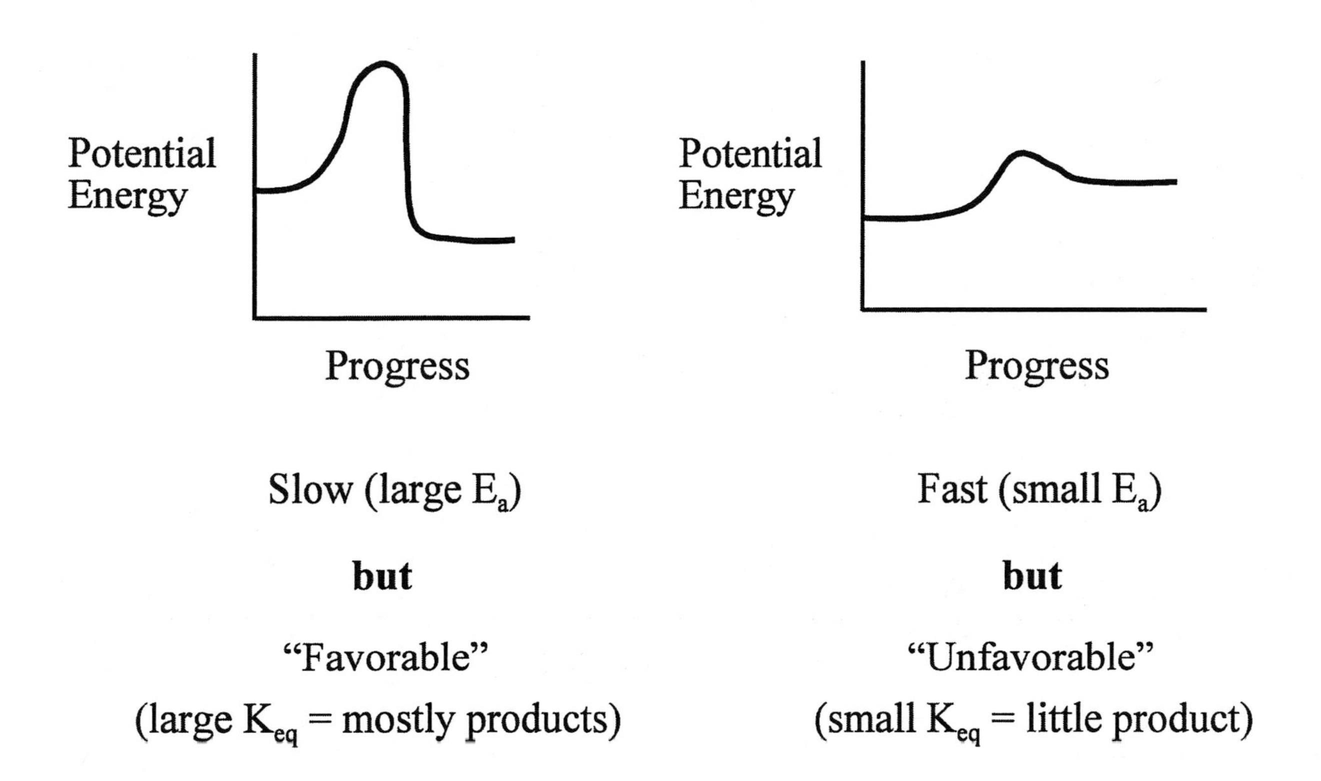

Slow (large E_a)	Fast (small E_a)
but	**but**
"Favorable"	"Unfavorable"
(large K_{eq} = mostly products)	(small K_{eq} = little product)

"Spontaneity" of Reaction

$$A + B \rightleftharpoons C + D$$

If you mix random amounts of A, B, C and D, there are three possibilities:

1. The reaction is **at** $\rightleftharpoons$, no shift. Amounts of A, B, C, and D **stay constant**.

   $Q = K_{eq}$ $\quad$ $\Delta G = 0$

2. The reaction **shifts to the right** to reach $\rightleftharpoons$

   $\uparrow$ [C], [D] $\quad$ $\downarrow$ [A], [B] $\quad$ $Q < K_{eq}$ $\quad$ $\Delta G = -$

   Spontaneous as written
   (Spontaneous in the forward direction)

3. The reaction **shifts to the left** to reach $\rightleftharpoons$

   $\uparrow$ [A], [B] $\quad$ $\downarrow$ [C], [D] $\quad$ $Q > K_{eq}$ $\quad$ $\Delta G = +$

   Nonspontaneous
   (Spontaneous in the reverse direction)

Gibbs Free Energy (ΔG)

ΔG is the Thermodynamic function that tells which will happen.

ΔG depends on two terms

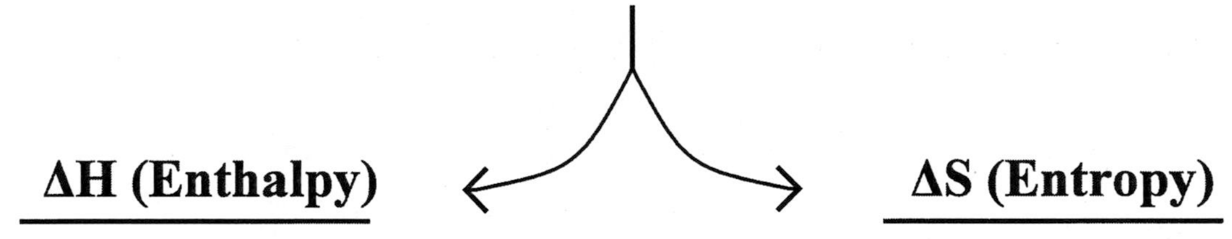

ΔH (Enthalpy)

"H" is for "Hemholtz"

Usually thought of as **"Heat"**
(Exothermic, Endothermic)

ΔS (Entropy)

"Statistical Mechanics" concept

Usually described as **"Disorder"**

The Enthalpy Term (ΔH)

I. Exothermic Reaction = gives off heat

$$C(s) + O_2(g) \longrightarrow CO_2(g) + \text{heat } (394 \text{ kJ})$$

$$\Delta H = -394 \text{ kJ}$$

1. Reaction vessel gets **hotter**.

2. Heat is written as a **product**.

3. ΔH is for the **number of moles** in the balanced equation.
   (1 mol C(s) releases 394 kJ)

   a. 2 mol C(s) would give off twice the heat.

   b. ½ mol C(s) would give off half the heat.

4. ΔH is – (negative).

Signs (+ and –) in Thermo

Always assigned from the perspective of the **system**, not the surroundings.

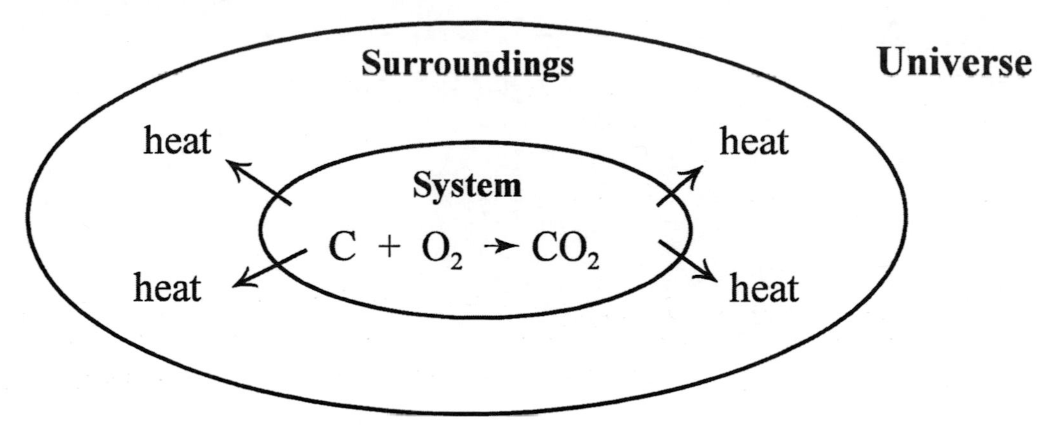

System **loses** heat, so ΔH is – (negative).

Units of heat

calorie = heat needed to raise the temp of 1 gram of water 1°C.

1 kcal = 1000 cal
4.184 J = 1 cal
1 kJ = 1000 J

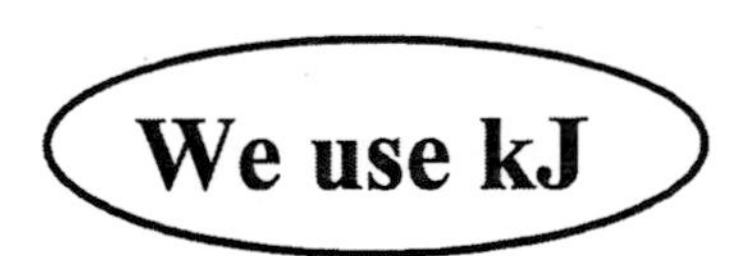

II. Endothermic Reaction = absorbs heat

$$2\ SO_3(g) + 198\ kJ \longrightarrow 2\ SO_2(g) + O_2(g)$$

$$\Delta H = +198\ kJ$$

1. Reaction vessel gets **colder**.
2. Heat is written as a **reactant**.
3. ΔH is for the **number of moles** in the balanced equation.
   (2 mol SO_3 (g) absorbs 198 kJ)
   a. 4 mol SO_3 (g) would absorb twice the heat.
   b. 1 mol SO_3 (g) would absorb half the heat.
4. ΔH is + (positive).

ΔH^o_{298} means under "Standard" conditions at 298 K. (K = °C + 273)

Standard Conditions

1) 1 atm gases
2) 1 M solutions.
3) All substances in their most stable state.

Calculating ΔH from Enthalpy of Formation (ΔH^o_f) Values

ΔH^o_f = heat absorbed or released when 1 mol of a substance forms from its elements.

$N_2(g) + 2\,H_2(g) \longrightarrow N_2H_4(\ell)$ $\quad \Delta H^o_f = +50.6$ kJ/mol

$K(s) + \frac{1}{2}\,Cl_2(g) + 1\frac{1}{2}\,O_2(g) \longrightarrow KClO_3(s)$ $\quad \Delta H^o_f = -397.7$ kJ/mol

Notes:

- Values are in **Table 6**
- For elements, $\mathbf{\Delta H^o_f = 0}$. **Examples:** C(s) Ca(s) $H_2(g)$
- There is no such thing as "absolute enthalpy." Values are **relative** to the elements.

For any reaction: Reactants ⟶ Products

$$\Delta H^o_{298} = (\Delta H^o_f)_{final} - (\Delta H^o_f)_{initial}$$

$$= \text{Products} - \text{Reactants}$$

Calculating ΔH For Any Reaction

Problem: Calculate ΔH°_{298} for the following reaction:

$$4\,NH_3(g) + 7\,O_2(g) \longrightarrow 4\,NO_2(g) + 6\,H_2O(g)$$

	$4\,NH_3(g)$	$7\,O_2(g)$	$4\,NO_2(g)$	$6\,H_2O(g)$
ΔH°_f values	-46.1	0	+33.2	-241.8

Products

4 x (33.2) + 6 x (-241.8) = 132.8 + (-1450.8) = -1318.0 kJ

Reactants

4 x (-46.1) + 7 x 0 = -184.4 + 0 = -184.4 kJ

ΔH°_{298} = Products - Reactants = -1318.0 - (-184.4)

= -1318.0 + 184.4 = **-1133.6 kJ**

ΔH = — tends to make reaction **spontaneous**.
favorable sign

ΔH = + tends to make reaction **nonspontaneous**.
unfavorable sign

Only a tendency ➡ ΔG gives the **final** answer.

ΔG involves **both** ΔH and ΔS.

Endothermic can still be spontaneous if ΔS **overrides** ΔH.

The Entropy Term (ΔS)

Second Law of Thermodynamics = all systems have a natural tendency to proceed toward a state of maximum disorder

Explanation: there are statistically more ways for a system to be disorderly than orderly.

$\Delta S = +$ ↑ disorder
Favorable sign

$\Delta S = -$ ↓ disorder, becomes more orderly
Unfavorable sign

(ΔH can override ΔS)

Predicting the sign of ΔS without calculating

1) **Solids** = least disorder (lowest entropy)
Liquids = more disorder
Gases = most disorder (highest entropy)

Example:

$$2\,H_2O(\ell) \xrightarrow{\text{electricity}} 2\,H_2(g) + O_2(g)$$

order **disorder**

$\Delta S = +$

2) **Dissolved substances have more disorder.**

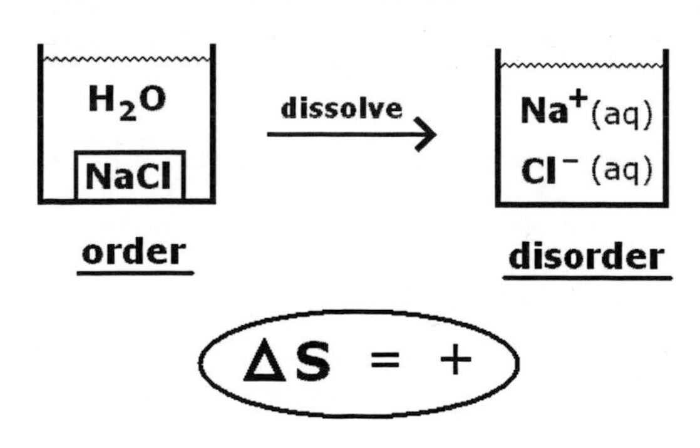

3) More gas molecules have more disorder.

$$N_2(g) + 3\ H_2(g) \longrightarrow 2\ NH_3(g)$$

4 gas molecules — **2 gas molecules**

disorder — **order**

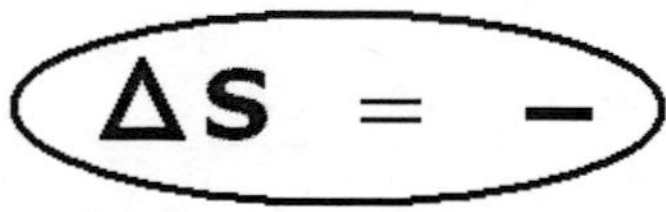

Absolute Entropies (not relative to elements like for ΔH) can be measured. No Δ in front of S in Table 6.

Third Law of Thermodynamics = the entropy of a perfect crystal at absolute zero is ZERO (no disorder).

Can also be stated, "Absolute zero cannot be reached in the physical world."

- Entropy of a pure substance ↑ with temp.
- **S** values in **Table 6** are **all +** (298 K).
- Elements are **NOT** ZERO.

S values in **Table 6** can be used to calculate **ΔS** for any reaction.

$$\Delta S = (S_{products}) - (S_{reactants})$$

Calculating ΔS For Any Reaction

Problem: Determine ΔS° for the following reaction:

$$4\ NH_3(g) + 7\ O_2(g) \longrightarrow 4\ NO_2(g) + 6\ H_2O(g)$$

	$4\ NH_3(g)$	$7\ O_2(g)$	$4\ NO_2(g)$	$6\ H_2O(g)$
S° values	.1923	.2050	.2400	.1887

Products

4 x (.2400) + 6 x (.1887) = .9600 + 1.1322 = 2.0922 kJ/K

Reactants

4 x (.1923) + 7 x (.2050) = .7692 + 1.435 = 2.2042 kJ/K

ΔS° = Products - Reactants = 2.0922 - 2.2042 = **-0.112 kJ/K**

ΔH and ΔS both have "favorable" and "unfavorable" signs. These are only **tendencies**. ΔG gives the final answer.

Gibbs Free Energy ΔG

$\Delta G = \Delta H - T\Delta S$ (T is Kelvin temp)

If		
ΔG	= −	Spontaneous
ΔG	= 0	At ⇌
ΔG	= +	Nonspontaneous

At 298 K, (products - reactants) can also be used for ΔG. (ΔG_f° for elements = ZERO).

$$\Delta G^\circ_{298} = (\Delta G_f^\circ)_{products} - (\Delta G_f^\circ)_{reactants}$$

Calculating ΔG for a Reaction at 298 K

Problem: Calculate ΔG°_{298} for the above reaction.

Method 1

$$\Delta G^\circ_{298} = \Delta H^\circ_{298} - T\Delta S^\circ$$

$$= -1133.6 \text{ kJ} - (298 \text{ K})(-0.112 \text{ kJ/K})$$

$$= -1133.6 \text{ kJ} + 33.4 \text{ kJ} = \mathbf{-1100.2 \text{ kJ}}$$

Method 2

	$4\ NH_3(g)$	+ $7\ O_2(g)$ $\longrightarrow$	$4\ NO_2(g)$	+ $6\ H_2O(g)$
ΔG°_f values	-16.5	0	+51.3	-228.6

Products

4 x (51.3) + 6 x (-228.6) = 205.2 + (-1371.6) = -1166.4 kJ

Reactants

4 x (-16.5) + 7 x 0 = -66.0 + 0 = -66.0 kJ

$$\Delta G^\circ_{298} = \text{Products} - \text{Reactants} = -1166.4 - (-66.0)$$

$$= -1166.4 + 66.0 = \mathbf{-1100.4 \text{ kJ}}$$

Changing ΔG for a reaction by changing conditions

1) Temperature

2) Concentrations of substances

Changing Temperature

$$\Delta G = \Delta H - T\Delta S$$

Varies with temp since **T** is in the equation (ΔG)

Do not change much with temp (ΔH, ΔS)

Use **Table 6** for **ANY** temp

Calculating ΔG At Any Temperature

Problem: Calculate $\Delta G°$ for the above reaction at 12,000 K.

At 12,000 K, we can use the same values as above for $\Delta H°$ and $\Delta S°$ (these values do not change much with temperature), but $\Delta G°$ will change dramatically:

$$\Delta G° = \Delta H° - T\Delta S°$$

$$= -1133.6 \text{ kJ} - (12{,}000 \text{ K})(-0.112 \text{ kJ/K})$$

$$= -1133.6 \text{ kJ} + 1344.0 \text{ kJ} = \mathbf{+210.4 \text{ kJ}}$$

At **298 K**, the reaction is **spontaneous** ($\Delta G°$ = -1100 kJ).

At **12,000 K**, the reaction is **nonspontaneous** or spontaneous in the reverse direction ($\Delta G°$ = +210.4 kJ).

Consider the reaction we have been discussing:

$$4\ NH_3(g) + 7\ O_2(g) \longrightarrow 4\ NO_2(g) + 6\ H_2O(g)$$

ΔH° = -1133.6 kJ

ΔS° = -0.112 kJ/K

This is an example of **Case 3** (both negative - See the table on the next page). Should be **spontaneous at low temperatures** and **nonspontaneous at high temperatures**. We calculated:

ΔG°_{298} = -1100 kJ and ΔG°_{12000} = +210.4 kJ

<u>Problem</u>: At what temperature will the reaction change from spontaneous to nonspontaneous? (This occurs at $\Delta G^\circ = 0$.)

$$\Delta G^\circ = \Delta H^\circ - T\Delta S^\circ$$

$$0 = \Delta H^\circ - T\Delta S^\circ$$

$$T\Delta S^\circ = \Delta H^\circ$$

Divide both sides by ΔS°.

$$\mathbf{T = \frac{\Delta H^\circ}{\Delta S^\circ} = \frac{-1133.6}{-0.112} = 10{,}121\ K}$$

For **ΔG** you can only use **<u>Table 6</u>** values at 298 K. For other temps, use

$$\mathbf{\Delta G = \Delta H - T\Delta S}$$

For the reaction we have been using:

ΔG°_{298} = -1100 kJ

$\Delta G^\circ_{?}$ = 0 ← Temp where $\Delta G^\circ = 0$ "Change in spontaneity"

$\Delta G^\circ_{12,000}$ = +210 kJ

Summary of Effect of Temperature on ΔG

$$\Delta G = \Delta H - T\Delta S$$

ΔH	ΔS	ΔG	
-	+	All temps -	(spontaneous)
+	-	All temps +	(nonspontaneous)
-	-	Low temp -	(spontaneous)
		High temp +	(nonspontaneous)
+	+	Low temp +	(nonspontaneous)
		High temp -	(spontaneous)

ΔG has different behavior as temp changes, depending on the signs of ΔH and ΔS

1) $\Delta H = -$ (favorable) $\Delta S = +$ (favorable)

Always + (Kelvin) → T

$$\Delta G = \Delta H + (-T\Delta S)$$
$$= (-) + (- \quad +)$$
$$= (-) + (-)$$
$$= \text{Always } -$$

Spontaneous at all temps

2) $\Delta H = +$ $\Delta S = -$

(unfavorable) (unfavorable)

Always + (Kelvin)

$$\Delta G = \Delta H + (-T\Delta S)$$
$$= (+) + (- \quad -)$$
$$= (+) + (+)$$

= Always **+** Nonspontaneous at all temps

3) $\Delta H = -$ $\Delta S = -$

(favorable) (unfavorable)

Always + (Kelvin)

$$\Delta G = \Delta H + (-T\Delta S)$$
$$= (-) + (- \quad -)$$
$$= (-) + (+)$$

Term becomes larger as T increases

= Low temp **–**

(2nd term small)

<u>Spontaneous</u>

High temp **+**

(2nd term large)

<u>Nonspontaneous</u>

4) $\Delta H = +$ (unfavorable) $\Delta S = +$ (favorable)

Always + (Kelvin)

$$\Delta G = \Delta H + (-T\Delta S)$$
$$= (+) + (- \quad +)$$
$$= (+) + (-)$$

Term becomes larger as T increases

= Low temp **+**
(2nd term small)
Nonspontaneous

High temp **–**
(2nd term large)
Spontaneous

	ΔH	ΔS	ΔG
favorable	-	+	-
unfavorable	+	-	+

Only tendencies (ΔH, ΔS)

Final Answer (ΔG)

Thermodynamics Part 2 and Electrochemistry Part 1

(Homework #13)

Effect of Reactant Concentration on ΔG

- Suppose the following reaction starts:

$$N_2(g) + 3\,H_2(g) \rightleftharpoons 2\,NH_3(g)$$

Initial	**1 atm**	**1 atm**	**1 atm**

- A later problem will show that

$$\Delta G^\circ_{298} = -33.0 \text{ kJ}$$

- When all the gases are at 1 atm (standard) the reaction is **spontaneous** ($-\Delta G$, rxn shifts to the right to reach $\rightleftharpoons$).

- Can ΔG be changed by changing concentrations (pressures for gases)?

- Suppose another reaction mixture contains:

$$N_2(g) + 3\,H_2(g) \rightleftharpoons 2\,NH_3(g)$$

Initial	**0**	**1 atm**	**1 atm**

- The standard ΔG°_{298} is still - 33 kJ. (This value is for the mixture where all gases are at 1 atm.)

- But under the new conditions (N_2 at 0, nonstandard) it is obvious that the rxn will shift to the left (toward the 0), so ΔG_{298} (no circle) must be **+** (nonspontaneous).

- Need a mathematical way to calculate the effect.

Equation for Changes in Concentration

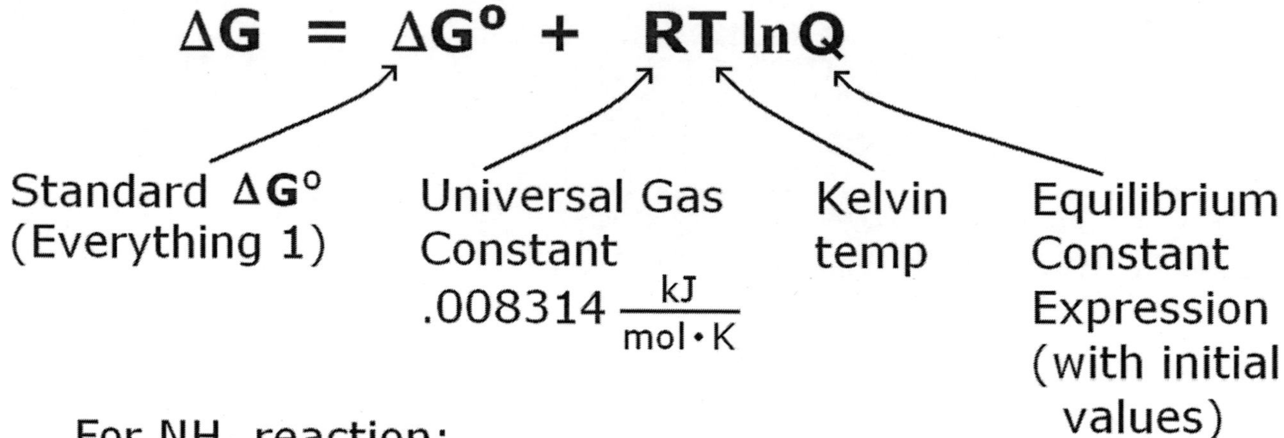

For NH_3 reaction:

$$Q = \frac{P(NH_3)^2}{P(N_2) \cdot P(H_2)^3}$$

If at standard conditions, $Q = \mathbf{1}$, $\ln \mathbf{1} = \mathbf{0}$
So, $\Delta \mathbf{G} = \Delta \mathbf{G}^{o}$, as expected when standard.

Problem: For the reaction:

$$N_2(g) + 3\,H_2(g) \longrightarrow 2\,NH_3(g)$$

a. Calculate ΔG^{o}_{298}

b. Calculate ΔG at 298 K if the partial pressures of gases are as follows:

$P(N_2) = .015$ atm $\quad P(H_2) = .013$ atm $\quad P(NH_3) = 4.28$ atm

c. Calculate ΔG^{o}_{800}. At what temperature does the reaction become nonspontaneous under standard conditions?

d. Calculate ΔG at 800 K if the partial pressures of gases are as follows:

$P(N_2) = 1.73$ atm $\quad P(H_2) = 2.98$ atm $\quad P(NH_3) = .003$ atm

e. Calculate K_{eq} at 298 K and at 800 K.

Solution:

a. $N_2(g) + 3\ H_2(g) \longrightarrow 2\ NH_3(g)$

	$N_2(g)$	$3\ H_2(g)$	$2\ NH_3(g)$
ΔH°_f	0	0	-46.1
S°	.1915	.1306	.1923
ΔG°_f	0	0	-16.5

ΔH°_{298}

Products = 2 x (-46.1) = -92.2

Reactants = 1 x 0 + 3 x 0 = 0

ΔH°_{298} = Products - Reactants = -92.2 - 0 = **-92.2 kJ**

ΔS°

Products = 2 x .1923 = .3846

Reactants = 1 x .1915 + 3 x .1306 = .5833

ΔS° = Products - Reactants = .3846 - .5833 = **-0.1987 kJ/K**

ΔG°_{298}

Products = 2 x (-16.5) = -33.0 kJ

Reactants = 0

ΔG°_{298} = Products - Reactants = -33.0 - 0 = **-33.0 kJ**

OR

$\Delta G^\circ_{298} = \Delta H^\circ_{298} - T\Delta S^\circ$

$= -92.2\text{ kJ} - (298\text{ K})(-0.1987\text{ kJ/K})$

$= -92.2\text{ kJ} + 59.2\text{ kJ} =$ **-33.0 kJ**

b.

$$Q = \frac{P(NH_3)^2}{P(N_2) \cdot P(H_2)^3} = \frac{(4.28)^2}{(.015)(.013)^3} = 5.56 \times 10^8$$

$$\Delta G = \Delta G^\circ_{298} + RT(\ln Q)$$

$$= -33.0 \text{ kJ} + (.008314 \text{ kJ/K})(298 \text{ K})[\ln(5.56 \times 10^8)]$$

$$= -33.0 \text{ kJ} + 49.9 \text{ kJ} = \mathbf{+16.9 \text{ kJ}}$$

c.

$$\Delta G^\circ_{800} = \Delta H^\circ - T\Delta S^\circ$$

$$= -92.2 \text{ kJ} - (800 \text{ K})(-.1987 \text{ kJ/K})$$

$$= -92.2 \text{ kJ} + 158.96 \text{ kJ} = \mathbf{+66.8 \text{ kJ}}$$

Becomes nonspontaneous when $T = \Delta H^\circ / \Delta S^\circ$:

$$T = \frac{\Delta H^\circ}{\Delta S^\circ} = \frac{-92.2}{-0.1987} = \mathbf{464 \text{ K}}$$

d.

$$Q = \frac{P(NH_3)^2}{P(N_2) \cdot P(H_2)^3} = \frac{(.003)^2}{(1.73)(2.98)^3} = 1.97 \times 10^{-7}$$

$$\Delta G = \Delta G^\circ_{800} + RT(\ln Q)$$

$$= 66.8 \text{ kJ} + (.008314 \text{ kJ/K})(800 \text{ K})[\ln(1.97 \times 10^{-7})]$$

$$= 66.8 \text{ kJ} + (-102.7 \text{ kJ}) = \mathbf{-35.9 \text{ kJ}}$$

Summary:

a) $\Delta G^\circ_{298} = -33.0$ kJ

b) ΔG becomes + (nonspontaneous, shift to the left) when ↓ reactants.

c) $\Delta G^\circ_{800} = +66.8$ kJ (nonspontaneous) Expected when ↑ temp and ΔH and ΔS are both – (see table on bottom of p. 94).

d) Becomes spontaneous at 800 K ($\Delta G_{800} = -35.9$ kJ) when ↓ products.

Relationship Between ΔG and K_{eq}

Major connection between Chemistry (K_{eq}) and Thermodynamics (ΔG) is shown by an equation that relates these quantities.

Spontaneous	$\Delta G = -$	$Q < K_{eq}$	(**Shift to the right**)
Equilibrium	$\Delta G = 0$	$Q = K_{eq}$	(**No Shift**)
Nonspontaneous	$\Delta G = +$	$Q > K_{eq}$	(**Shift to the left**)

Substitute "equilibrium" line into equation for changing concentrations.

$$\Delta G = \Delta G^\circ + RT\ln Q$$

$$0 = \Delta G^\circ + RT\ln K_{eq}$$

$$-\Delta G^\circ = RT\ln K_{eq}$$

$$\boxed{\Delta G^\circ = -RT\ln K_{eq}}$$

$-$: large K_{eq} (lots of product) ($K_{eq} > 1$) $\ln K_{eq}$ is $+$

$+$: small K_{eq} (little product) ($K_{eq} < 1$) $\ln K_{eq}$ is $-$

Summary reactants ⟶ products $K_{eq} = \frac{\text{products}}{\text{reactants}}$

$\Delta G = -$	spontaneous shift ⟹	lots of product	large K_{eq}
$\Delta G = +$	nonspontaneous ⟸ shift	little product	small K_{eq}

e. **ΔG°_{298}**

$$\Delta G^\circ_{298} = -RT(\ln K_{eq})$$

$$-33.0 \text{ kJ} = -(.008314 \text{ kJ/K})(298 \text{ K})(\ln K_{eq})$$

$$\ln K_{eq} = \frac{-33.0 \text{ kJ}}{-.008314 \text{ kJ} \times 298} = 13.32$$

$$K_{eq} = \text{2nd } \ln(13.32) = \mathbf{6.1 \times 10^5}$$

Large K_{eq} for a Spontaneous Reaction.

ΔG°_{800}

$$\Delta G^\circ_{800} = -RT(\ln K_{eq})$$

$$66.8 \text{ kJ} = -(.008314 \text{ kJ/K})(800 \text{ K})(\ln K_{eq})$$

$$\ln K_{eq} = \frac{66.8 \text{ kJ}}{-.008314 \text{ kJ} \times 800} = -10.04$$

$$K_{eq} = \text{2nd } \ln(-10.04) = \mathbf{4.4 \times 10^{-5}}$$

Small K_{eq} for a Nonspontaneous Reaction.

	ΔH	ΔS	ΔG	K_{eq}
favorable	-	+	-	large
unfavorable	+	-	+	small
	Only tendencies		**Final Answer**	

The Haber Process

$$N_2(g) + 3\,H_2(g) \rightleftharpoons 2\,NH_3(g)$$

N_2 is cheap H_2 is expensive

Known Data

- Δ**H** and Δ**S** both –
- $\Delta G^o_{298} = -33.0\ kJ$ $K_{eq} = 6.1 \times 10^5$
  (Favorable at room temp)
- Rxn is too slow to use at room temp.
- Rxn becomes nonspontaneous if heated too much. $\Delta G^o_{800} = +66.8\ kJ$

Solutions

1) Catalyst. But still too slow at room temp.

2) Temp increase. Must not be too high due to nonspontaneity.

3) High pressure. Shifts rxn toward fewer gas molecules. (LeChatelier's Principle)

4) Remove NH_3 as it forms.

   BP NH_3 = -33°C
   BP N_2 and H_2 ≈ -200°C

   If mixture is cooled below -33°C, NH_3 liquifies.
   Removes NH_3 (g). Shifts rxn to the right.
   (LeChatelier's Principle)

Summary of Thermodynamics Equations

$\Delta G = \Delta H - T\Delta S$ (changing temp)

$\left[\text{Temp where spontaneity changes is: } T = \dfrac{\Delta H}{\Delta S}\right]$

$\Delta G = \Delta G^{o} + RT \ln Q$ (changing concentrations)

$\Delta G^{o} = -RT \ln K_{eq}$ (calculate ΔG^{o} from K_{eq} or K_{eq} from ΔG^{o})

$\Delta G^{o} = -nFE^{o}_{cell}$ (calculate ΔG^{o} from voltage)

$E_{cell} = E^{o}_{cell} - \dfrac{.0591}{n} \log Q$ (calculate voltage at different concentrations)

Mathematics of Electrochemistry

Equation:

$$Zn(s) + Cu^{2+}(aq) \longrightarrow Zn^{2+}(aq) + Cu(s)$$

Half-Reactions:

$$Zn(s) \longrightarrow Zn^{2+}(aq) + 2e^- \quad \text{(oxidation)}$$

$$Cu^{2+}(aq) + 2e^- \longrightarrow Cu(s) \quad \text{(reduction)}$$

Cell Shorthand:

$Zn \mid Zn^{2+}(aq) \parallel Cu^{2+}(aq) \mid Cu$

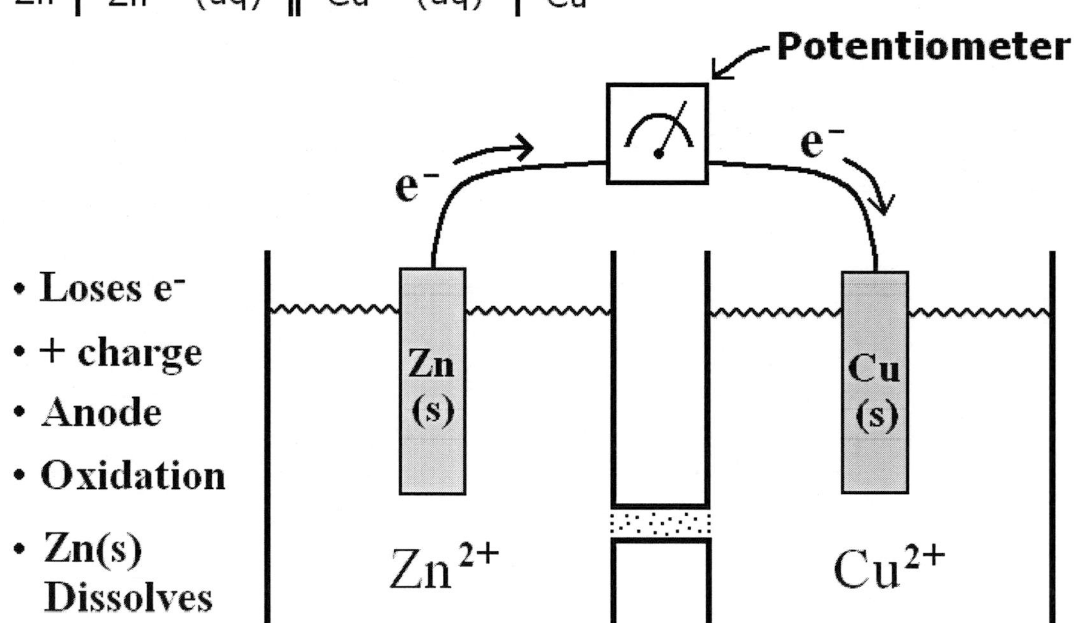

Potential:

$$Zn(s) \longrightarrow Zn^{2+}(aq) + \cancel{2e^-} \qquad E^o_{ox} = 0.763\ V$$

$$Cu^{2+}(aq) + \cancel{2e^-} \longrightarrow Cu(s) \qquad E^o_{red} = 0.337\ V$$

$$Zn(s) + Cu^{2+}(aq) \longrightarrow Zn^{2+}(aq) + Cu(s)$$

$$E^o_{cell} = E^o_{ox} + E^o_{red} = 0.763 + 0.337 = \mathbf{1.10\ V}$$

Redox Reactions and Thermodynamics

- Redox reactions can be analyzed by Thermo in ways other reactions cannot.
- Redox reactions have a property called **Voltage.** (Electromotive force, EMF, or just E.)
- Voltage is involved in Thermo equations.

Typical Voltages

AA, C, and D cells = 1.5 V

Rectangular with two posts = 9 V

Car Battery = 12 V

Wall socket = 115 V (220 V in Europe)

Voltage

★ Measures the tendency of electrons to flow from one point to another.

★ Each pair of half-reactions, when used as electrodes in a cell, has a different voltage than other pairs.

★ Voltage is similar to Potential Energy because it measures a "tendency." It is not a force, energy, or pressure. Often called "electrical potential" or a "potential difference" between points.

★ The voltage of a cell is labeled "E_{cell}."

Voltage can be measured with a "voltmeter."

High resistance instrument = requires a lot of current flow

Usually use a **"Potentiometer."** Measures voltage "balance point" = no current required.

Potentiometer measures:

1) Size of voltage
2) Direction of electron flow

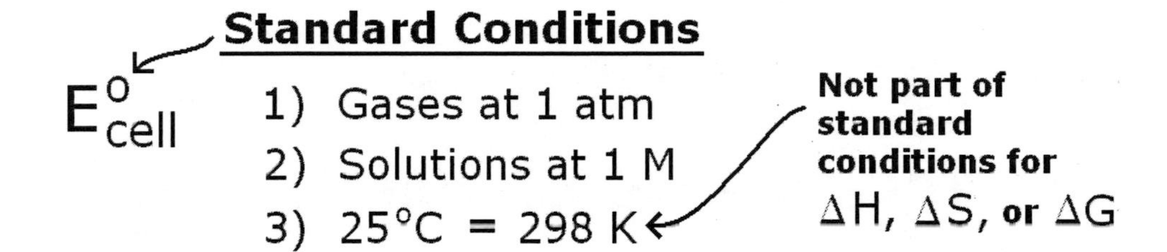

Signs of E

E = + means **spontaneous**
just like $\Delta G = -$
(Final answer)

E = − means **nonspontaneous**
just like $\Delta G = +$
(Final answer)

In picture:

$$Zn(s) + Cu^{2+} \longrightarrow Zn^{2+} + Cu(s)$$

$E^{o}_{cell} = +1.10\ V$ (spontaneous as written)

If reaction is turned around, change sign of E:

$$Zn^{2+} + Cu(s) \longrightarrow Zn(s) + Cu^{2+}$$

$E^{o}_{cell} = -1.10\ V$ (nonspontaneous, occurs in reverse)

	ΔH	ΔS	ΔG	K_{eq}	E_{cell}
favorable	-	+	-	large	+
unfavorable	+	-	+	small	-
	Only tendencies		Final Answer		

Measuring the Voltage of Half-Reactions

Chemists specify the Standard Hydrogen Electrode as 0.00 V and compare all the others to it:

$$2\,H^+ + 2\,e^- \longrightarrow H_2(g) \qquad 0.00\ V$$

$$H_2(g) \longrightarrow 2\,H^+ + 2\,e^- \qquad 0.00\ V$$

Attach the electrode to be tested to the SHE and measure the voltage and direction of electron flow.

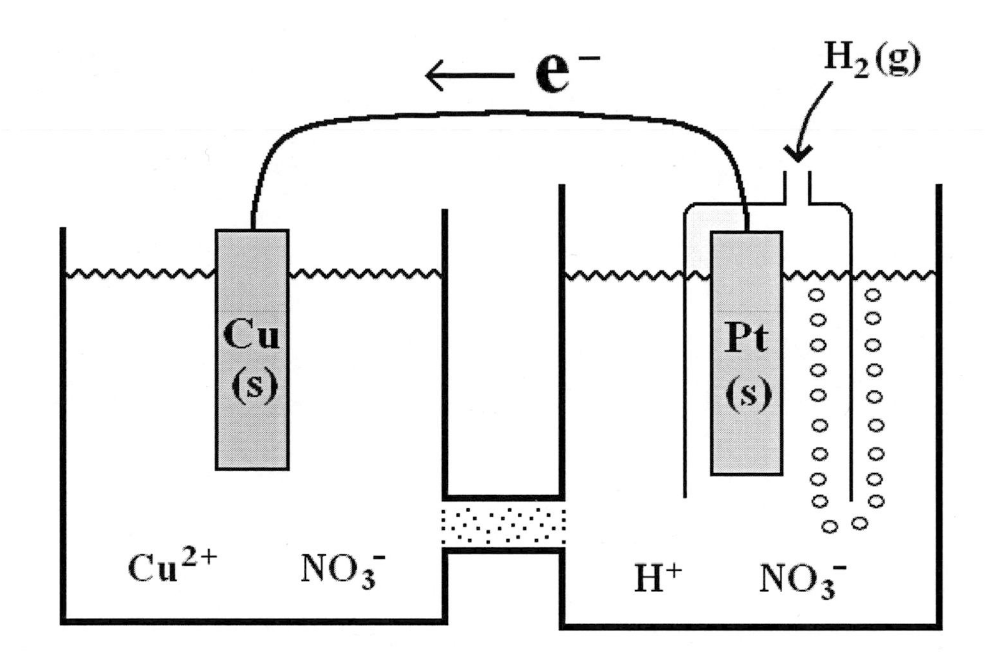

$$Cu^{2+}(aq) + \cancel{2e^-} \longrightarrow Cu(s) \qquad E^o_{red} = \;?$$

$$H_2(g) \longrightarrow 2H^+(aq) + \cancel{2e^-} \qquad E^o_{ox} = 0.000\ V$$

$$Cu^{2+}(aq) + H_2(g) \longrightarrow Cu(s) + 2H^+(aq) \qquad E^o_{cell} = 0.337\ V$$

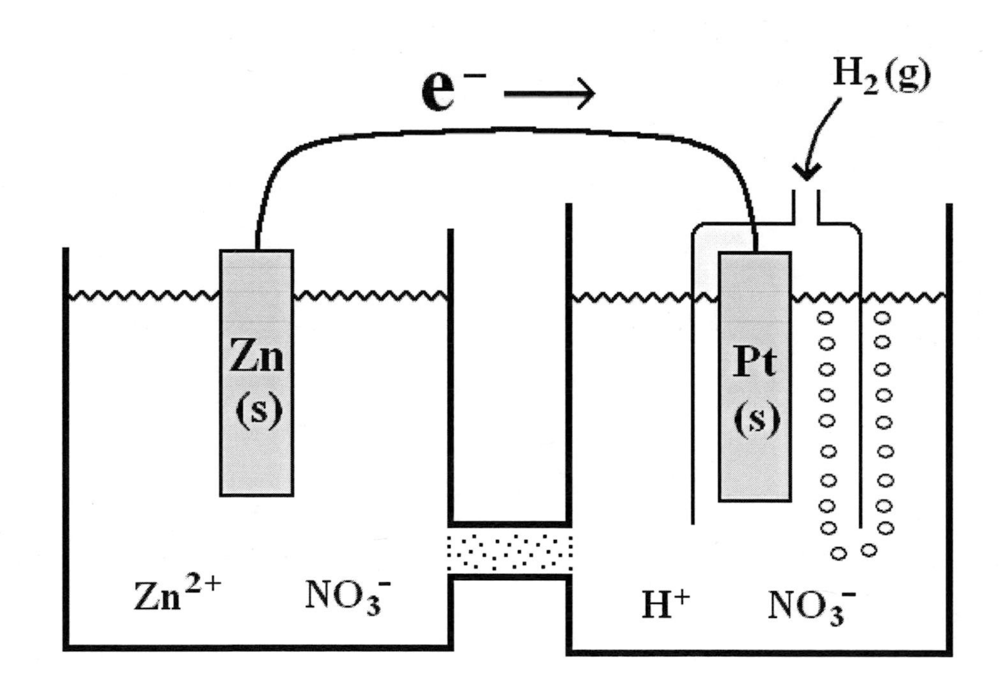

$$2H^+(aq) + \cancel{2e^-} \longrightarrow H_2(g) \qquad E^o_{red} = 0.000\ V$$

$$Zn(s) \longrightarrow Zn^{2+}(aq) + \cancel{2e^-} \qquad E^o_{ox} = \;?$$

$$Zn(s) + 2H^+(aq) \longrightarrow Zn^{2+}(aq) + H_2(g) \qquad E^o_{cell} = 0.763\ V$$

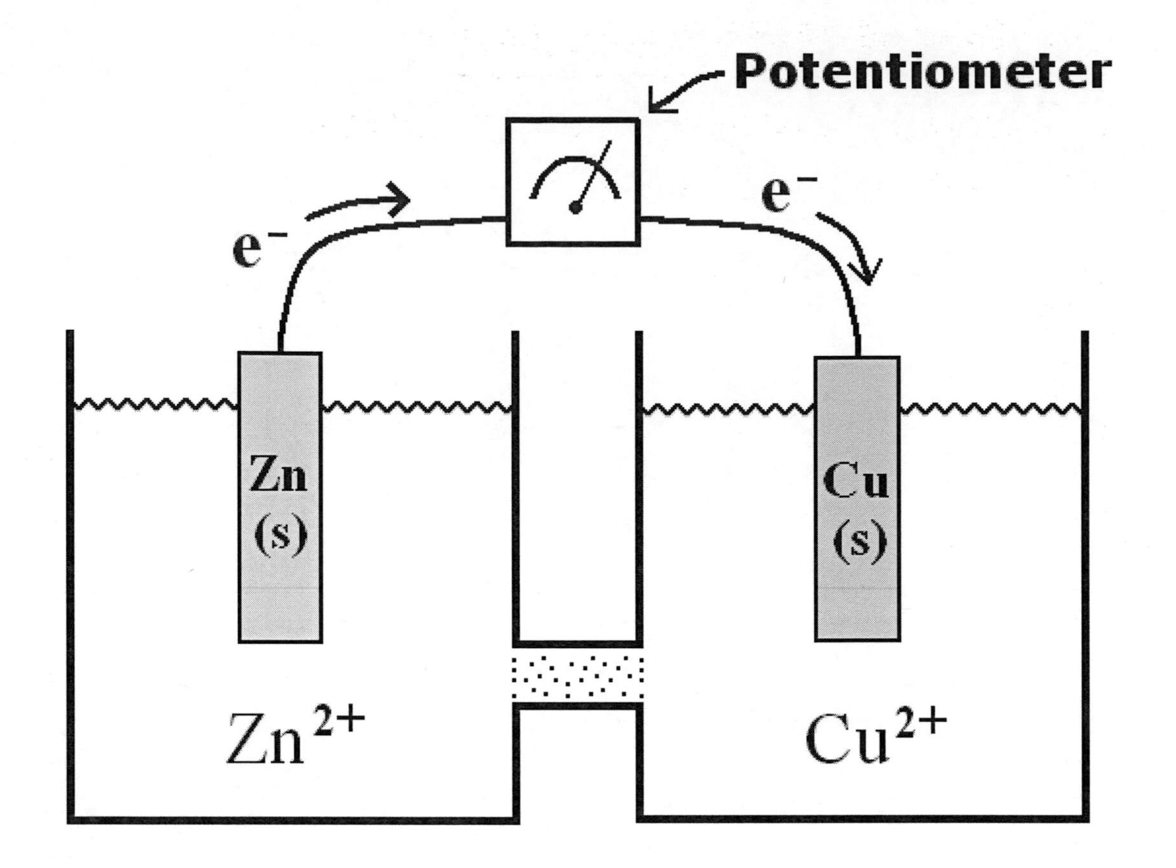

Potential:

$$Zn(s) \longrightarrow Zn^{2+}(aq) + \cancel{2e^-} \qquad E^o_{ox} = 0.763\ V$$

$$Cu^{2+}(aq) + \cancel{2e^-} \longrightarrow Cu(s) \qquad E^o_{red} = 0.337\ V$$

$$Zn(s) + Cu^{2+}(aq) \longrightarrow Zn^{2+}(aq) + Cu(s)$$

$$E^o_{cell} = E^o_{ox} + E^o_{red} = 0.763 + 0.337 = \mathbf{1.10\ V}$$

Tables of Half-Reactions

Written as reductions, gain electrons, e^- on left in half-reactions.

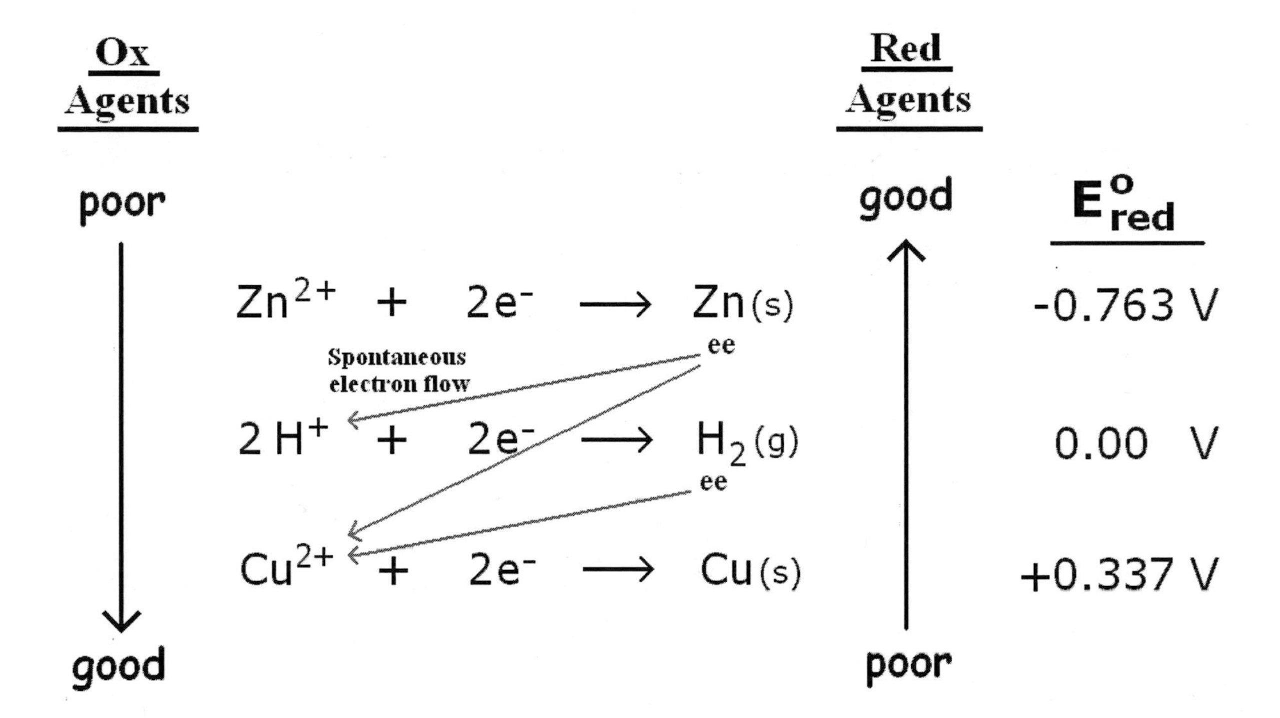

Spontaneous Direction of e^- Flow

Rule 1 = when an "above" electrode is attached to a "below" electrode, e^-'s flow spontaneously from "above" to "below." (**Down** the table)

Rule 2 = it must be the **reducing agent** (right side) of the "above" electrode that **loses e^-** and the **oxidizing agent** (left side) of the "below" electrode that **gains e^-**.

Summary

When half-reactions are written as reductions and arranged in order of voltage with the most negative E^o_{red} at the top, the **spontaneous direction** of e^- flow is **upper right to lower left**.

Example:

			E^{o}_{red}
$Hg^{2+} + 2e^{-}$	$\longrightarrow$	$Hg(\ell)$	+ 0.854 V
$Au^{3+} + 3e^{-}$	$\longrightarrow$	$Au(s)$	+ 1.50 V

If Hg^{2+}, Au^{3+}, $Hg(\ell)$ and $Au(s)$ are mixed, the spontaneous reaction will be for Au^{3+} taking electrons from $Hg(\ell)$.

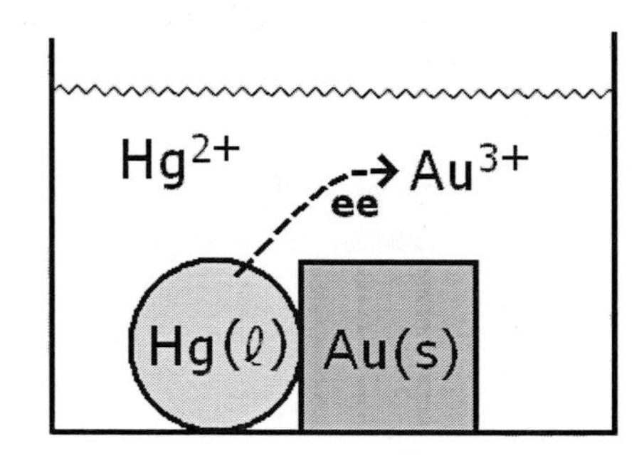

Arrow shows spontaneous e⁻ flow.

Calculating E^{o}_{cell} for a Redox Reaction

Calculate E^{o}_{cell} for the following Redox Reaction:

$$Br_2(\ell) + 2\,Ag(s) \longrightarrow 2\,Br^{-} + 2\,Ag^{+}$$

Step 1

Copy half-reactions from Table 3 or 4 with E^{o}_{red}:

$Br_2(\ell) + 2e^{-}$	$\longrightarrow$	$2\,Br^{-}$	+ 1.0652 V
$Ag^{+} + e^{-}$	$\longrightarrow$	$Ag(s)$	+ 0.7991 V

Step 2

Turn around whichever rxn is needed to place all substances on the correct side. Change the sign of the voltage of the rxn that was turned around.

$$Br_2(\ell) + 2e^- \longrightarrow 2\,Br^- \qquad +1.0652\ V$$

$$Ag(s) \longrightarrow Ag^+ + e^- \qquad -0.7991\ V$$

Step 3

Multiply to equalize e^-. Multiplying DOES NOT change the voltage. Voltage is only a tendency and does not vary with the size of a cell.

$$Br_2(\ell) + 2e^- \longrightarrow 2\,Br^- \qquad +1.0652\ V$$

$$\mathbf{2x}\left[Ag(s) \longrightarrow Ag^+ + e^-\right] \qquad -0.7991\ V$$

Step 4

Add the equations to get the balanced equation, and add the voltages to get the final E°_{cell}.

$$Br_2(\ell) + \cancel{2e^-} \longrightarrow 2\,Br^- \qquad +1.0652\ V$$

$$2\,Ag(s) \longrightarrow 2\,Ag^+ + \cancel{2e^-} \qquad -0.7991\ V$$

$$Br_2(\ell) + 2\,Ag(s) \longrightarrow 2\,Br^- + 2\,Ag^+$$

$$E^\circ_{cell} = +1.0652 + (-0.7991)$$

$$= \boxed{+0.2661\ V}$$

Spontaneous as written.

Problem: Calculate E^{o}_{cell} and write the overall cell reaction for

$$Co \mid Co^{2+}(aq) \parallel Fe^{2+}(aq);\ Fe^{3+}(aq) \mid Pt$$

$$Co^{2+} + 2\,e^{-} \longrightarrow Co \qquad E^{o}_{red} = -0.277\ V$$

$$Fe^{3+} + e^{-} \longrightarrow Fe^{2+} \qquad E^{o}_{red} = +0.771\ V$$

Turn the first equation around because Co is to the left of the ‖

$$Co \longrightarrow Co^{2+} + 2\,e^{-} \qquad E^{o}_{ox} = +0.277\ V$$

$$Fe^{3+} + e^{-} \longrightarrow Fe^{2+} \qquad E^{o}_{red} = +0.771\ V$$

Multiply the second equation by **2**.

$$Co \longrightarrow Co^{2+} + \cancel{2\,e^{-}} \qquad E^{o}_{ox} = +0.277\ V$$

$$2\,Fe^{3+} + \cancel{2\,e^{-}} \longrightarrow 2\,Fe^{2+} \qquad E^{o}_{red} = +0.771\ V$$

$$2\,Fe^{3+} + Co \longrightarrow 2\,Fe^{2+} + Co^{2+} \qquad E^{o}_{cell} = 0.277 + 0.771$$

$$= \mathbf{+1.048\ V}$$

Problem: Calculate E^{o}_{cell} for the reaction:

$$5\,Cl_2 + 2\,Mn^{2+} + 8\,H_2O \longrightarrow 10\,Cl^{-} + 2\,MnO_4^{-} + 16\,H^{+}$$

Half-reactions:

$$Cl_2 + 2\,e^{-} \longrightarrow 2\,Cl^{-} \qquad E^{o}_{red} = +1.3595\ V$$

$$MnO_4^{-} + 8\,H^{+} + 5\,e^{-} \longrightarrow Mn^{2+} + 4\,H_2O \qquad E^{o}_{red} = +1.51\ V$$

Turn the Mn equation around:

$$Cl_2 + 2\,e^{-} \longrightarrow 2\,Cl^{-} \qquad E^{o}_{red} = +1.3595\ V$$

$$Mn^{2+} + 4\,H_2O \longrightarrow MnO_4^{-} + 8\,H^{+} + 5\,e^{-} \qquad E^{o}_{ox} = -1.51\ V$$

Multiply the first equation by **5** and the second equation by **2**.

$$5\,Cl_2 + \cancel{10\,e^{-}} \longrightarrow 10\,Cl^{-} \qquad E^{o}_{red} = +1.3595\ V$$

$$2\,Mn^{2+} + 8\,H_2O \longrightarrow 2\,MnO_4^{-} + 16\,H^{+} + \cancel{10\,e^{-}} \qquad E^{o}_{ox} = -1.51\ V$$

$$5\,Cl_2 + 2\,Mn^{2+} + 8\,H_2O \longrightarrow 10\,Cl^{-} + 2\,MnO_4^{-} + 16\,H^{+}$$

$$E^{o}_{cell} = +1.3595 + (-1.51) = \mathbf{-0.15\ V}$$

E_{cell} and ΔG

Faraday's Equation

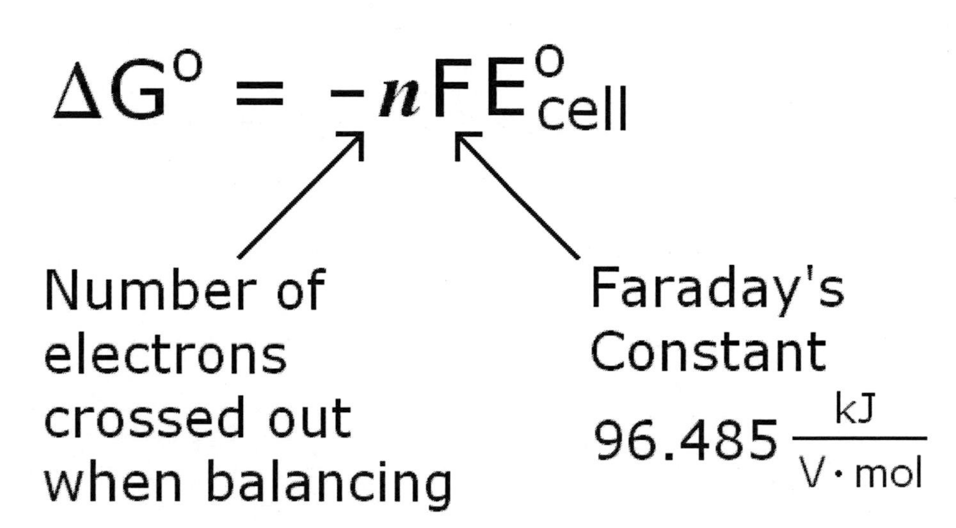

Signs of ΔG^o and E^o_{cell}

$$\Delta G^o = -nFE^o_{cell}$$

ΔG^o	E^o_{cell}	
$-$	$+$	(spontaneous, Large K_{eq})
$+$	$-$	(nonspontaneous, Small K_{eq})

Meaning of Faraday's Constant

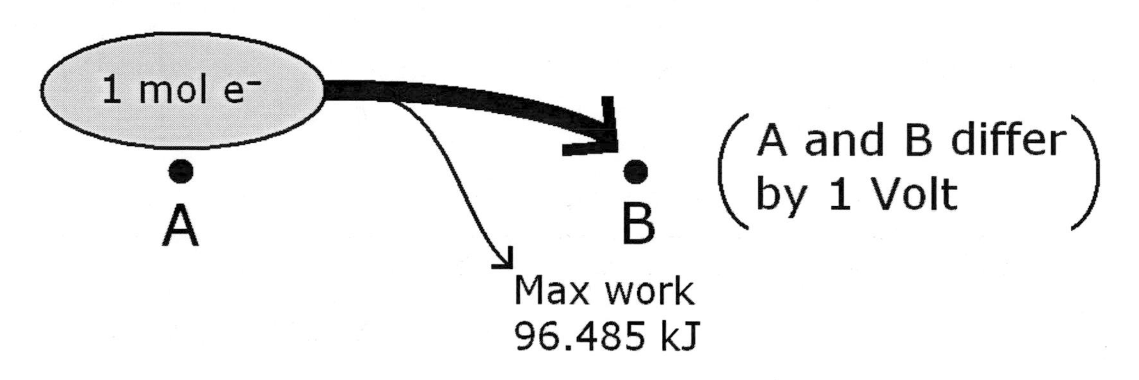

Problem: Calculate ΔG° and K_{eq} at 25°C (298 K) for the reaction:

$$Br_2(\ell) + 2\,Ag(s) \longrightarrow 2\,Br^- + 2\,Ag^+$$

In balancing, **2 mol** of e^- were in the equations.

To get ΔG°:

$$\Delta G^\circ = -nFE^\circ_{cell} = -(2\,\cancel{mol})(96.485\,\frac{kJ}{\cancel{V}\cdot\cancel{mol}})(0.2661\,\cancel{V}) = \mathbf{-51.3\ kJ}$$

To get K_{eq}:

$$\Delta G^\circ = -RT(\ln K_{eq})$$

$$-51.3\ kJ = -(0.008314\ kJ/\cancel{K})(298\ \cancel{K})(\ln K_{eq})$$

$$\ln K_{eq} = \frac{-51.3\ \cancel{kJ}}{-(.008314\ \cancel{kJ})(298)} = 20.7$$

$$K_{eq} = \mathbf{9.83 \times 10^8} \quad \text{(favors products)}$$

Problem: Calculate ΔG° and K_{eq} at 25°C (298 K) for the reaction:

$$5\,Cl_2 + 2\,Mn^{2+} + 8\,H_2O \longrightarrow 10\,Cl^- + 2\,MnO_4^- + 16\,H^+$$

As calculated earlier, $\mathbf{E^\circ_{cell} = -0.15\ V}$ and **10** $\mathbf{e^-}$ were involved in balancing the equation.

To get ΔG°:

$$\Delta G^\circ = -nFE^\circ_{cell} = -(10\,\cancel{mol})(96.485\,\frac{kJ}{\cancel{V}\cdot\cancel{mol}})(-0.15\,\cancel{V}) = \mathbf{+144.7\ kJ}$$

To get K_{eq}:

$$\Delta G^\circ = -RT(\ln K_{eq})$$

$$144.7\ kJ = -(0.008314\ kJ/\cancel{K})(298\ \cancel{K})(\ln K_{eq})$$

$$\ln K_{eq} = \frac{144.7\ \cancel{kJ}}{-(.008314\ \cancel{kJ})(298)} = -58.4$$

$$K_{eq} = \mathbf{4.32 \times 10^{-26}} \quad \text{(favors reactants)}$$

Electrochemistry Part 2

(Homework #14)

Derivation of the Nernst Equation

Suppose a redox reaction with a potential E°_{cell}. Then,

$$\Delta G = \Delta G^\circ + RT(\ln Q)$$

$$-nFE_{cell} = -nFE^\circ_{cell} + RT(\ln Q)$$

$$E_{cell} = E^\circ_{cell} - \frac{RT}{nF}\ln Q$$

Substituting R = 0.008314 kJ/K, T = 298 K, and F = 96.485 kJ/(V·mol):

$$E_{cell} = E^\circ_{cell} - \frac{0.02568\ V}{n}\ln Q$$

Converting to a base 10 log gives:

$$E_{cell} = E^\circ_{cell} - \frac{0.0591\ V}{n}\log Q$$ **(Final Form of Nernst Equation)**

Problem: Calculate E°_{cell} for the reaction:

$$Pb^{2+} + Ni(s) \longrightarrow Pb(s) + Ni^{2+}$$

a. What is E_{cell} when $[Pb^{2+}]$ = .0001 M and $[Ni^{2+}]$ = 2.50 M?

b. What is E_{cell} when $[Pb^{2+}]$ = 0.541 M and $[Ni^{2+}]$ = 1.31×10^{-7} M?

Solution:

$$Pb^{2+} + \cancel{2e^-} \longrightarrow Pb(s) \qquad E^\circ_{red} = -0.126\ V$$

$$Ni(s) \longrightarrow Ni^{2+} + \cancel{2e^-} \qquad E^\circ_{ox} = +0.250\ V$$

$$Pb^{2+} + Ni(s) \longrightarrow Pb(s) + Ni^{2+} \qquad E^\circ_{cell} = -0.126 + 0.250 = \mathbf{+0.124\ V}$$

a. $$Q = \frac{[Ni^{2+}]}{[Pb^{2+}]} = \frac{2.50}{.0001} = 25{,}000$$

$$E_{cell} = E^\circ_{cell} - \frac{0.0591\ V}{n}\log Q$$

$$= .124\ V - \frac{.0591\ V}{2}\log(25{,}000)$$

$$= .124\ V - .130\ V = \mathbf{-0.006\ V}$$

b. $$Q = \frac{[Ni^{2+}]}{[Pb^{2+}]} = \frac{1.31 \times 10^{-7}}{0.541} = 2.42 \times 10^{-7}$$

Substituting in the Nernst Equation:

$$E_{cell} = .124\ V - \frac{.0591\ V}{2}\log(2.42 \times 10^{-7})$$

$$= .124\ V + .196\ V = \mathbf{+0.320\ V}$$

Electrochemistry Practice Problem

a. Calculate E^o_{cell}, ΔG^o, and K_{eq} for the following reaction:

$$2\ MnO_4^- + 3\ Ni(OH)_2(s) \longrightarrow 2\ MnO_2(s) + 3\ NiO_2(s) + 2\ OH^- + 2\ H_2O(\ell)$$

b. What is E_{cell} when $[OH^-] = 3.00\ M$ and $[MnO_4^-] = 0.200\ M$?

__Solution__:

a. The **half-reactions** (turned the right way) are:

$$MnO_4^- + 2\ H_2O + 3\ e^- \longrightarrow MnO_2(s) + 4\ OH^- \qquad E^o_{red} = +0.588\ V$$

$$Ni(OH)_2(s) + 2\ OH^- \longrightarrow NiO_2(s) + 2\ H_2O + 2\ e^- \qquad E^o_{ox} = -0.49\ V$$

Multiply the **first** equation by **2** and the **second** equation by **3**.

$$2\ MnO_4^- + \cancel{4\ H_2O} + \cancel{6\ e^-} \longrightarrow 2\ MnO_2(s) + \overset{2}{\cancel{8}}\ OH^- \qquad E^o_{red} = +0.588\ V$$

$$3\ Ni(OH)_2(s) + \cancel{6\ OH^-} \longrightarrow 3\ NiO_2(s) + \overset{2}{\cancel{6}}\ H_2O + \cancel{6\ e^-} \qquad E^o_{ox} = -0.49\ V$$

$$2\ MnO_4^- + 3\ Ni(OH)_2(s) \longrightarrow 2\ MnO_2(s) + 3\ NiO_2(s) + 2\ OH^- + 2\ H_2O$$

$$E^o_{cell} = .588 + (-.49) = \mathbf{0.098\ V}$$

To calculate ΔG°:

$$\Delta G^\circ = -nFE^\circ_{cell} = -(6\ \cancel{mol})(96.485 \frac{kJ}{\cancel{V}\cdot\cancel{mol}})(0.098\ \cancel{V}) = \mathbf{-56.7\ kJ}$$

To calculate K_{eq}:

$$\Delta G^\circ = -RT(\ln K_{eq})$$

$$-56.7\ kJ = -(.008314\ kJ/\cancel{K})(298\ \cancel{K})(\ln K_{eq})$$

$$\ln K_{eq} = \frac{-56.7\ \cancel{kJ}}{-(.008314\ \cancel{kJ})(298)} = 22.9$$

$$K_{eq} = \mathbf{8.7 \times 10^9}$$

b.

$$Q = \frac{[OH^-]^2}{[MnO_4^-]^2} = \frac{(3.00)^2}{(0.2)^2} = 225$$ **(NOTE! Keep the power 2!)**

$$E_{cell} = E^\circ_{cell} - \frac{.0591\ V}{6}\log Q$$

$$= .098\ V - \frac{.0591\ V}{6}\log(225)$$

$$= .098\ V - .023\ V = \mathbf{.075\ V}$$

Examples of Commercial Cells

Car Battery

$$PbO_2(s) + SO_4^{2-} + 4\,H^+ + \cancel{2e^-} \longrightarrow PbSO_4(s) + 2\,H_2O \qquad E^\circ_{red} = +1.685\ V$$

$$Pb(s) + SO_4^{2-} \longrightarrow PbSO_4(s) + \cancel{2e^-} \qquad E^\circ_{ox} = +0.356\ V$$

$$PbO_2(s) + Pb(s) + 2\,SO_4^{2-} + 4\,H^+ \longrightarrow 2\,PbSO_4(s) + 2\,H_2O \qquad E^\circ_{cell} = +2.041\ V$$

Hearing Aide Alkaline Battery

$$Zn(s) + \cancel{2\,OH^-} \longrightarrow Zn(OH)_2(s) + \cancel{2e^-} \qquad E^\circ_{ox} = +1.245\ V$$

$$HgO(s) + H_2O + \cancel{2e^-} \longrightarrow Hg(\ell) + \cancel{2\,OH^-} \qquad E^\circ_{red} = +.0984\ V$$

$$HgO(s) + Zn(s) + H_2O \longrightarrow Hg(\ell) + Zn(OH)_2(s) \qquad E^\circ_{cell} = +1.3434\ V$$

Nickel-Cadmium Rechargable Battery

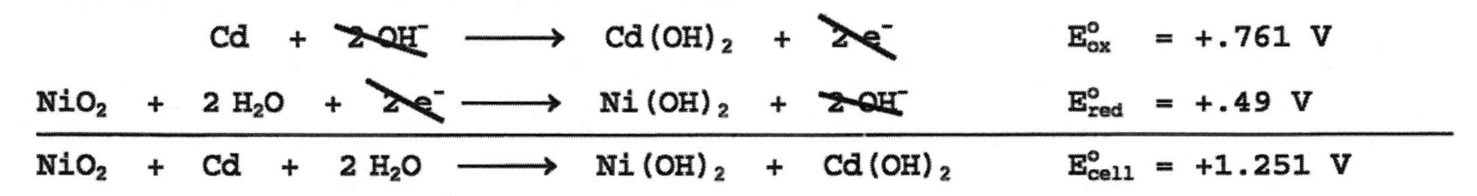

$$Cd + \cancel{2\,OH^-} \longrightarrow Cd(OH)_2 + \cancel{2e^-} \qquad E^\circ_{ox} = +.761\ V$$

$$NiO_2 + 2\,H_2O + \cancel{2e^-} \longrightarrow Ni(OH)_2 + \cancel{2\,OH^-} \qquad E^\circ_{red} = +.49\ V$$

$$NiO_2 + Cd + 2\,H_2O \longrightarrow Ni(OH)_2 + Cd(OH)_2 \qquad E^\circ_{cell} = +1.251\ V$$

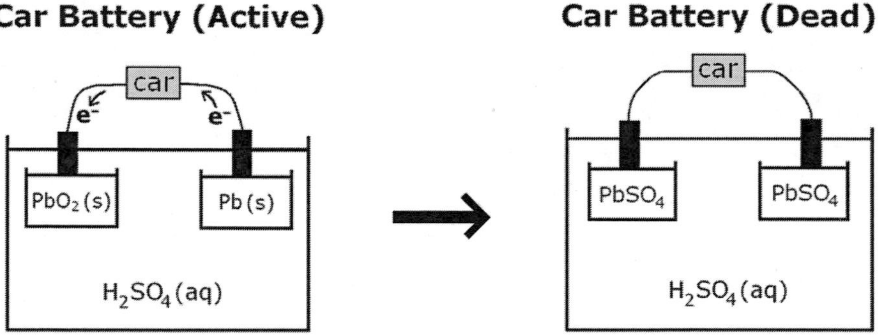

Recharge (Electrolytic Cell)

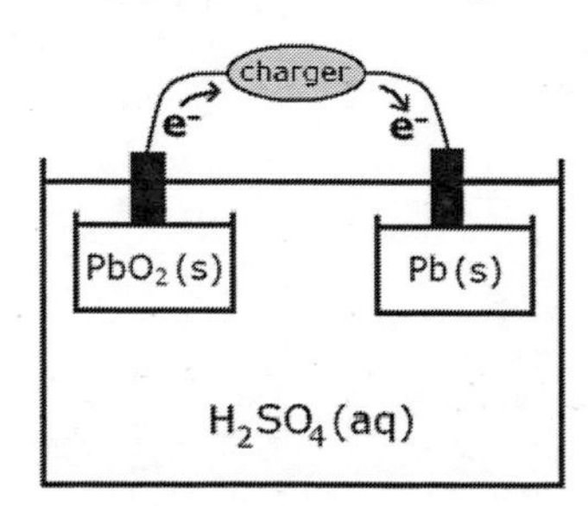

Determining Direction of e⁻ Flow

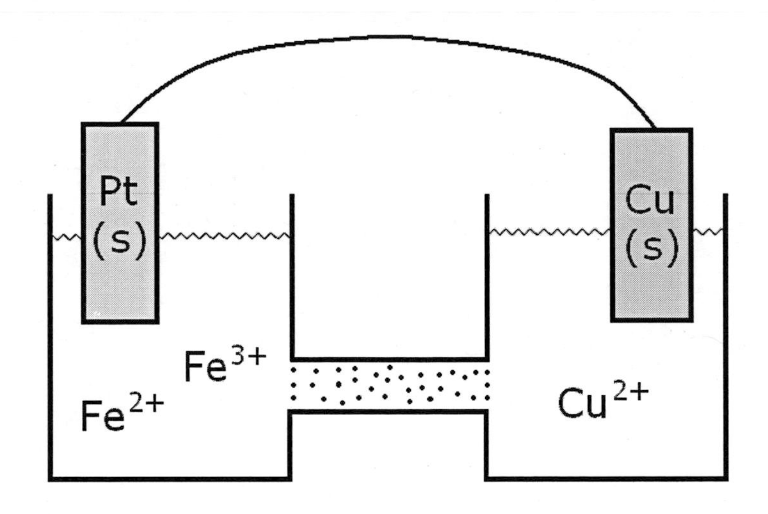

a. Which way will e⁻'s flow spontaneously?

b. What voltage will be measured?

Half-Reactions as Found in the Redox Table

$$Fe^{3+} + e^- \longrightarrow Fe^{2+} \quad +0.771\text{ V}$$

$$Cu^{2+} + 2e^- \longrightarrow Cu(s) \quad +0.337\text{ V}$$

- To have a spontaneous reaction, must have a positive (+) E_{cell}.
- To get a + E_{cell}, must turn around the Cu reaction.
- Multiplying by 2 has no effect on voltage:

$$2Fe^{3+} + 2e^- \longrightarrow 2Fe^{2+} \quad +0.771\text{ V}$$

$$Cu(s) \longrightarrow Cu^{2+} + 2e^- \quad -0.337\text{ V}$$

$$2Fe^{3+} + Cu(s) \longrightarrow 2Fe^{2+} + Cu^{2+} \quad +0.434\text{ V}$$

(E°_{cell})

Since the half-reactions show that Cu(s) loses e^- (e^- on **right** in half-reaction) and Fe^{3+} gains e^- (e^- on **left** in half-reaction), e^- flow out of the Cu electrode and into the Pt (Fe^{2+}; Fe^{3+}) electrode.

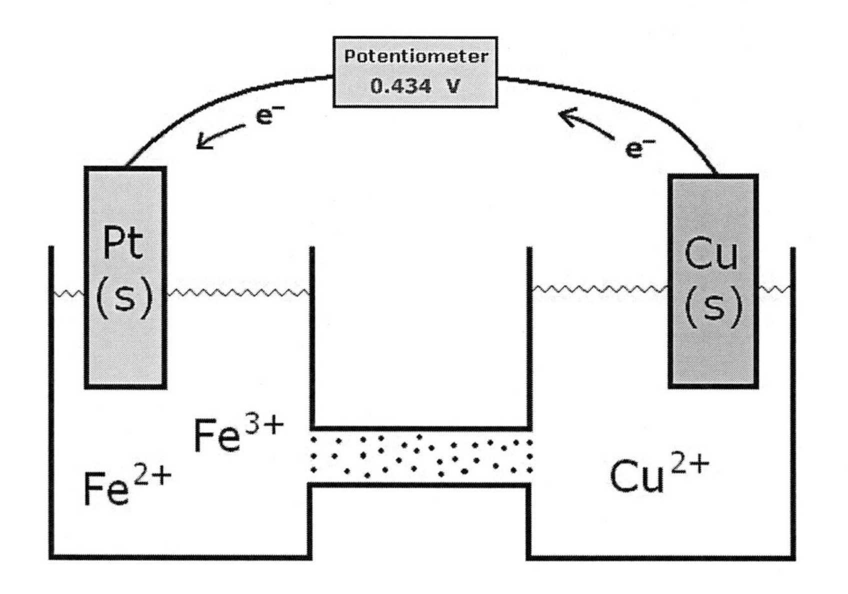

Answers:

a. e^- flow from right to left. (←------)

b. Measured votage is 0.434 V.

3 Ways To Tell Which Half-Reaction To Turn Around

1. For a redox reaction, turn around whichever equation keeps everything on the same side as given.

2. For a cell written with a ‖ for the salt bridge, always turn around the equation for the stuff on the LEFT (usually the first half-reaction you write.)

3. For a picture with the actual beakers drawn, the electrons could go either way. Turn around whichever equation makes the sum of the voltages come out + (spontaneous).

Electrolytic Cells

- An e^- pump is placed in the circuit to force e^- to flow in the nonspontaneous direction.
- Makes the half-reactions and the overall reaction go in the opposite direction of the spontaneous cell.

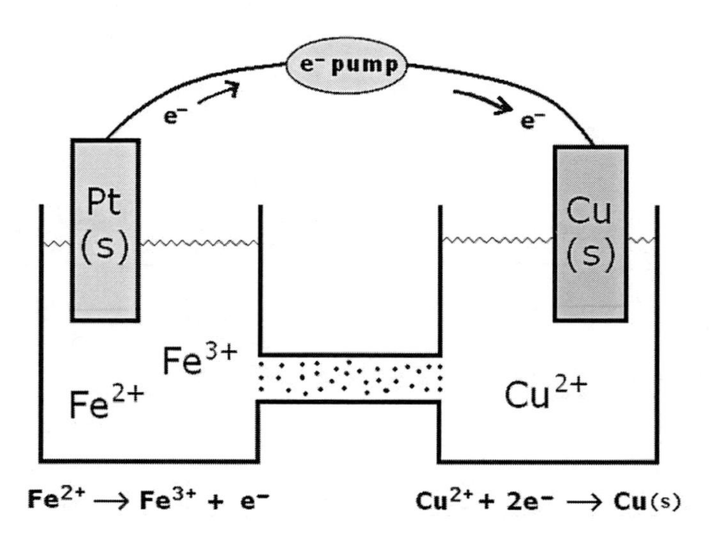

Because e^-'s now flow into the Cu electrode, Cu^{2+} gains e^-'s and Cu(s) plates out on the copper strip.

Faraday's Law of Electrolysis

The amount of metal plated out in an electrolytic cell is proportional to the # mol e^- that pass through the circuit.

Reaction	# mol e⁻ needed to plate out 1 mol of metal
$Ag^+ + e^- \longrightarrow Ag(s)$	**1**
$Cu^{2+} + 2e^- \longrightarrow Cu(s)$	**2**
$Au^{3+} + 3e^- \longrightarrow Au(s)$	**3**

How many grams of Cu(s) will plate out from a Cu^{2+} solution in an electrolytic cell when 6.72 mol e^- pass through the circuit?

$$6.72 \cancel{\text{mol } e^-} \times \frac{1 \cancel{\text{mol Cu}}}{2 \cancel{\text{mol } e^-}} \times \frac{63.55 \text{ g Cu}}{1 \cancel{\text{mol Cu}}} = \boxed{214 \text{ g Cu}}$$

How would the problem change if Au(s) were plating out from a solution of Au^{3+}?

$$6.72 \cancel{\text{mol } e^-} \times \frac{1 \cancel{\text{mol Au}}}{3 \cancel{\text{mol } e^-}} \times \frac{196.97 \text{ g Au}}{1 \cancel{\text{mol Au}}} = \boxed{441 \text{ g Au}}$$

Note: # mol e^- required for each ion depends on the charge of the ion.

Radiation and Nuclear Chemistry

(Homework #15)

Difference Between Chemical and Nuclear Reactions

Chemical Reactions

$$C(s) + O_2(g) \longrightarrow CO_2(g)$$

Nuclear Reactions

$$^{14}_{6}C \longrightarrow {}^{14}_{7}N + \text{Radiation}$$

Radiation = stream of submicroscopic particles traveling in the same direction.

Types of Radiation

Particles with mass

- **Alpha (α)**
- **Beta (β)**
- **Positron(β^+)**
- **Neutron**

Particles with no mass

Photons = particles of ***Electromagnetic Radiation*** with no mass, only energy. "Small packages of energy"

High Energy

- **Gamma (γ) Rays**
- **X-Rays**
- Ultraviolet (UV)
  Visible
  Infrared (IR)
  Microwaves
  Radio, TV, Radar

Low Energy

The radiation types shown in bold type are called **Ionizing Radiation** = have enough energy to knock electrons completely off of atoms to form ions.

The others are called **Non-Ionizing Radiation** = do not have enough energy to cause electrons to be completely ejected from atoms.

Non-ionizing radiations cause:

a. **electron transitions** = promotion of electrons into higher energy levels of the same atom (UV and visible)
b. "**stretching**" and "**bending**" of covalent bonds (IR)
c. **rotation of molecules** (microwaves)
d. **changes in nuclear "spin"** (radio waves) = Observed in Nuclear Magnetic Resonance (NMR) and Magnetic Resonance Imaging (MRI)

Although non-ionizing radiation can have biological effects, such as mutations caused by UV and heating of water caused by microwaves, ionizing radiation is the type mainly associated with nuclear reactions.

Ionizing radiation cannot be detected by human senses (that is, it cannot be seen, heard, felt, tasted, or smelled), but it causes significant biological effects.

Biological Effects of Ionizing Radiation

All significant biological effects of ionizing radiation result from **DNA damage**.

1. **Mutation**
   Responsible for genetic defects in offspring and for cancer development. All cancer is ultimately caused by mutation (activation of oncogenes and/or deactivation of tumor-suppressor genes).

2. **Cell death**

Because radiation affects DNA, **cells that reproduce the fastest** are affected most.

Examples:
Hair follicles
Digestive tract cells
Blood-forming cells
Reproductive cells

Radiation sickness (loss of hair, nausea, diarrhea, dehydration) occurs within a few days of exposure.

Cancer development may occur years after exposure.

Most radiation types cause an essentially linear dose-response curve in animals when death or cancer development is measured.

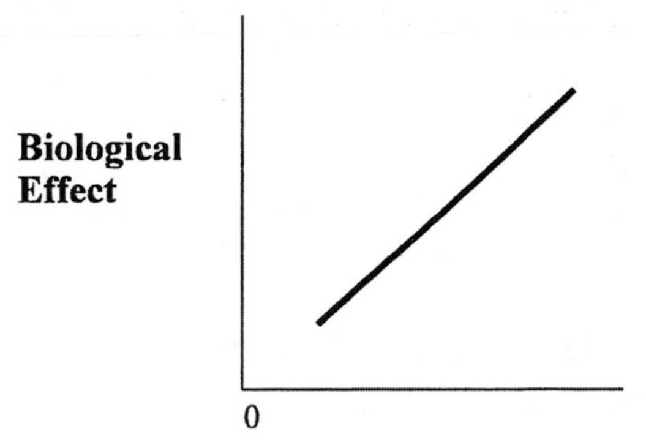

In the lower dose ranges, effects of radiation cannot be statistically distinguished from background.

It is likely that the effects of small radiation doses are negligible because of the effectiveness of natural DNA repair mechanisms in cells. However, the alternative hypothesis held by some people in the field is that the danger of radiation exposure is cumulative, so that any dose, no matter how small, is capable of causing permanent damage.

Natural Background Radiation

1. Cosmic Rays
2. Uranium, Thorium, and other radioactive deposits in the earth

Normal background radiation is probably a negligible source of risk compared to other risk factors in life.

Examples of Ways To Increase Radiation Dose

1. Change of location
2. Smoking
3. Frequent X-rays and other medical tests
4. Nuclear accidents

Measurement of Radiation

1. Geiger Counter
2. Liquid Scintillation Counter
3. Gamma counter
4. Scanning of exposed photographic film

Uses of Radiation in Medicine

1. **Cancer therapy**.
   Because rapidly growing cells are most affected, radiation is used in cancer therapy to kill cancer cells in preference to normal cells.

   Because normal cells are also affected, patients often experience side-effects of radiation sickness.

2. **Destruction of overactive tissue**.
   (Example: destruction of thyroid tissue by radioactive iodine in hyperthyroidism.)

3. **Imaging**.
   Examples include X-rays, PET scanning and scanning of bodily organs such as thyroid, heart and gall bladder.

4. **Identification of specific gene sequences**.
   Used in determination of paternity, in forensics, and in diagnosis of genetic diseases.

5. **Radioimmunoassay**.
   Clinical labs measure levels of substances in body fluids and tissues by using assays based on radioactive isotopes.

Four Types of Nuclear Reactions

1. **Nuclear Decay or Emission**
   Changes in individual nuclei of atoms causes the atoms to emit radiation.

2. **Nuclear Fission**
   Large amounts of energy are produced when large nuclei split into smaller ones.

3. **Nuclear Fusion**
   Small atoms (hydrogen) combine into larger atoms (helium) with release of even more energy than Fission.

4. **Nuclear Bombardment**
   Smaller nuclei are forced to collide at high energy to form larger nuclei. (Used to produce man-made elements.)

Review of the Atomic Nucleus

Nucleus = protons ($\mathbf{p^+}$) and neutrons ($\mathbf{n^o}$) are packed into a relatively tiny space. The electron ($\mathbf{e^-}$) "cloud" is **HUGE** in size by comparison.

Analogy: If the nucleus were the size of a period (.), the atom would be about the size of half of Soldier Field!

But, almost all the **mass** of an atom is in the **nucleus.**

mass $\mathbf{p^+} \cong$ **mass** $\mathbf{n^o} \cong$ **1 amu** (atomic mass unit)

- Protons and neutrons each have a mass almost 2000 times larger than electrons.
- For many purposes, **mass e^-** can be ignored relative to **mass p^+** or **mass n^o.**

Atomic # (Z) = # p^+ in the nucleus. Makes elements unique (different from one another).

Mass # (A) = # p^+ plus # n^o

Isotopes = atoms of an element (same # p^+) with different # n^o (and, therefore, different mass #'s).

- All elements have more than one isotope (even hydrogen).
- No matter where on earth a sample of an element comes from, the % of each isotope is the same.

Example: Carbon

	Carbon-12	Carbon-13	Carbon-14
	6 p^+	6 p^+	6 p^+
	6 n^o	7 n^o	8 n^o
Mass #	12 amu	13 amu	14 amu
Abundance	98.9 %	1.1 %	(trace)
Symbol	${}^{12}_{6}C$	${}^{13}_{6}C$	${}^{14}_{6}C$

Atomic mass = weighted average of the masses of isotopes. (The masses of more abundant isotopes have more influence on the number.)

Carbon = **12.011**

For mass calculations (grams, moles, stoichiometry, etc.), carbon is assumed to weigh 12.011.

In **Nuclear Chemistry**, the behavior of each individual isotope is studied, not all isotopes as a group.

"Isotopic Notation"

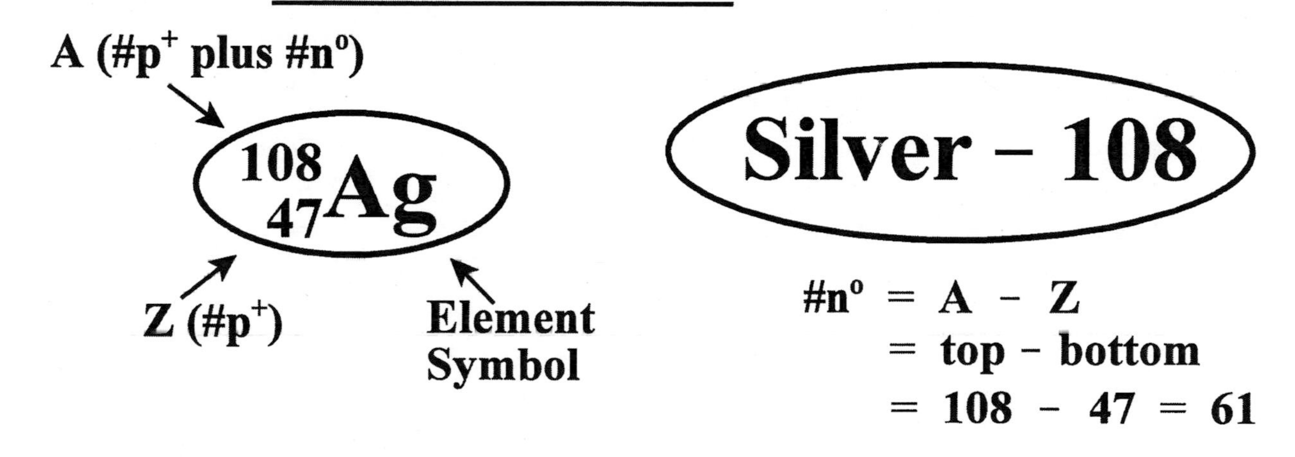

Two Kinds of Nuclei (Isotopes)

Stable isotopes = do not emit radiation

Radioactive isotopes = emit radiation spontaneously

Radioactive nuclei have "too much energy." So, they "package" the energy into a particle and "shoot" it out of the nucleus like a bullet. The particle "carries away" excess energy as radiation.

Most nuclei are **radioactive**. They emit radiation in one or more steps (emissions, decays) in an attempt to become **stable**.

Most stable nuclei (except some small ones) have **slightly more n^o than p^+.** [An element could theoretically have any number of (neutral) neutrons and still be the same element (same # p^+).]

Band of Stability

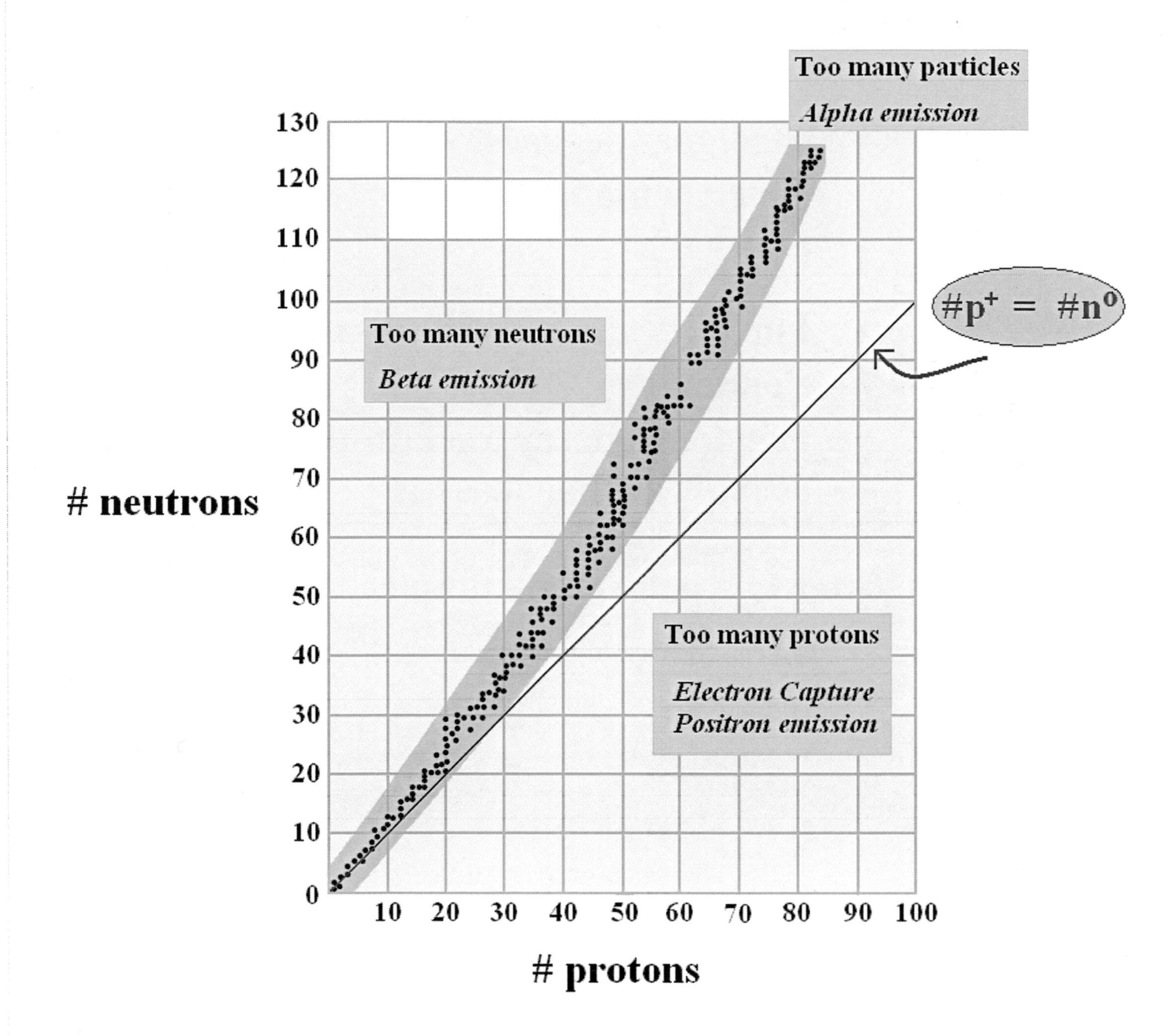

Notice:

1) All nuclei **larger than #83 (Bi) are radioactive.**

2) The type of decay process a nucleus undergoes depends on whether there are **too many p^+ or too many n^o.**

3) **The largest naturally-occurring element is #92 (U).** It has isotopes that do not decay too fast to get an accurate atomic mass.

What Is Nuclear "Instability"?

3 Forces in Physics

1) **Gravity**
2) **Electroweak** (Electricity, Magnetism, + and – charges)
3) **Nuclear Force**

   30 – 40 times stronger than electroweak but acts only over very short distances (as in the nucleus).

If electroweak forces were all that were involved, nuclei should "fly apart"

➔ many + particles (p^+) "crammed" into a very small space. Why don't they?

Answer: **Nuclear Force** holds the nucleus together.

Origin of the Nuclear Force

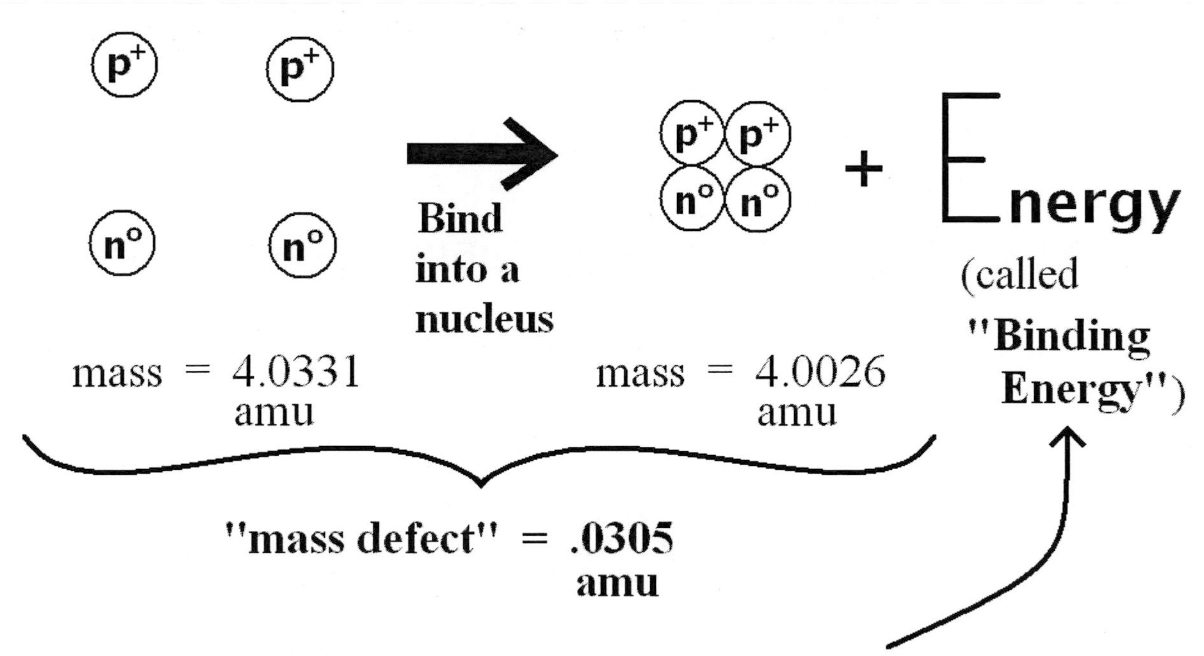

This mass is converted into a HUGE amount of energy.

$E = mc^2$ (c is the speed of light)

- Called "Binding Energy" (BE) because you would have to put that much energy back in to break the nucleus back apart.

- In Nuclear Chemistry,

  Nucleus releases Energy ($E = mc^2$) → ↑BE → Nucleus more stable

- Nuclei must release **excess** **energy** to become more **stable**.

- Energy is released as **radiation**.

Stable isotopes = already have enough BE and do not need to emit radiation and become any more stable.

Radioactive isotopes = contain "too much energy" and must release energy as radiation to ↑BE and become more stable. (They "don't have enough BE" to start with.)

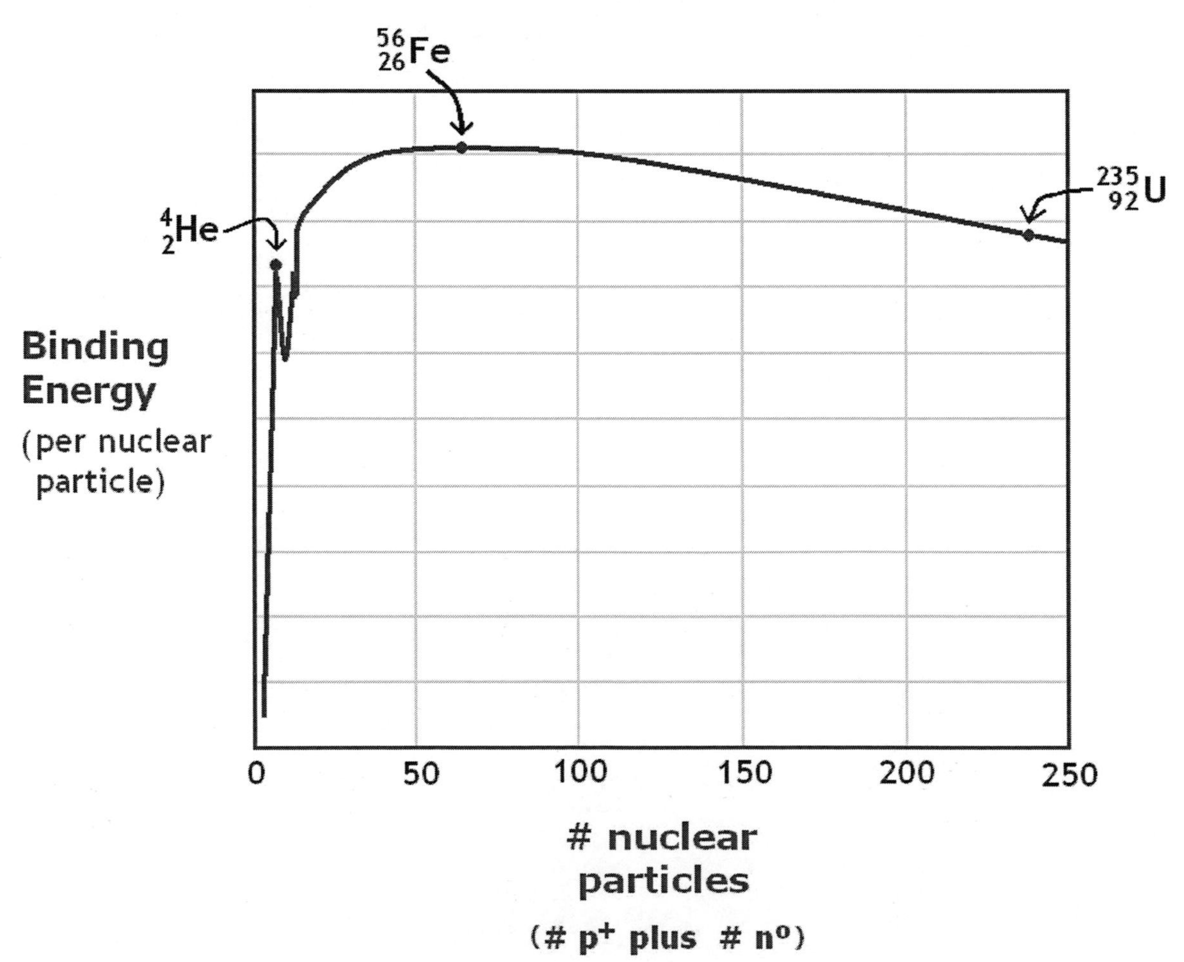

1) **Alpha (α) radiation** = consists of particles that contain 2 protons, 2 neutrons, and no electrons

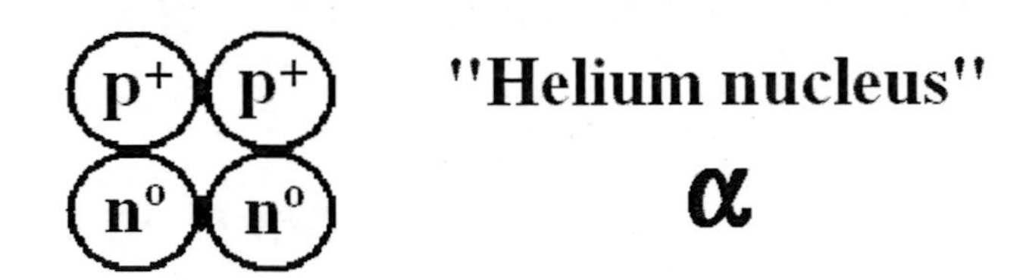

small piece of the nucleus "breaks off"

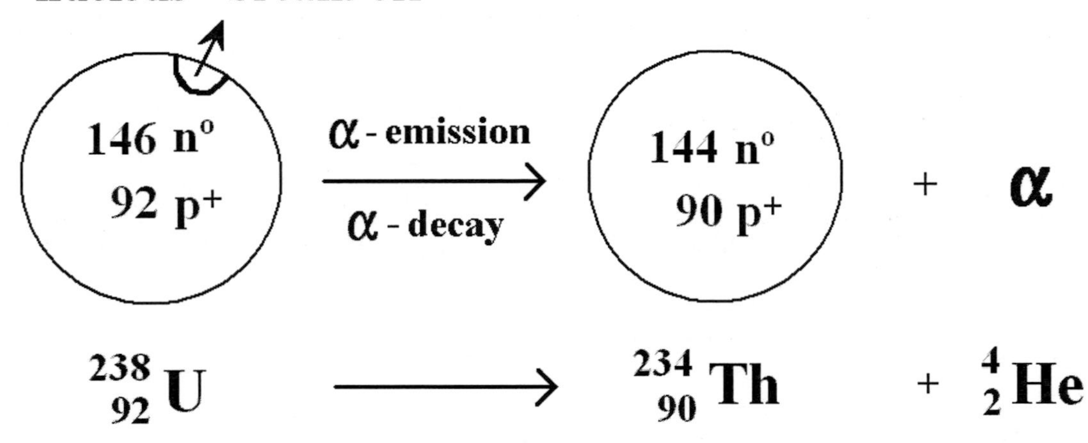

$$^{238}_{92}U \longrightarrow \, ^{234}_{90}Th + \, ^{4}_{2}He$$

2) **Beta (β) radiation** = consists of particles that are identical to electrons

$$^{0}_{-1}e \qquad \beta$$

17 n° 15 p+	β - emission → β - decay	16 n° 16 p+	+	β

$$^{32}_{15}P \longrightarrow \, ^{32}_{16}S + \, ^{0}_{-1}e$$

- In Beta emissions, the parent nucleus loses 1 n^o and gains 1 p^+.
- Protons and neutrons are made of "quarks" which can change "spins."
- The net result is that a <u>neutron</u> in the nucleus changes into a <u>proton</u> and an <u>electron</u>.

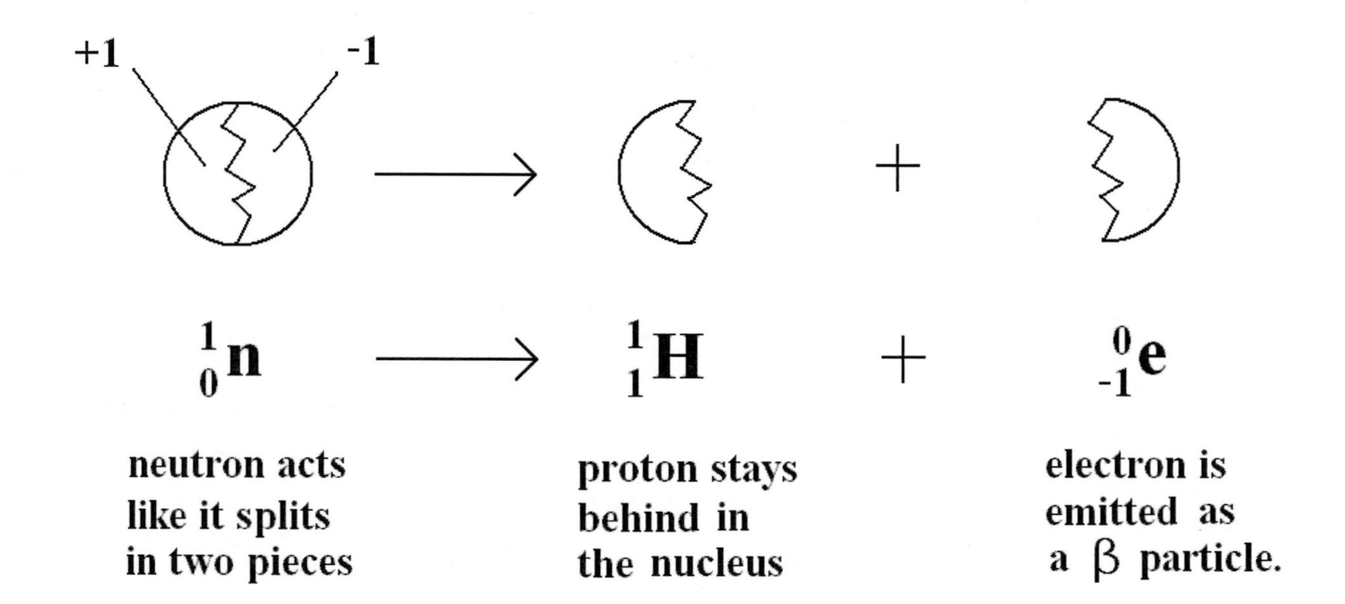

The key to balancing nuclear equations is that the top numbers add up to be equal on each side. The same is true of the bottom numbers.

Radon-222 is an α-emitter. Write a balanced equation.

$$^{222}_{86}Rn \longrightarrow ^{218}_{84}Po + ^{4}_{2}He$$

Carbon-14 is a β-emitter. Write a balanced equation.

$$^{14}_{6}C \longrightarrow ^{14}_{7}N + ^{0}_{-1}e$$

3) **Gamma (γ) radiation** = consists of particles that are electromagnetic radiation. The particles are photons = "packages" of energy with no mass and no charge.

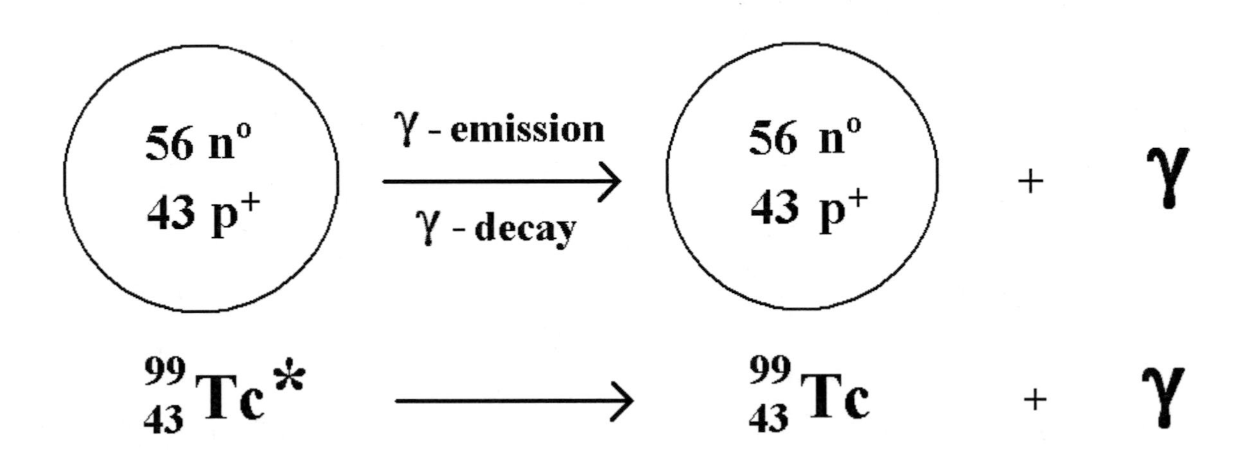

4) **Positron (β^{+}) emission** = consists of particles that are positively charged electrons

$$^{0}_{+1}e \qquad \beta^{+}$$

9 n° 9 p^{+} $\xrightarrow[\beta^{+}\text{- decay}]{\beta^{+}\text{- emission}}$ 10 n° 8 p^{+} + β^{+}

$$^{18}_{9}F \longrightarrow ^{18}_{8}O + ^{0}_{+1}e$$

- In positron emissions, the parent nucleus loses 1 p^+ and gains 1 n^o.
- Again, "quarks" change "spins."
- The net result is that a proton in the nucleus changes into a neutron and a positron.

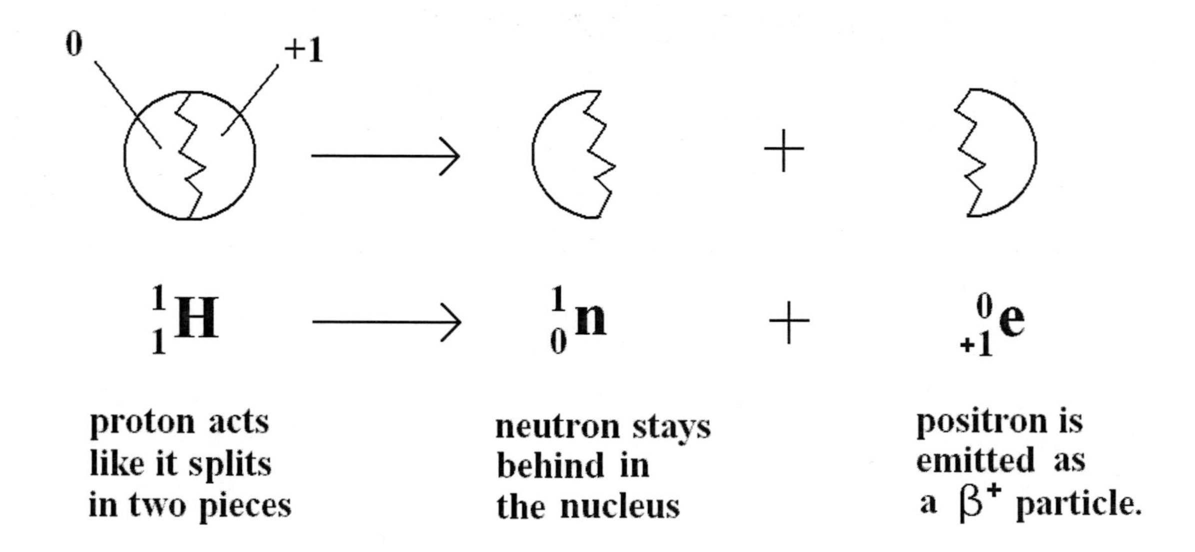

Positrons are particles of "antimatter."

Antimatter

positrons	+ electrons
antineutrons	
antiprotons	- protons

When antimatter collides with matter, they "annihilate" each other to produce 100% $E = mc^2$ energy. This is the most energetic process presently known to man.

$$^{0}_{+1}e + ^{0}_{-1}e \longrightarrow \text{Energy } (E = mc^2)$$

Positron Electron

PET (positron emission tomography) scanning

- **Glucose is "labeled" with emitting fluorine and injected.**
- **Labeled glucose accumulates in rapidly metabolizing tissues (brain, heart, cancer cells)**
- **Differences between "normal" and "abnormal" tissue can be detected. Also, differences between patients with various medical conditions can be visualized.**

5) **Electron capture** or **K capture** = the nucleus "absorbs" an electron from the 1s orbital.

(the first shell in the Bohr Model is called the "K shell")

EC

$$\boxed{\begin{matrix} 19\ n^o \\ 18\ p^+ \end{matrix}} + {}^{0}_{-1}e \xrightarrow{EC} \boxed{\begin{matrix} 20\ n^o \\ 17\ p^+ \end{matrix}}$$

$${}^{37}_{18}Ar + {}^{0}_{-1}e \longrightarrow {}^{37}_{17}Cl$$

- **In electron capture, the parent nucleus loses 1 p^+ and gains 1 n^o .**
- **The net result is that a proton in the nucleus "combines" with the incoming electron to form a neutron .**
- **The overall process is the reverse of β emission.**

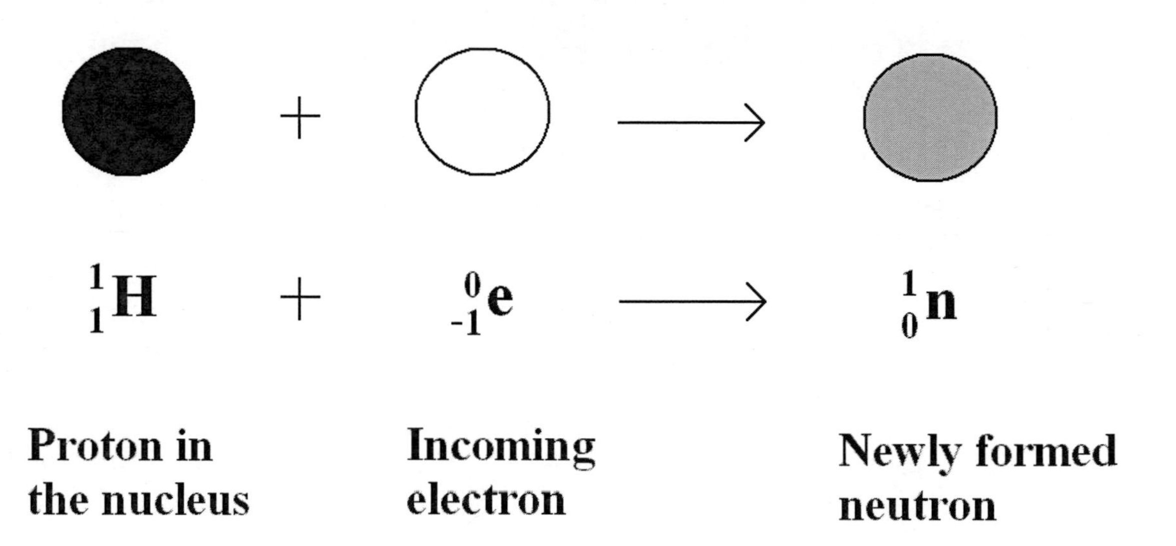

In electron capture, absorption of a 1s electron creates an "electron hole" close to the nucleus. Electrons from higher energy levels fall into lower levels, and the energy is released as X-rays.

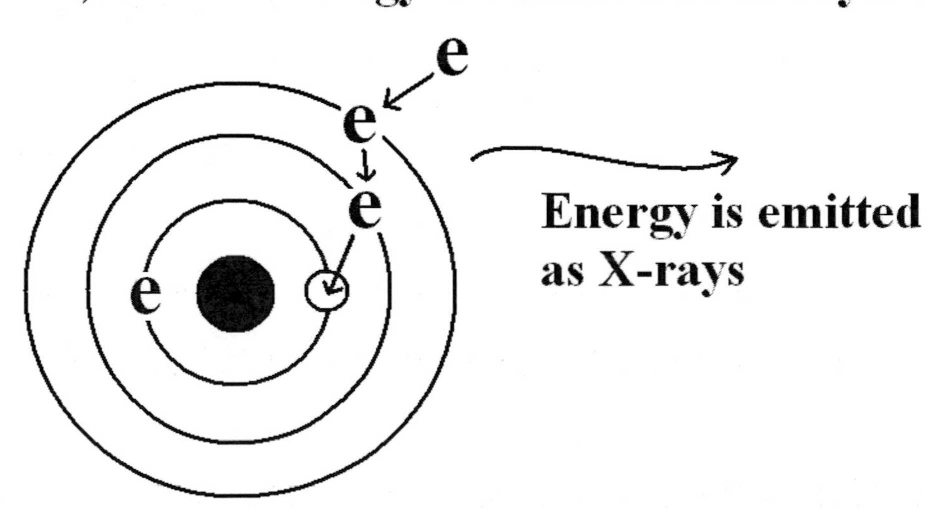

Antimony-114 decays to Tin-114. What two decay processes could account for this change?

$$^{114}_{51}Sb \longrightarrow {}^{114}_{50}Sn + {}^{0}_{+1}e \qquad (\beta^+)$$

$$^{114}_{51}Sb + {}^{0}_{-1}e \longrightarrow {}^{114}_{50}Sn \qquad (EC)$$

Positron emission and Electron capture always produce the same daughter nucleus.

Kinetics of Radioactive Isotopes

Measuring Amounts of Radioactivity

1) Can be measured as grams, moles, or atoms
2) Usually measured as Activity = the number of decays a sample undergoes per unit time

1 Curie (Ci) = 3.7×10^{10} decays per second (DPS)

1 millicurie (mCi) = one thousandth of a Curie

1 microcurie (μCi) = one millionth of a Curie

1 nanocurie (nCi) = one billionth of a Curie

In kinetic equations, amount of radioactivity is usually written as X, not molarity.

Kinetic Equations for Radioactive Decay

All decay processes follow first order kinetics, so the same equations are used for radioactivity as are used in chemical kinetics.

$$\ln \frac{X_0}{X_t} = kt$$

$$t_{1/2} = \frac{.693}{k} \qquad k = \frac{.693}{t_{1/2}}$$

Kinetics of Radioactive Isotopes

Problem: Cobalt-60 is a β-emitting isotope used in cancer therapy:

$$^{60}_{27}\text{Co} \longrightarrow \, ^{60}_{28}\text{Ni} + \, ^{0}_{-1}\text{e}$$

The half-life ($t_{½}$) is 5.26 years.

a. What is the rate constant **k**?
b. If you start with a 200 µCi sample, how much is left after 14.2 years?
c. How long will it take for the activity to reach 3.4 µCi?

Solution:

a.

$$t_{½} = \frac{0.693}{k}$$

$$k = \frac{0.693}{t_{½}} = \frac{0.693}{5.26 \text{ yr}} = 0.132 \text{ yr}^{-1}$$

b.

$$\ln\frac{X_o}{X_t} = kt$$

$$\ln\frac{200}{X_t} = (0.132 \text{ yr}^{-1})(14.2 \text{ yr}) = 1.87$$

$$\frac{200}{X_t} = \text{INV ln } 1.87$$

$$\frac{200}{X_t} = 6.49$$

$$6.49 \times X_t = 200$$

$$X_t = \frac{200}{6.49} = \mathbf{30.8\ \mu Ci}$$

c.

$$\ln\frac{X_o}{X_t} = kt$$

$$\ln\frac{200}{3.4} = (0.132\ yr^{-1})t$$

$$4.075 = (0.132\ yr^{-1})t$$

$$t = \frac{4.075}{0.132\ yr^{-1}} = \mathbf{30.9\ yr}$$

<u>Problem</u>: A sample of 3.42 mg of radioactive isotope decays to 1.79 mg in 10.3 seconds. What are **k** and **$t_{½}$**?

Solution:

$$\ln\frac{X_o}{X_t} = kt$$

$$\ln\frac{3.42}{1.79} = k(10.3\ s)$$

$$0.647 = k(10.3\ s)$$

$$k = \frac{0.647}{10.3\ s} = \mathbf{0.0628\ s^{-1}}$$

$$t_{½} = \frac{0.693}{k} = \frac{0.693}{0.0628\ s^{-1}} = \mathbf{11.0\ s}$$

Problem: What percent of the above isotope is left after 30.0 seconds?

Solution:

Assume you start with 100. Then, whatever is left will be the desired percent (parts out of 100).

$$\ln\frac{X_o}{X_t} = kt$$

$$\ln\frac{100}{X_t} = (0.0628\ s^{-1})(30.0\ s) = 1.884$$

$$\frac{100}{X_t} = \text{INV}\ \ln 1.884$$

$$\frac{100}{X_t} = 6.58 \quad \rightarrow \quad 6.58 \times X_t = 100 \quad \rightarrow \quad X_t = \frac{100}{6.58} = \mathbf{15.2\%}$$

Problem: How long will it take an isotope with $t_{1/2} = 123$ yr to decay to 2.2% of its original activity?

Solution:

First calculate **k**:

$$t_{1/2} = \frac{0.693}{k} \quad \text{and} \quad k = \frac{0.693}{t_{1/2}} = \frac{0.693}{123\ \text{yr}} = 0.00563\ \text{yr}^{-1}$$

If you start with 100, you can use 2.2 for X_t. (2.2% is 2.2 parts out of 100.)

$$\ln\frac{100}{2.2} = (0.00563\ \text{yr}^{-1})t$$

$$3.82 = (0.00563\ \text{yr}^{-1})t$$

$$t = \frac{3.82}{0.00563\ \text{yr}^{-1}} = \mathbf{679\ yr}$$

Carbon-14 Dating

1. Animals break down food molecules to CO_2 and H_2O, but cannot make food from these substances.

2. Plants can make food molecules from CO_2 and H_2O through Photosynthesis.

3. Plants incorporate CO_2 as long as they are alive (Photosynthesis does not occur after a plant dies.)

4. $^{12}CO_2$ and $^{14}CO_2$ are incorporated at almost exactly the same rate during Photosynthesis.

5. When the plant dies, the ratio of ^{14}C to ^{12}C declines as ^{14}C decays. (The half-life is 5720 yr.)

6. The ratio of ^{14}C to ^{12}C in a once-living plant substance gives an estimate of the age of the sample.

Nuclear Fission

1. Provides the energy source for nuclear power plants and "atomic" bombs (the "first generation" bombs like those used on Hiroshima and Nagasaki).

2. Only a few known atoms will undergo fission. The one used in power plants is Uranium-235.

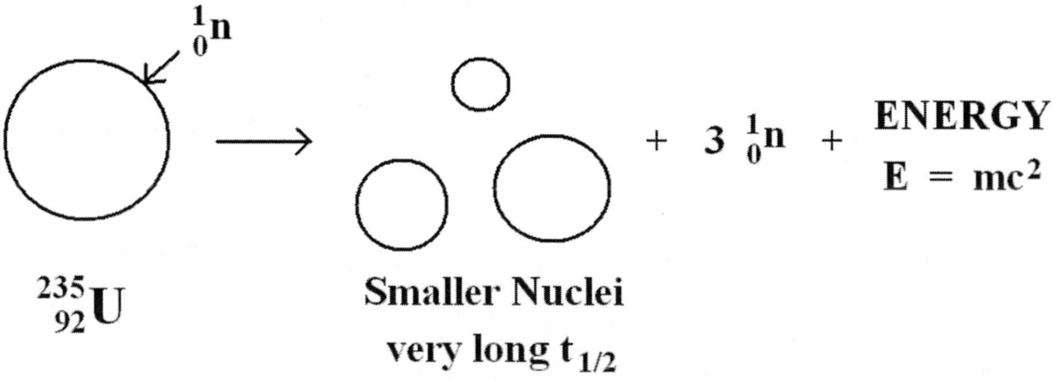

$${}^{1}_{0}n + {}^{235}_{92}U \longrightarrow \text{Smaller Nuclei} + 3\,{}^{1}_{0}n + \text{ENERGY} \quad (E = mc^2)$$

Smaller Nuclei: very long $t_{1/2}$

3. Reaction continues by a "chain reaction" = the 3 neutrons released cause fission of 3 more atoms. Now there are 9 neutrons. Number of neutrons keeps increasing exponentially.

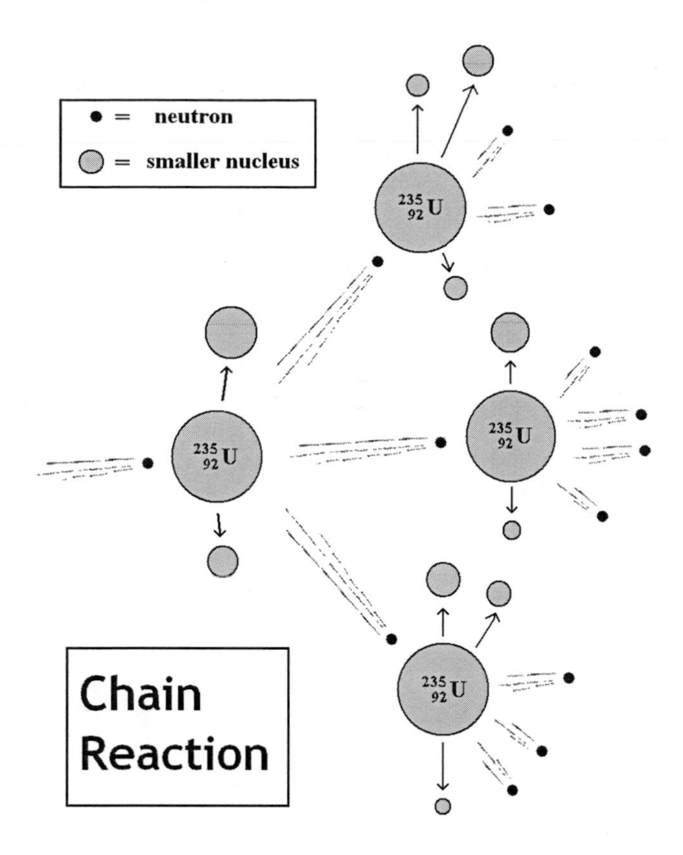

4. Reaction will not begin unless there is a "critical mass" = enough material to start the chain reaction

5. To make a bomb, subcritical masses are forced together to start the fission. Reaction does not stop until all fissionable material is gone.

6. In a power plant, fission is controlled in two ways.

7. Uranium-238 will not undergo fission, but makes up over 99% of a sample of uranium ore. U-235 must be purified (expensive process) in order to get fissionable material.

8. The purification is stopped before the U-235 is pure enough to make a bomb. It can be used in a power plant, but will not explode like a bomb.

9. "Control rods" made of Carbon and Boron "soak up" neutrons to limit the chain reaction.

Nuclear Fusion

1. Used as the energy source in stars and in "Hydrogen Bombs" (H-bombs).

2. The only known atoms capable of these reactions are the isotopes of hydrogen.

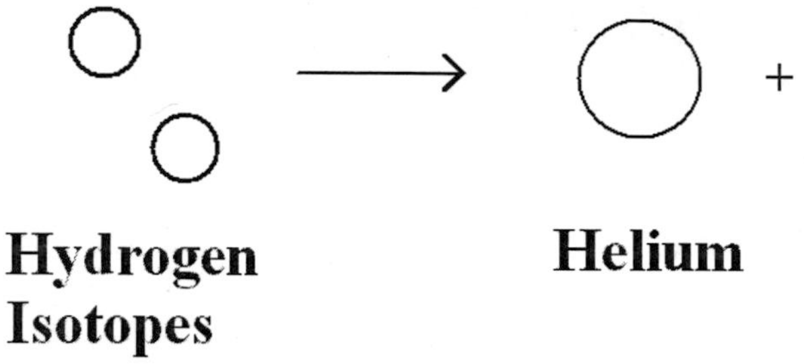

Hydrogen Isotopes ⟶ Helium + **ENERGY**

$E = mc^2$

Even more than in fission

3. The reaction does not continue by means of a chain reaction -- it continues by means of HEAT.

4. A fusion reaction does not start until the temperature reaches about 100 million ^{0}C. At such temperatures, a new state of matter called "plasma" exists. The temp is so hot that covalent bonds cannot exist, and even electrons are removed from atoms so that plasma is a mixture of ions and electrons.

5. Stars are at a high enough temp to continue the reaction.

6. An H-bomb achieves the required temp by explosion of a fission bomb (the "fuse") which then begins the fusion reaction.

7. Power plants based on fusion do not yet exist. Many practical problems would have to be worked out. The reaction can be contained in a magnetic field, and a sufficient temp can be achieved by using lasers. At present, however, so much energy must be put in to continue the reaction that the amount of energy produced is insufficient by comparison.

Nuclear Bombardment

1. **Nuclear particles or entire nuclei are forced to collide with specific atoms to produce larger atoms.**

2. **Particles can be accelerated in a "cyclotron" and forced to collide with atoms imbedded on a target.**

3. **Atoms of any size can be produced this way. An example is the element Technetium, which does not occur in nature.**

$$^{96}_{42}\text{Mo} + {}^{2}_{1}\text{H} \longrightarrow {}^{97}_{43}\text{Tc} + {}^{1}_{0}\text{n}$$

4. **The largest known elements in the periodic table are also "man-made" elements produced by bombardment. An example is Mt (#109):**

$$^{209}_{83}\text{Bi} + {}^{58}_{26}\text{Fe} \longrightarrow {}^{266}_{109}\text{Mt} + {}^{1}_{0}\text{n}$$

The Periodic Table of the Elements

	IA	IIA	IIIB	IVB	VB	VIB	VIIB	VIIIB			IB	IIB	IIIA	IVA	VA	VIA	VIIA	VIIIA
	1	2	3	4	5	6	7	8	9	10	11	12	13	14	15	16	17	18
1	1 H 1.01																	2 He 4.00
2	3 Li 6.94	4 Be 9.01											5 B 10.81	6 C 12.01	7 N 14.01	8 O 16.00	9 F 19.00	10 Ne 20.18
3	11 Na 22.99	12 Mg 24.31											13 Al 26.98	14 Si 28.09	15 P 30.97	16 S 32.07	17 Cl 35.45	18 Ar 39.95
4	19 K 39.10	20 Ca 40.08	21 Sc 44.96	22 Ti 47.88	23 V 50.94	24 Cr 52.00	25 Mn 54.94	26 Fe 55.85	27 Co 58.93	28 Ni 58.69	29 Cu 63.55	30 Zn 65.39	31 Ga 69.72	32 Ge 72.61	33 As 74.92	34 Se 78.96	35 Br 79.90	36 Kr 83.80
5	37 Rb 85.47	38 Sr 87.62	39 Y 88.91	40 Zr 91.22	41 Nb 92.91	42 Mo 95.94	43 Tc (98)	44 Ru 101.07	45 Rh 102.92	46 Pd 106.42	47 Ag 107.87	48 Cd 112.41	49 In 114.82	50 Sn 118.71	51 Sb 121.76	52 Te 127.60	53 I 126.90	54 Xe 131.29
6	55 Cs 132.91	56 Ba 137.33	57 La* 138.91	72 Hf 178.49	73 Ta 180.95	74 W 183.85	75 Re 186.21	76 Os 190.2	77 Ir 192.22	78 Pt 195.08	79 Au 196.97	80 Hg 200.59	81 Tl 204.38	82 Pb 207.2	83 Bi 208.98	84 Po (209)	85 At (210)	86 Rn (222)
7	87 Fr (223)	88 Ra (226)	89 Ac** (227)	104 Rf (261)	105 Db (262)	106 Sg (266)	107 Bh (264)	108 Hs (269)	109 Mt (268)									

*Lanthanides	58 Ce 140.12	59 Pr 140.91	60 Nd 144.24	61 Pm (145)	62 Sm 150.36	63 Eu 151.97	64 Gd 157.25	65 Tb 158.93	66 Dy 162.50	67 Ho 164.93	68 Er 167.26	69 Tm 168.93	70 Yb 173.04	71 Lu 174.97
**Actinides	90 Th 232.04	91 Pa (231)	92 U 238.03	93 Np (237)	94 Pu (244)	95 Am (243)	96 Cm (247)	97 Bk (247)	98 Cf (251)	99 Es (252)	100 Fm (257)	101 Md (258)	102 No (259)	103 Lr (262)